MANUAL OF INSTRUCTION

FOR

EWAGE TREATMENT PLANT OPERATORS

NEW YORK STATE
DEPARTMENT OF ENVIRONMENTAL CONSERVATION

NELSON A. ROCKEFELLER,
Governor

HENRY L. DIAMOND,
Commissioner of Environmental Conservation

CONTENTS

v

INDEX OF FIGURES

INDEX OF TABLES

PREFACE

This Manual was prepared specifically for use in the Grade II Sewage Treatment Plant Operators Courses conducted by the Office of Environmental Manpower of the New York State Department of Environmental Conservation, in cooperation with the College of Engineering, New York University; the Great Lakes Laboratory of the State University College at Buffalo, and the Department of Civil Engineering, Syracuse University. It was written primarily as a text to be used in study assignments and to augment lecture and laboratory exercises given during the course. The material should be useful as a reference work by those attending the course and others interested in the field of sewage and waste treatment.

Some of the students attending the Grade II Sewage Treatment Plant Operators Courses do not have strong scientific backgrounds. Every attempt, therefore, was made to keep from being too technical and to present concise and readily understandable material. The appendices contain a brief discussion of arithmetic, chemistry and bacteriology and a glossary of common terms relating to sewerage and sewage treatment.

Many individuals assisted in the preparation of the Manual and many standard textbooks and technical publications were used for reference. These references are given at the end of the chapters or in the bibliography at the back of the Manual.

CHAPTER 1

SEWAGE

Sewage is largely the water supply of a community after it has been fouled by various uses. From the standpoint of source, it may be a combination of the liquid or water-carried wastes from residences, business buildings and institutions, together with those from industrial establishments, and with such ground water, surface and storm water as may be present.

Volume. The amount or volume of sewage produced varies in different communities depending on a number of factors. A strictly residential community with well constructed sewers from which storm waters are excluded might average 40 gallons per person per day while an industrial community or one in which the domestic use of water is unusually high may have 200 gallons or more per person per day requiring disposal. In the United States, a figure of 100 gallons per person per day has been considered a reasonable average, though this figure is tending to increase with the growing use of automatic laundry and dishwashing machines and garbage grinders. Where storm waters are admitted to the sewers carrying domestic and industrial wastes the average is, of course, much higher.

SOURCES OF SEWAGE AND WASTES

Sewage orignates from several different sources:

(a) Human and animal wastes
(b) Household wastes
(c) Storm flows
(d) Ground water infiltration
(e) Industrial wastes

(a) *Human and animal wastes.* These consist of the body discharges which become part of sewage through flushing of toilet facilities, and to some extent those of animals which are washed into sewers from soil or streets. These wastes are the most important as affecting public health because they may contain organisms which produce disease in man and their safe and effective treatment constitutes a major problem in conditioning sewage for disposal.

(b) *Household wastes.* These are derived from home laundry operations, bathing, kitchen wastes, from washing and cooking foods and dishwashing. Most of these contain soaps, synthetic detergents usually containing foaming agents now generally used in housekeeping. Kitchen wastes have particles of food and grease which are becoming a more significant and increasing part of household wastes with the growing use of home garbage grinding units.

1

(c) *Street washings and storm flows.* Rains and storms deposit varying amounts of water on the land, much of which drains or washes over the surface and carries with it grit, sand, leaves, and other debris that may be lying on the drained surfaces. In some communities this storm drainage is allowed to flow into the sewers or collecting devices for the community wastes and becomes an important component of the sewage. In other communities these flows are collected separately for disposal and do not become a part of the community sewage. Storm flow volume varies with the intensity of rainfall, topography, and pavements and roof areas. Storm waters from roof areas are of particular significance with respect to the volume of sewage to be treated when they are connected. usually illegally, to sewers from which they are supposedly excluded.

(d) *Ground water infiltration.* Sewers. the collecting devices for sewage, are buried in the ground and in many instances are laid below ground water levels. particularly when such levels are high because of excessive seasonal rainfall. Since the joints between sections of the pipe forming the sewers are not all tight, an opportunity exists for the flow of ground water, or infiltration, into the sewers. Collecting sewers are usually not under pressure, the flow in them being by gravity only, and consequently such infiltration is not only possible but at times is considerable. The volume of ground water infiltration cannot be determined accurately. It is influenced by soil composition, the type of sewer construction, ground water conditions. and rainfall and other weather conditions.

(e) *Industrial wastes.* The waste products of manufacturing processes are an important part of community sewage and their effective disposal must be provided for. In many areas industrial or manufacturing wastes are collected with other community components of sewage for ultimate treatment and disposal. These wastes vary widely in type and volume, depending on the manufacturing establishments located in the community. In some instances the volume and character of industrial wastes are such that separate collecting and disposal devices must be provided. Many types of industrial wastes contain frothing or foaming agents. detergents. and other chemical substances that interfere with the final disposal of the community sewage or damage sewers and other structures. Thus they cannot be added directly to the sewage but must be given a preliminary treatment or disposed of by separate and special means.

DEFINITIONS

Descriptive names have been given to the various types of sewage depending on their sources as described above. These are defined as follows:

Domestic sewage is that containing human and animal wastes and household wastes. Ground water infiltration is also included. This sewage is typical of residential areas where there are no or only very minor industrial operations.

Sanitary sewage is commonly considered to be the same as domestic sewage. It includes all of the domestic sewage but may also contain much, if not all of the industrial wastes of the community.

2

Storm waters consist of the surface run off from storms, flowing from roofs, pavements and over natural ground surfaces.

Combined sewage is a mixture of domestic or sanitary sewage and storm waters when both are collected in the same sewers.

Industrial wastes are the waste waters from manufacturing processes. They may be collected and disposed of by themselves or may be added to and become part of sanitary or combined sewage.

APPEARANCE OF SEWAGE

Sewage is a turbid liquid containing solid material in suspension. When fresh it is gray in color, and has a musty and not unpleasant odor. It carries varying amounts and kinds of floating matter; fecal solids, bits of food, garbage, paper, sticks, and other types of material disposed of in the daily life of a community of people. With the passage of time, the color gradually changes from gray to black, foul and unpleasant odors develop and black solids appear floating on the surface or throughout the liquid. In this state it is termed septic sewage.

COMPOSITION OF SEWAGE

Sewage consists of water plus solids which are dissolved or carried in suspension in the water. The solids are very small in amount, usually less than 0.1 per cent by weight, but they are the part of the sewage that presents the major problems in its adequate treatment and disposal. The water provides only the volume and a vehicle for the transportation of the solids.

These solids may be dissolved, suspended, or floating. Advertising slogans for a certain brand of soap has established as an acceptable standard the idea of 99.44 per cent pure. An average domestic sewage, consisting of over 99.94 per cent water meets an even stricter standard of purity. However, the less than 0.1 per cent solids portion of sewage is a much more potent and significant impurity than the 0.56 per cent impurity of the soap product.

SOLIDS IN SEWAGE

The solids in sewage may be divided into two general groups depending on their composition or on their physical condition. Thus we have the organic and inorganic solids which may in turn be suspended and dissolved solids. These groupings are shown in Figure I with definitions following the Figure.

DEFINITIONS OF SOLIDS IN SEWAGE

Organic solids. These are generally of animal or vegetable origin including the waste products of animal and vegetable life, dead animal matter, plant tissue or organisms, but may include synthetic organic compounds. They are substances which contain carbon, hydrogen and oxygen, some of which may be combined with nitrogen, sulphur or phosphorus. The principal groups are proteins, carbohydrates and fats together with the products of their decomposition. They are subject to decay or decomposition through the activity of bacteria and other living organisms and are combustible, that is, they can be burned.

3

FIGURE I

PHYSICAL CONDITION AND COMPOSITION OF SOLIDS IN AN

AVERAGE DOMESTIC SEWAGE

(Numbers are in parts per million)

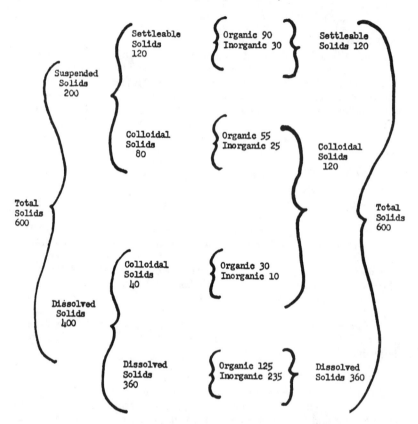

Inorganic solids are those substances which are inert and not subject to decay. Exceptions to this characteristic are certain mineral componds or salts—such as sulfates—which under certain conditions, to be discussed in detail later, can be broken down to simpler substances such as the reduction of sulfates to sulfides. Inorganic solids are frequently designated as mineral substances and include sand, gravel, silt and the mineral salts in the water supply which produce the hardness and mineral content of the water. In general, they are noncombustible.

The amount of these solids, both organic and inorganic, in sewage, imparts to it what is frequently termed its *strength*. Actually the amount or concentration of the organic solids and their capacity to undergo decay or decomposition is the principal part of this strength. The greater the concentration of organic solids, the stronger the sewage. A *strong*

4

sewage can be defined as one containing a large amount of solids, particularly organic solids. A *weak sewage* is one containing only a small amount of organic solids.

As already noted, solids can be grouped depending on their physical state as suspended solids, colloidal solids and dissolved solids, each of which may include both organic and inorganic solids.

Suspended solids are those which are visible and in suspension in the water. They are the solids which can be removed from the sewage by physical or mechanical means, such as sedimentation or filtration. More exactly, they are the solids which are retained on the asbestos mat filter in a Gooch crucible as detailed under the laboratory determination for suspended solids in Chapter 11. They include the larger floating particles and consist of sand, grit, clay, fecal solids, paper, sticks of wood, particles of food and garbage, and similar materials. They are about 70 per cent organic solids and 30 per cent inorganic solids, the latter being principally sand and grit.

Suspended solids are divided into two parts—settleable solids and colloidal solids.

Settleable solids are that portion of the suspended solids which are of sufficient size and weight to settle in a given period of time, usually one hour. As used in this Manual they are those which will settle in an Imhoff cone in one hour (see determination of settleable solids in Chapter 11). They are usually reported as milliliters of solids per liter of sewage, but may be reported as parts per million by weight as given in Figure I. They are about 75 per cent organic and 25 per cent inorganic.

Colloidal suspended solids. These are somewhat loosely defined as the difference between the total suspended solids and the settleable solids. There is, at present, no simple or standard laboratory test to specifically determine colloidal matter. Some will settle out if the quiescent period in the Imhoff cone test is longer than one hour, but most will remain in suspension over long periods of several days or more. They constitute that portion of the total suspended solids (about 40 per cent) which are not readily removed by physical or mechanical treatment facilities but will not pass the asbestos mat filter in a Gooch crucible. In composition they are about two-thirds organic and one-third inorganic, are subject to rapid decay and are an important factor in the treatment and disposal of sweage.

Dissolved solids. The term "dissolved solids" as commonly used in discussing sewage is not technically correct. All of these solids are not in true solution but they include some solids in the colloidal state. As used, the term means all of the solids which pass through the asbestos filter in a Gooch crucible. Of the total dissolved solids, about 90 per cent are in true solution and about ten per cent colloidal. Dissolved solids, as a whole, are about 40 per cent organic and 60 per cent inorganic. The colloidal portion is higher in per cent organic matter than the solids in true solution as the latter includes all of the mineral salts in the water supply.

Total solids, as the term implies, includes all of the solid constituents of sewage. They are the total of the organic and inorganic solids or the total of the suspended and dissolved solids. In an average domestic sewage they are about half organic and half inorganic, and about two-thirds in solution and one-third in suspension. It is the organic half of the solids, which are subject to decay, that constitute the main problem in sewage treatment.

As already noted, the weights of the various types of solids as given in Figure I, and as carried through the definitions, are based on an average domestic sewage, equivalent to approximately 100 gallons per capita per day. Addition of storm water flows or ground water infiltration may change those solids relationships markedly. Similarly, the introduction of industrial wastes may increase the solids content, particularly the organic solids, with very definite variations in the strength of the sewage. Also, sewage varies widely in both composition and volume from hour to hour, depending upon changes in community activities. Obviously, sewage is likely to be at its maximum strength and flow during the daytime and be at a minimum during the night hours. Also, sewage may vary in its composition from day to day with corresponding changes in the industrial and community activities from which the sewage originates. On Sundays and weekends and holidays, flows and strengths are frequently reduced because of the lowered rate of communal activity. Any table of sewage composition can give only an average composition. The amounts of solids indicated cannot be applied equally to all sewages at all times.

DISSOLVED GASES

Sewage contains small and varying concentrations of dissolved gases. Among the most important of these is oxygen, present in the original water supply and also dissolved from air in contact with the surface of flowing sewage. This oxygen, familiarly known as *dissolved oxygen*, is an exceedingly important component of sewage and its functions will be discussed in detail below. In addition to dissolved oxygen, sewage may contain other gases, such as *carbon dioxide* resulting from the decomposition of organic matter; *nitrogen* dissolved from the atmosphere; *hydrogen sulfide* formed by the decomposition of organic and certain inorganic sulfur compounds. These gases, although small in amount, function importantly in the decomposition and treatment of sewage solids and signify to a major degree the progress of such treatment procedures.

Volatile liquids. Sewage may contain volatile liquids. These are, in general, liquids which boil at less than 212 degrees Fahrenheit, as, for example, gasoline.

BIOLOGICAL COMPOSITION OF SEWAGE

Sewage also contains countless numbers of living organisms, most of them too small in size to be visible except when viewed under a microscope. They are a natural living part of the organic matter found in sewage and their presence is of utmost importance because they are one of the reasons for sewage treatment and the success of such treatment, involving decay or decomposition, is dependent upon their activities. It can well be said that they are the workers used by a sewage treatment plant operator and his success may be measured by his knowledge of and attention to their likes and dislikes in their eating habits and environment.

These microscopic living organisms may be considered to be of two general types: bacteria and other more complex living organisms.

Bacteria. Bacteria are living organisms, microscopic in size, which consist of a single cell and are similar in functions and life processes to plants. Some bacteria are *motile*, able to move about freely by their own power, and others are *non-motile*. Like all living organisms. bacteria require food. oxygen and water. They can exist only when the environment provides these necessities. In turn, they produce waste products as the result of their life processes.

Bacteria can be divided into two main groups: Parasitic bacteria and Saprophytic bacteria.

Parasitic bacteria are those which normally live off of another living oragnism, known as the host, since they require a food supply already prepared for their consumption, and generally do not develop outside the body of the host. The parasitic bacteria of importance in sewage. originate in general in the intestinal tract of human beings and animals and reach the sewage by means of body discharges. Included among the parasitic bacteria are certain specific types which, during their growth within the body of the host, produce toxic or poisonous compounds that cause disease in the host. These bacteria are called *pathogenic bacteria*. They may be present in sewage receiving the body discharges of persons ill with such diseases as typhoid fever, dysentery, cholera, or other intestinal infections. The possible presence of these microorganisms in sewage is one of the principal reasons why sewage must be carefully collected, adequately treated, and disposed of safely, to prevent any transfer by sewage flows of these pathogenic or disease-producing bacteria from one person to another.

The *saprophytic bacteria* are those which feed on dead organic matter. thus decomposing organic solids to obtain their needed nourishment, and producing in turn waste substances which consist of both organic and inorganic solids. By this activity they are of utmost importance in sewage treatment methods designed to facilitate or hasten natural decomposition of the organic solids in sewage. Such processes of decomposition will not progress without their activity. In the absence of bacterial life—sterility—decomposition will not take place. Sterile sewage is not subject to the type of decomposition upon which the familiar methods of sewage treatment are based. There are many species of saprophytic bacteria, each of which plays a specific role in the breakdown of the organic solids of sewage. Each species tends to die away following completion of its part in the process of decomposition.

All of the bacteria, parasitic and saprophytic, require, in addition to food, oxygen for respiration. Certain of them can use only oxygen dissolved in water, termed *dissolved oxygen* and sometimes called free or molecular oxygen. These organisms are known as *aerobic bacteria* and the process of degradation of organic solids which they carry out is

7

termed *aerobic decomposition,* oxidation or decay. This type of decomposition proceeds in the presence of dissolved oxygen without the production of foul odors or unsightly conditions. Other types of bacteria cannot exist in the presence of dissolved oxygen but must obtain the required supply of this element from the oxygen content of organic and some inorganic solids which is made available by their decomposition. Such microorganisms are termed *anaerobic bacteria* and the process of degradation of solids which they bring about is called *anaerobic decomposition* or putrefaction, that is, decomposition in the absence of dissolved oxygen, which results in the production of foul odors and unsightly conditions.

To complicate the reactions involved in the decay of organic matter, certain aerobic types can adjust themselves to live and function in the absence of dissolved oxygen and are termed *facultative aerobic bacteria.* Conversely, some varieties of anaerobic bacteria can become accustomed to live and grow in the presence of dissolved oxygen and are thus termed *facultative anaerobic bacteria.*

Such adaptability of the saprophytic bacteria to various sources of oxygen is of great importance in the decomposition of organic solids in sewage and thus in the various treatment procedures.

In addition to food and oxygen, bacteria require moisture to remain alive. This is adequately provided in sewage by its water component.

In order to function at maximum efficiency bacteria require a favorable temperature. They are very susceptible to changes in temperature in that their rate of growth and reproduction, which is directly proportional to the amount of work done, is definitely and sharply affected by such variations. The larger proportion of the saprophytic types thrive best at temperatures from 20°C. to 40°C., or 68°F. to 104°F. These are known as *mesophilic* types. Variations from this temperature range limit the activity of mesophilic bacteria, practically eliminating it at extremely low temperatures and at high temperatures. Mesophilic sludge diegestion proceeds most rapidly at 35°C. or 95°F. Other bacteria live best at high temperatures, in the range of 55°C. to 60°C., or 130°F. to 140°F. These are known as *thermophilic types.* Thermophilic bacteria function in sewage treatment principally in high temperature digestion of sludge solids. A very few types of bacteria find their optimum conditions at low temperatures, 0°C. to 5°C., or 32°F. to 40°F. There are known as *psychrophylic* bacteria. Temperatures, consequently, are of major importance in the operation of sewage treatment processes.

When all of these environmental conditions of food supply, oxygen, moisture, and temperature are properly maintained at their optimum amounts for the full functioning of the bacteria, decomposition of the sewage solids proceeds in a natural orderly manner.

Other Microscopic Organisms. In addition to the bacteria, other living organisms, usually so small in size as to require microscopic viewing, are found in sewage. They are present in large numbers also, although not in as great densities as the various species of bacteria. These other microorganisms tend to be larger and more complex in structure than the bacteria. Some of them are plants and some are animals. All originate in the soil or in the organic wastes that go to make up sewage. Some are motile (able to move about), others are not. All require food, oxygen and moisture. They can be either aerobic or anaerobic or facultative in their oxygen requirements. Their growth is affected by the temperature of the environment in much the same degree as the bacteria. These organisms also function in the decomposition and degradation of the organic solids in sewage. They use these solids as food, and produce waste products simpler in chemical structure. These waste products, in turn, frequently serve as food for certain types of saprophytic bacteria. Many of the larger forms are predatory by nature and prey upon other organisms, especially the bacteria.

Macroscopic Organisms. In addition to the two groups of microscopic organisms described above, many larger more complex organisms play a part in the decomposition of organic matter. These are termed *macroscopic*, that is, visible to the naked eye. They include varieties of worms and insects in various stages of development. Some are active in sewage treatment plant facilities and others are prevalent in streams highly polluted by sewage or other organic wastes.

Some forms of all of these organisms, microscopic and macroscopic, are essential to the orderly decomposition of organic matter in nature, and hence are equally essential for the proper functioning of the usual methods of sewage treatment. In fact, biological organisms actually carry on the processes of treatment and the only responsibility of the operator is to provide the environmental condition best suited to them.

Viruses. There is one other form of life found in sewage that is of interest to the sewage treatment plant operator. These are *viruses*. They are smaller than any of the microscopic organisms, too small to be seen under the ordinary microscope used in bacteriological work. They do not play a significant part in sewage treatment processes, but are important in that they are, like pathogenic bacteria, the causative agents of a number of diseases of man. Some, such as the virus of hepatitis, originate in the intestines of man and are carried with intestinal wastes to the sewage.

CONDITION OF SEWAGE

The extent and nature of the bacterial decomposition of solids in sewage has given rise to certain terms descriptive of the condition of the sewage.

Fresh sewage is, as the name indicates, the first stage after waste solids have been added to water to produce sewage. It contains the dissolved oxygen present in the water supply and remains fresh as long as there is sufficient oxygen to maintain aerobic decomposition. Such sewage is turbid with solids in suspension or floating, greyish in color, and has a musty, not unpleasant odor.

Septic sewage describes a sewage in which the dissolved oxygen has been completely exhausted so that anaerobic decomposition of the solids has been established with the production of hydrogen sulfied and other gases. Such sewage is characterized by a blackish color, foul and unpleasant odor and with black floating and suspended solids.

9

Stable sewage is sewage in which the solids have decomposed to relative inert solids which are subject to no further decomposition or are only slowly decomposable. Dissolved oxygen is again present by absorption from the atmosphere, there is little or no odor and few suspended solids.

CHEMICAL CHANGES IN SEWAGE COMPOSITION

The activities of biological life in sewage produce many changes in the chemical composition of its solids. These chemical changes or, as they should be called, biochemical changes (since they are brought about by biological growth) not only indicate the activities of the micro-organisms but likewise measure the degree of decomposition of the solids and thus the effectiveness of any particular treatment process.

In sewage treatment the physical force of gravity materially reduces the suspended solids in sewage especially the settleable portion. With the colloidal or non-settleable solids, biochemical changes result in the removal of molecules of water bound in them. This loss of water causes them to stick together or flocculate to form heavier or settleable solids. These settled solids, both organic and inorganic, which are removed are called respectively, sludge and grit.

Under anaerobic decomposition, oxygen is removed from complex compounds and simpler ones are formed. Such biochemical reactions continue, and step by step complex compounds are broken down until the final end product of stable inorganic and organic substances is produced.

The complex organic solids originally added to water to form sewage are compounds of the element *carbon* combined with other elements such as nitrogen, sulfur, phosphorus, hydrogen, oxygen, and others, and frequently tightly bound molecules of water. In the process of aerobic decomposition, oxygen is combined with these elements so that the final end products of biochemical change when carried to completion are carbon dioxide, water, nitrates, sulfates, phosphates, and other similar substances usually designated as mineral salts. These are in general quite similar to or the same as the inorganic solids of the sewage and serve as fertilizers or food for the production of new complex organic matter by plant growth.

During the steps of biochemical decomposition intermediate products are formed. They include organic and inorganic acids, gases such as hydrogen sulfide, methane, carbon dioxide, and in many instances very foul smelling gases resulting from the biochemical changes in organic sulfur compounds. It is these by-products of decomposition which appear in the different stages of sewage treatment, particularly the digestion of sludge solids, and affect, sometimes adversely and sometimes not, the progress of the digestion reactions. The particular compounds produced and the amounts of each are dependent upon the type of microorganisms carrying on the reactions. Thus, the appearance of excessive concentrations of acid in sludge digestion indicates that decomposition of the organic matter is being carried on by organisms that will not produce a rapid and orderly anaerobic destruction of the solids but will cause incomplete digestion and the formation of by-products detrimental to good treatment—such as the production of non-combustible gas which is disagreeably odorous from sludge digestion.

The intermediate products of biochemical decomposition of organic solids provide an excellent indication of the progress of biological activity and the type and degree of treatment resulting.

The process of biochemical changes is well illustrated by the nitrogen, carbon and sulfur cycles, Figures 2, 3, and 4, which show the steps or stages through which organic matter containing nitrogen, carbon or sulfur pass from dead organic matter through decomposition to products used by plant life upon which animal life depends. Animal life in turn through waste products, death and decay ends up as dead organic matter to start the cycles over again.

In all three cycles the left half of the figures pertain to living matter while the right half of the figures is concerned with dead or waste material. Sewage treatment and disposal lie in the right half.

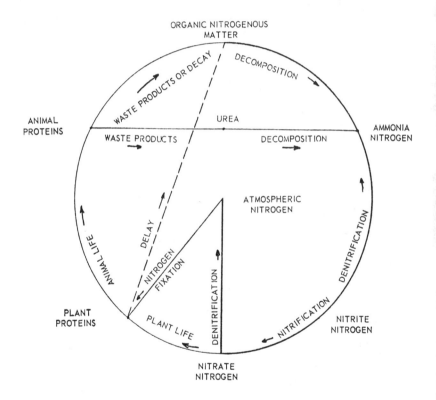

NITROGEN CYCLE

FIGURE 2

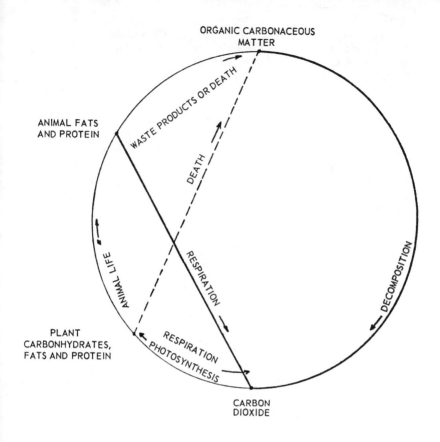

ORGANIC CARBONACEOUS
MATTER

WASTE PRODUCTS OR DEATH

DEATH

ANIMAL FATS
AND PROTEIN

RESPIRATION

DECOMPOSITION

ANIMAL LIFE

PLANT
CARBONHYDRATES,
FATS AND PROTEIN

RESPIRATION
PHOTOSYNTHESIS

CARBON
DIOXIDE

CARBON CYCLE

FIGURE 3

The three cycles illustrate nature's conservation of matter. The products of death are changed to become the support of plant and animal life. Air and water serve as a huge reservoir in which oxygen, nitrogen, carbon dioxide and other gases produced in one part of the cycle can be stored till needed in another part.

Sewage treatment does not alter or modify natural processes. A treatment plant is merely a device to localize in a most suitable place a workshop in which the natural processes of decomposition of dead organic matter can be carried on as far as necessary and to some extent be controlled and accelerated.

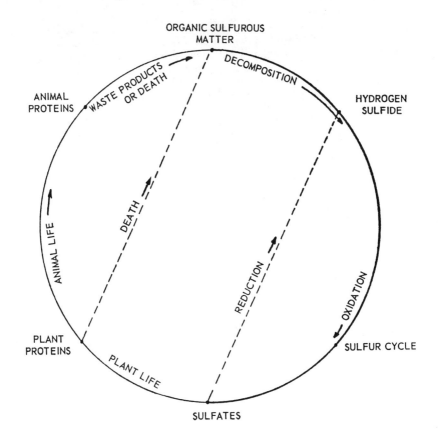

SULFUR CYCLE

FIGURE 4

In the biochemical changes in sewage the dissolved gases play an important role. This is especially true of dissolved oxygen which, when present in the sewage or when added to it by treatment devices, insures the growth and activities of the aerobic microorganisms and thus the progress of aerobic decomposition without the production of putrefactive conditions. When dissolved oxygen is completely exhausted, the aerobic organisms are displaced by anaerobic varieties, and anaerobic decomposition takes place with the rapid development of putrefaction and the accompanying unsightly black appearance of the sewage together with foul odors. Although the other gases dissolved in the water fraction of the sewage do not control biological activities to the extent of the dissolved oxygen, they also play a part. Hydrogen sulfide, a foul-smelling gas, is the result of anaerobic decomposition of sulfur-bearing compounds and produces acid conditions which may affect further biochemical reactions and which will exert corrosive action on the sewage structures. Carbon dioxide, if present in excessive amounts, indicates that acid decomposition of the solids is taking place, with resulting reduction in the rate of decay. In the case of sludge digestion, carbon dioxide production reduces the generation of combustible gas which is a valuable by-product of such operations.

The chemical or biochemical changes in sewage solids are best measured by chemical analyses. Such chemical analyses will:

(a) Detect and measure biochemical reactions.

(b) Detect and measure the chemical compounds formed during such biochemical reactions.

(c) Measure the degree and rate of the decomposition of organic solids.

(d) Measure the efficiencies of various methods and devices used in sewage treatment.

Details of the various chemical tests which may be used for these purposes, will be discussed in Chapter 11.

CHAPTER 2

SEWAGE DISPOSAL

As discussed in Chapter I, sewage is the waste water of community life. In composition it includes dissolved and suspended organic solids, which are putrescible and therefore will decay. Sewage also contains countless numbers of living organisms—bacteria and other microorganisms whose life activities cause the process of decomposition. When decay proceeds under anaeronic conditions, that is, in the absence of dissolved oxygen in the sewage, offensive conditions result and odors and unsightly appearances are produced. When decay proceeds under aerobic conditions, that is, in the presence of dissolved oxygen, offensive conditions do not result and the process is greatly accelerated.

The promotion of cleanliness by the removal of filth and wastes to an area remote from the center of activity is important. It is only by such practices that the environment can be maintained in an acceptable and safe condition. Among the waste products of life are the disease-producing (pathogenic) bacteria and viruses which can be readily transferred by sewage from sick individuals to well ones. Properly regulated procedures for disposal of sewage are necessary to protect the health of the people and to maintain the cleanliness of the environment and the comfort of the inhabitants.

A sharp distinction must be made between the term "sewage disposal" which is the subject of this Chapter and "sewage treatment" which is covered in subsequent chapters. All sewage has to be disposed of. Some sewage is subjected to various types of treatment *before* disposal, but some sewage receives no treatment before disposal.

SEWAGE TREATMENT

Sewage treatment is a process in which the solids in sewage are partially removed and partially changed by decomposition from complex highly putrescible organic solids to mineral or relatively stable organic solids. The extent of this change is dependent on the treatment processes involved. After all treatment processes have been completed, it is still necessary to dispose of the liquid and the solids which have been removed.

SEWAGE DISPOSAL

There are three methods by which final disposal of sewage can be accomplished.

Disposal by Irrigation. This involves spreading the sewage over the surface of the ground, generally by irrigation ditches. There is some evaporation, but most of the sewage soaks into the ground and supplies moisture with small amounts of fertilizing ingredients for plant life. Use of this method is largely restricted to small volumes of sewage from a relatively small population and where land area is available. It has its best use in arid or semi-arid areas where the moisture added to the soil is of special value. If crops are cultivated on the disposal area, industrial wastes which would be toxic or impair the growth of vegetation must be excluded from sewers. Because of the ever present possibility that sewage may contain pathogenic organisms, the production of foods for human consumption which may be eaten without cooking is not desirable.

Subsurface Disposal. By this method sewage is introduced into the ground below its surface through pits or tile fields. It is commonly used for disposal of settled sewage from residences or institutions where there is only a limited volume of sewage. Because it has little application for municipalities, any discussion of the many details involved would be of little value in this manual.

Disposal by Dilution. Disposal by dilution is the simple method of discharging sewage into a surface water such as a river, lake or ocean. This results in the pollution of the receiving water. The degree of pollution depends on the dilution, the volume and composition of sewage as compared to the volume of water with which it is mixed. When the volume and organic content of the sewage is small, compared with the volume of the receiving water, the dissolved oxygen present in the receiving water is adequate to provide for aerobic decomposition of the organic solids in the sewage so that nuisance conditions do not develop. However, in spite of the continued aerobic status of the receiving water, the bacterial pollution remains a health menace and floating solids in the sewage, if not previously removed, are visible evidence of the pollution.

Where the dissolved oxygen in the receiving water is inadequate to maintain aerobic decomposition, anaerobic decomposition takes place and putrefaction with objectionable conditions results. It is not so much the volume of sewage that is the critical factor as the amount of readily decomposable organic matter in the sewage. Thus a volume of sewage that has been treated to remove or reduce this organic matter can be discharged to a natural surface water without creating objectionable conditions, while the same volume of raw or untreated sewage might produce a nuisance. The dissolved oxygen in the receiving water is the determining factor.

ROLE OF DISSOLVED OXYGEN IN RECEIVING WATERS

When sewage solids are discharged into water, decay and decomposition proceed owing to activities of the bacteria and microorganisms present in the sewage and in the receiving water. Oxygen is required for the functioning of all such biological and biochemical reactions. As discussed previously, when dissolved oxygen is present, aerobic organisms carry on the work, and aerobic decomposition of the organic solids proceeds. When oxygen is absent, anaerobic organisms take over and putrefaction results. Thus, when sewage is discharged into a stream, the reactions depend upon the dissolved oxygen present in the water.

16

Oxygen is dissolved in water from air in contact with the water surface until the point of saturation at a given temperature is reached. At a temperature of 0°C., water contains 14.6 ppm of dissolved oxygen at saturation. This concentration is reduced as the water temperature increases, so that at a temperature of 15°C., the dissolved oxygen concentration at saturation is 10.00 ppm. When the dissolved oxygen concentration is reduced below the saturation value, more is dissolved from the air. Turbulent flow of a stream over stones, riffles, and rapids increase the rate of solution of oxygen, or reaeration. By means of reaeration, additional oxygen is made available for the biochemical decomposition of putrescible organic solids.

BIOCHEMICAL OXYGEN DEMAND—BOD

The amount of oxygen required for the aerobic biological oxidation of the organic solids in a sewage or waste is the *biochemical oxygen demand (BOD)*. It is determined by a laboratory test which is detailed in Chapter 11. Since this decomposition extends over a long period of time and is dependent on temperature, BOD values from laboratory tests should state the time and temperature used in making the test. Those most commonly used are 5 days and 20°C. (68°F.) and unless other time and temperature are specifically mentioned, these are generally assumed to have been the time and temperature used.

SELF-PURIFICATION

When sewage is discharged into a stream, decay and decomposition continue and proceed towards completion. A stream polluted at a given point would, as a result of the decomposition of the polluting organic matter, tend to return to a state similar to that before the pollution occurred. This is generally designated as the process of *self-purification*. It proceeds by physical, chemical and biological means. The physical reactions are essentially those of sedimentation of suspended solids to form deposits called sludge banks, the bleaching and other effects of sunlight, and reaeration.

The chemical and biological reactions are more complex. Here the living organisms feed on the organic solids, producing waste products which may destroy them and at the same time serve as food for succeeding types, which carry on the process of decomposition to a further degree—until finally the complex organic compounds are reduced to stable inorganic salts, such as nitrates, sulfates, phosphates, etc. These, in turn, serve as food for other biological forms, such as the algae, which during the process of their growth and metabolism produce oxygen as a waste product. This then dissolves in the water, adding to that obtained through reaeration. These reactions return the stream or water to a condition of relative cleanliness, and self-purification may be considered complete. The progress of self-purification is dependent upon time, temperature, oxygen supply, and the other environmental factors which regulate biological growths.

Self-purification of a stream is generally considered to take place in four stages with the stream divided into four zones which merge into

17

each other. These are called the zones of degradation, decomposition, recovery and clean water. As noted below under zone of decomposition this zone is not always present.

Zone of Degradation. The first of these zones occurs immediately below the point of pollution and is designated as the *Zone of Degradation.* This zone is characterized by visible evidences of pollution. Floating solids, such as bits of garbage, sticks, paper, and possibly fecal solids are present. The turbidity of the stream is markedly increased by the sewage discharge. Oxygen is reduced but is not immediately exhausted. Fish life decreases and is limited to those species which can survive in water with relatively little dissolved oxygen. Biological life, although not visible, abounds. Bacteria are present in large numbers—including those pathogenic ones that were in the sewage. Fungus organisms also are present and in time long stringy growths of these will be found clinging to rocks and shrubs on the shoreline. Active growth of the microbiological life absorbs and gradually exhausts the dissolved oxygen. If the flow in the stream in this section is slow, sedimentation of the suspended solids takes place to create sludge banks. This accumulation of sewage solids putrefies and further contributes to the degradation of the stream.

Zone of Decomposition. As the dissolved oxygen supply is exhausted, the *Zone of Degradation* passes into the *Zone of Decomposition* where anaerobic decomposition or putrefaction is initiated.

With a heavy load of pollution this occurs quickly. With a smaller discharge of sewage relative to the volume of the stream, the change to the second zone proceeds more slowly. When the volume of sewage discharged is relatively very small so that dissolved oxygen is continuously adequate to sustain aerobic life, the stream may not pass into the *Zone of Decomposition,* and the *Zone of Degradation* may pass directly into the *Zone of Recovery.*

The *Zone of Decomposition* is characterized by the development of anaerobic decomposition. Dissolved oxygen is almost or entirely depleted and all fish life disappears. The water turns black, and foul odors are produced as a result of the decomposition of the organic solids by anaerobic organisms which are present in large numbers. Sedimentation of suspended solids continues with sludge deposits appearing which are similar to those occurring in the first zone. As decomposition of organic matter progresses, the putrescible solids are reduced in amount and putrefactive reactions begin to decline in rate. Oxygen from reaeration first equals and then exceeds the rate at which it is being used for biochemical decomposition so that some dissolved oxygen is present at the lower edge of this zone, which merges into the third zone, the *Zone of Recovery.*

Zone of Recovery. In the *Zone of Recovery* dissolved oxygen appears in gradually increasing amounts, organic solids decrease, and a favorable appearance of the stream is attained. Microorganisms in reduced numbers are present but the anaerobes are dying and aerobic species are present. Fish can again survive, and other higher forms of organisms appear in large numbers. Sedimentation of solids continues, and the organic solids in the sludge banks and bottom deposits are acted on by worms and larvae which are large enough to be visible, to affect further decomposition.

As previously indicated, if aerobic conditions are always present in the stream, the *Zone of Recovery* follows immediately after the *Zone of Degradation*.

Zone of Clean Water. In the *Zone of Recovery* decomposition of organic solids is largely completed and mineral and stable inorganic solids are found in major concentrations. The stream then flows into the fourth and final zone, the Zone of Clean Water. Here the water is similar in appearance to what it was before it received the polluting material. Visible floating solids are absent, the water is clear, free from suspended matter, and has returned to its original color. Oxygen is at or near the point of saturation. Living microscopic organisms, including bacteria, are present but in relatively small numbers. Larger organisms are abundant, principally the algae and other forms which find in clean water their optimum environment and which use as food the stable inorganic compounds resulting from decomposition of the complex organic solids characteristic of the sewage that produced the pollution. Fish are generally more abundant than before the pollution occurred because of the increase in the population of macroscopic organisms which serves to increase the food supply for the fish.

The time required for self-purification of a stream or the distance it must flow to pass through the four zones is dependent upon the strength and relative volumes of pollution and stream flow, on the turbulence of flow, the temperature of the water, and, of major importance, on whether or not additional pollution is discharged into the stream during the progress of self-purification.

Possibility of Residual Pollution. The process of self-purification affects primarily the putrescible matter in the sewage. Some pathogenic organisms and viruses may survive. Other polluting substances, especially metallic and other compounds not completely organic in nature originating from industrial and manufacturing processes, are not changed by the biochemical processes. These substances, if present in sufficient concentration, interfere with and inhibit biological decomposition and may remain as a residual pollution which can impair the quality of the receiving stream to such a degree that the water is not suitable for use for water supply, recreational, industrial and other purposes.

NEED FOR SEWAGE TREATMENT

The problem of sewage disposal developed with the use of water to pick up and carry away waste products of human life. Prior to that the volume of wastes, without the water vehicle, was small and disposal was largely restricted to the individual's or family's excreta. The earliest method was to leave body waste and garbage on the surface of the ground where it was gradually decayed by bacteria, mostly the saprophytic anaerobic type. This caused the production of foul odors. Later experience showed that if these wastes were promptly buried the development of these odors was prevented. The next step was the development of the earth privy, a method for the disposal of excremental wastes which is still widely used.

With the development of community water supplies and the use of water to flush or transport wastes from habitations, it became necessary to find disposal methods not only for the wastes themselves but for the water which carried them. All of the three possible methods—irrigation, subsurface disposal and dilution—were employed.

As urban communities increased in population, with proportional increase in the volume of sewage and amount of organic waste, all methods of disposal resulted in such unsatisfactory conditions that remedial measures became essential and the development of methods of treatment of sewage prior to ultimate disposal was started.

The objectives sought in sewage treatment include:

(1) Maintenance of sources for use as domestic water supplies

(2) Prevention of disease

(3) Prevention of nuisances

(4) Maintenance of clean waters for bathing and other recreational purposes

(5) Maintenance of clean waters for the propagation and survival of fish life

(6) Conservation of water for industrial and agricultural uses

(7) Prevention of silting in navigable channels

A sewage treatment plant is designed to remove from the sewage enough organic and inorganic solids so that it can be disposed of without infringing upon the objectives sought.

The various processes used in sewage treatment parallel closely the processes involved in the self-purification of a polluted stream. Treatment devices merely localize and confine these processes to a restricted, controlled, suitable area and provide favorable conditions for the acceleration of the physical and biochemical reactions.

The extent or degree of treatment needed varies greatly from place to place. Basically there are three determining factors.

(1) The character and amount of the solids carried by the sewage

(2) The objectives sought

(3) The ability or capacity of the land (in disposal by irrigation and subsurface disposal) or the receiving water (in disposal by dilution) to handle by self-purification or dispersal the water and solids in the sewage without infringing on the objectives sought.

The removal of floating solids by screens may be adequate for sewage discharged into coastal sea waters. A very high removal of suspended solids, decomposition of dissolved organic solids and destruction of pathogenic organisms may be required, however, before discharge to a river which is used downstream as a source of public water supply. Adequate treatment prior to disposal to attain objectives is becoming a must, but excessive overtreatment is an unwarranted extravagance.

20

After the disposal of the sewage effluent from a treatment plant, there still remain in the plant the solids and water constituting the sludge which has been removed from the sewage. This too, must be disposed of safely and without nuisance.

The progress of self-purification of a stream can be measured by appropriate physical, chemical and biological laboratory tests. Similar tests are used to measure and control the progress of sewage treatment plant processes.

LEGAL ASPECTS OF SEWAGE DISPOSAL

The serious problem involving the disposal of sewage and other wastes by adequate and effective means that will eliminate nuisances and not violate the rights and welfare of individuals and communities has led to the development of laws and regulations governing such disposal.

It is presumed that in ancient times, customs slowly developed which regulated the disposal of the wastes of the individuals and of the group. As time went, on custom took on the force of law, and led, over the years, to the formulation of legal regulations—first as common law and then as statutory law.

Mosaic Law. One of the earliest recorded regulations pertaining to waste disposal can be found in the 23rd chapter of Deuteronomy. Moses, as the leader of a great community of people, found it necessary to establish rules for the conduct of his followers. Verses 12 to 14 of this chapter contain that portion of the Mosaic Law which placed the responsibility for proper disposal of excrement with the individual and required that it be buried. Modern research has not changed the fundamental principles involved. Increased knowledge of the transmission of disease from man to man and the need for personal cleanliness in community life have led to better practices and regulation for disposal of these waste products.

Common Law. Perhaps the earliest regulations related to sewage disposal and water pollution were based on the common law as related to the use of streams by owners of property bordering the stream. These specified (a) that every riparian owner is entitled to reasonable use of the water flowing past his property, and (b) that every riparian owner is entitled to have the waters of the stream reach his property in their natural condition and unimpaired as to quality and quantity.

Modern Legal Practice. The general principles of Common Law have been further clarified and modified by many specific statutory laws and regulations concerned with the disposal of sewage into streams and other bodies of water. Large numbers of lawsuits based on instances of pollution have led to legislation in most states governing the treatment and disposal of community wastes. Such legislation usually applies not only to pollution of waterways but controls the installation of treatment facilities by requiring approval of design and supervision of operation by some government body. Disposal of industrial waste as well as of domestic sewage is included in the legislation.

New York State now has stringent laws relating to this important matter of sewage and wastes disposal. Articles 11 and 12 of the Public

Health Law regulate sewage disposal for the prevention and control of water pollution.

Article 11, Title III, prohibits the discharge of sewage into waters of the State unless a permit for such discharge has been granted by the State Commissioner of Health. The legal procedures for the control of pollution and regulations relative to construction of sewers and sewage treatment facilities are included.

Article 12 is concerned with the control of water pollution. Section 1200 outlines the policy of the State in this regard, and Section 1201 states the purpose of these regulations.

"Section 1200. Declaration of policy. It is declared to be the public policy of the State of New York to maintain reasonable standards of purity of the waters of the state consistent with public health and public enjoyment thereof, the propagation and protection of fish and wild life, including birds, mammals and other terrestial and aquatic life, and the industrial development of the state, and to that end require the use of all known available and reasonable methods to prevent and control the pollution of the waters of the State of New York."

"Section 1201. Statement of purpose. It is the purpose of this article to safeguard the waters of the state from pollution by: (a) preventing any new pollution, and (b) abating polluting existing when this chapter is enacted, under a program consistent with the declaration of policy above stated in the provisions of this article."

The ensuing sections of the New York State Public Health Law delineate the procedures that must be followed to control pollution of the State's water resources. The principle of classification of the surface and ground water resources of the State in accordance with the usage to which a specific water should be put is established. Various degrees of permissible pollution of streams, lakes, and ground waters are recognized.

In 1950 there were established seven classes of standards for fresh surface waters, four for tidal salt waters and two for ground waters. Several others have subsequently been established to meet spacial local conditions. The classes are based on the best use of the waters. The standards do not specify the character of polluting material discharged but are those which the waters must meet after such material has had an opportunity for reasonable dilution and mixture with the waters. Indirectly, however, this does not indicate the treatment pollutional material must have prior to discharge.

Best usages include use for drinking, culinary, food processing, bathing, fishing, agriculture, production of shellfish for marketing, agriculture and industry, navigation, sewage and wastes disposal.

Laws and regulations governing pollution and sewage disposal have become more and more essential with population increase. Only by such legal procedures and their enforcement can a clean, comfortable, and healthy environment be assured for all people.

CHAPTER 3

SEWAGE TREATMENT METHODS

Satisfactory disposal of sewage, whether by irrigation, subsurface methods or dilution, is dependent on its treatment prior to disposal. For disposal by dilution, adequate treatment is necessary to prevent contamination of receiving waters to a degree which might interfere with their best use, whether it be for water supply, recreation, fishing or any other required purpose. Even when a body of water has no other use than for the disposal of sewage or liquid industrial wastes, some treatment is necessary to avoid creating offensive conditions.

Sewage treatment is a means whereby in a limited segregated area, and under controlled conditions, it is possible to carry out the various stages, described in Chapter 2, as taking place in the self-purification of a stream.

The purpose of sewage treatment prior to disposal by dilution is to remove from the sewage enough solids to permit the remainder to be discharged to receiving waters without interfering with its best or proper use, taking into consideration the capacity of the receiving waters to assimilate the added load. The solids which are removed are primarily organic but include also inorganic solids. As the best use of a receiving water may vary from use of the water for drinking and culinary purposes to use, primarily, for the disposal of sewage and industrial wastes, the amount or degree of treatment provided for the sewage or wastes must be varied accordingly. Treatment must be provided for the solids and liquids which are removed as sludge, and treatment to control odors, to retard biological activity or destroy pathogenic organisms may also be needed.

While the devices used in sewage treatment are numerous they may all be included under five methods:

(1) Preliminary treatment
(2) Primary treatment
(3) Secondary treatment
(4) Chlorination
(5) Sludge treatment

PRELIMINARY TREATMENT

At most plants preliminary treatment is used to protect pumping equipment and facilitate subsequent treatment processes. Preliminary devices are designed to remove or cut up the larger suspended and floating solids: to remove the heavy inorganic solids: and to remove excessive amounts of oils or greases. In some few instances where, for example, disposal by dilution is into tidal waters, the results accomplished by preliminary treatment may be adequate.

To effect the objectives of preliminary treatment, the following devices are commonly used:

(1) Screens—rack, bar or fine
(2) Comminuting devices—grinders, cutters, shredders
(3) Grit chambers
(4) Pre-aeration tanks

In addition to the above, chlorination may be used in preliminary treatment. Since chlorination may be used at all stages in treatment, it is considered to be a method by itself and is covered in a separate section in this Manual.

Preliminary treatment devices require careful design and operation. Detailed discussion of them is contained in Chapter 4.

PRIMARY TREATMENT

By this treatment most of the settleable solids or about 40 to 60 per cent of the suspended solids are separated or removed from the sewage by the physical process of sedimentation in settling tanks. When certain chemicals are used with primary tanks much of the colloidal as well as the settleable solids or a total of 80 to 90 per cent of the suspended solids are removed. Biological activity in the sewage is of negligible importance.

The purpose of primary devices is to reduce the velocity of the sewage sufficiently to permit solids to settle. Therefore, primary devices may be called settling tanks. Because of variations in design and operation, settling tanks can be divided into four general groups.

(1) Septic tanks
(2) Two story tanks—Imhoff and several patented units
(3) Plain sedimentation tank with mechanical sludge removal
(4) Upward flow clarifiers with mechanical sludge removal

When chemicals are used, other auxiliary units are employed. These are:

(1) Chemical feed units
(2) Mixing devices
(3) Flocculators

The results obtained by primary treatment, together with anaerobic sludge digestion as described later, are such that they can be compared with the zone of degradation in stream self-purification. The use of chlorine with primary treatment is discussed under the section on Chlorination.

In many cases, primary treatment is adequate to permit the discharge of the effluent to the receiving waters without interfering with the proper subsequent uses of the waters.

SECONDARY TREATMENT

This must be used where sewage after primary treatment still contains more organic solids in suspension or solution than the receiving waters can assimilate without infringing upon their normal proper use. Secondary treatment depends primarily upon biological aerobic organisms for the biochemical decomposition of organic solids to inorganic or stable organic solids. It is comparable to the zone of recovery in the self-purification of a stream.

The devices used in secondary treatment may be divided into four groups.

(1) Trickling filters with secondary settling tanks
(2) Aeration tanks—(a) activated sludge with final settling tanks, and, (b) contact aeration
(3) Intermittent sand filters
(4) Stabilization ponds

The use of chlorine with secondary treatment is discussed under the chapter on Chlorination.

CHLORINATION

This is a method of treatment which may be employed for many purposes in all stages in sewage treatment, and even prior to preliminary treatment. It involves the application of chlorine to the sewage for the following purposes.

(1) Disinfection or destruction of pathogenic organisms
(2) Prevention of sewage decomposition—(a) odor control, (b) protection of plant structures
(3) Aid in plant operation—(a) sedimentation, (b) trickling filters, (c) activated sludge bulking
(4) Reducation or delay of biochemical oxygen demand

SLUDGE TREATMENT

The solids removed from sewage in both primary and secondary treatment units, together with the water removed with them, constitute sewage sludge. While in some few instances satisfactory disposal without treatment is practical, it is generally necessary to subject sludge to some treatment to prepare or condition it for disposal without creating unsatisfactory conditions. Such treatment has two objectives—the removal of part or all of the water in the sludge to greatly reduce its volume, and the decomposition of the putrescible organic solids to mineral solids or to relatively stable organic solids. This is accomplished by a combination of two or more of the following methods.

(1) Thickening
(2) Digestion with or without heat
(3) Drying on sand bed—open or covered
(4) Conditioning with chemicals

(5) Elutriation

(6) Vacuum filtration

(7) Heat drying

(8) Incineration

(9) Wet oxidation

(10) Floatation with chemicals and air

(11) Centrifuging

PACKAGE UNITS

The term "package units" has come into quite common use in recent years to describe equipment which has been put on the market by a number of manufacturers. There is no universally accepted definition of the term. One meaning is a complete installation including both mechanisms and pre-fabricated containers. This term is also applied to installations where only the mechanisms are purchased and the containers constructed by the purchaser in accordance with plans and specifications prepared by the manufacturer. The latter appears to be the more generally accepted interpretation.

Though specific limitations have not been established, individual package units have, in general, been small installations serving a limited population.

Package units have been adapted to practically all the treatment devices, either singly or in various combinations, listed in this chapter.

CHAPTER 4

PRELIMINARY TREATMENT

The purpose of preliminary treatment is to remove from the sewage some of its constitutents which can clog or damage pumps, or interfere with subsequent treatment processes. Preliminary treatment devices are, therefore, designed to:

(1) remove or to reduce in size the large suspended or floating organic solids. These solids consist of pieces of wood, cloth, paper, garbage, together with some fecal matter.

(2) remove heavy inorganic solids such as sand, gravel and possible metallic objects all of which are called grit.

(3) remove excessive amounts of oils or greases.

A number of devices or types of equipment are used to obtain these objectives.

RACKS AND BAR SCREENS

These consist of bars usually spaced three-quarter inches to six inches. Those most commonly used provide clear openings of one to two inches. Although large screens are sometimes set vertically, screens are usually set at an angle of 45 to 60 degrees with the vertical. They may be cleaned either manually or by means of automatically operated rakes. It has been recommended that hand cleaned screens, except those for emergency use, should be placed on slopes of 30 to 45 degrees with the vertical. The solids removed by these units can be disposed of by burial or incineration or they may be reduced in size by grinders or shredding devices and returned to the sewage.

FINE SCREENS

Screens with openings of one-eighth inch or less have been used in sewage treatment. They can be classified as bandscreens, disk screens and drum screens, and are mentioned here because there are a few in operation at existing sewage treatment plants in New York State. They are commonly used in the treatment of many types of industrial wastes, but are no longer considered for sewage treatment except in special cases, because of the limited results obtained.

COMMINUTING DEVICES

Grinders, Cutters and Shredders. These are devices to break or cut up solids to such size that they can be returned to the sewage without danger of clogging pumps or piping or affecting subsequent treatment devices. They may be separate devices to grind solids removed by screens or a combination of screen and cutters installed within the sewage flow channel in such a manner that the objective is accomplished without actually removing these larger solids from the sewage. These latter devices are made by a number of manufacturers under various trade names and, in most cases, consist of fixed, rotating or oscillating teeth or blades, acting together to reduce the solids to a size which will pass through fixed or rotating screens or grids having openings of about one-fourth inch. Some of these devices are even designed to operate as a low-lift pump.

GRIT CHAMBERS

Sewage usually contains a relatively large amount of inorganic solids such as sand, cinders and gravel which are called grit. The amount varies greatly depending on a number of factors, but primarily on whether the collecting sewer system is of the sanitary or combined type. Grit will damage pumps by abrasion and cause serious operation difficulties in sedimentation tanks and with sludge digestion by accumulation around and plugging of outlets. It is, therefore, common practice to remove this material by grit chambers. They are usually located ahead of pumps or comminuting devices, and if mechanically cleaned as described below, should be preceded by coarse bar rack screens. Grit chambers are generally designed as long channels. In these channels the velocity is reduced sufficiently to deposit heavy inorganic solids but to retain organic material in suspension. Channel type chambers should be designed to provide controlled velocities as close as possible to 1.0 foot per second. The detention period should be based on size of particle to be removed and is usually between 20 seconds to 1.0 minute. This is attained by providing several chambers to accommodate variation in flow or by proportional weirs at the end of the chamber or other flow control devices which permit regulation of flow velocity. There are also patented devices to remove grit. A recent development is the injection of air several feet above the floor of a tank type unit. The rolling action of the air keeps the lighter organic matter in suspension and allows the grit relatively free from organic matter to be deposited in the quiescent zone beneath the zone of air diffusion.

Cleaning. Grit chambers are designed to be cleaned manually or by mechanically operated devices. If cleaned manually, storage space for the deposited grit is usually provided. Grit chambers for plants treating wastes from combined sewers should have at least two hand-cleaned units or a mechanically cleaned unit with by-pass. Mechanically cleaned grit chambers are recommended. Single hand-cleaned chambers with by-pass are acceptable for small sewage treatment plants serving sanitary sewer systems. Chambers other than channel type are acceptable, if provided with adequate and flexible controls for agitation and/or air supply devices and with grit removal equipment.

There are a number of mechanical cleaning units available which remove grit by scrapers or buckets while the grit chamber is in nomal operation. These require much less grit storage space than manually operated units.

Washing Grit. Grit always contains some organic matter which decomposes and creates odors. To facilitate economical disposal of grit without causing nuisance, the organic matter is sometimes washed from the grit and returned to the sewage. Special equipment is available to wash grit. Mechanical cleaning equipment generally provides for washing grit with sewage as it is removed from the chamber.

Quantity of Grit. This depends on the type of tributary sewer system, the condition of the sewer lines and other factors. Strictly domestic sewage collected in well constructed sewers will contain little grit, while combined sewage will carry large volumes of grit reaching a peak at times of severe storms. In general 1.0 to 4.0 cu ft of grit per million gallons can be expected.

Operation. Manually cleaned grit chambers for combined sewage should be cleaned after every large storm. Under ordinary conditions these grit chambers should be cleaned when the deposited grit has filled 50 to 60 per cent of the grit storage space. This should be tested at least every ten days.

When mechanically cleaned chambers are used they must be cleaned at regular intervals to prevent undue load on the cleaning mechanism. Recommendations of the manufacturer should be rigidly observed. This plus experience will determine the cleaning schedule.

A grit in which marked odors develop indicates that too much organic matter is being removed in the grit chamber. If sludge from settling tank is excessively high in inorganic matter, or if there is excessive wear in pumps, comminutors, sludge collectors or other mechanical equipment, the reason is likely to be inefficient functioning of the grit chamber in removing grit and a study of this unit should be made.

Disposal of Screenings and Grit. Screenings decompose rapidly with foul odors. They should be kept covered in cans at the screens and removed at least daily or oftener for disposal by burial, incineration or through grinders. The walls and platforms of the screen chamber and screen itself should be hosed down and kept clean. Grit containing much organic matter may have to be buried to prevent odor nuisances.

PRE-AERATION TANKS

Pre-aeration of sewage, that is aeration before primary treatment, is sometimes provided for the following purposes:

(1) To obtain a greater removal of suspended solids in sedimentation tanks.

(2) To assist in the removal of grease and oil carried in the sewage.

(3) To freshen up septic sewage prior to further treatment.

(4) BOD Reduction.

Pre-aeration is accomplished by introducing air into the sewage for a period of 20 to 30 minutes at the design flow. This may be accomplished by forcing compressed air into the sewage at a rate usually taken as 0.10 cu ft per gallon of sewage when 30 minutes of aeration is provided or by mechanical agitation whereby the sewage is stirred or agitated so that new surfaces are continually brought into contact with the atmosphere for absorption of air. To insure proper agitation when compressed air is forced into the sewage, air is usually supplied at the rate of 1.0 to 4.0 cubic feet per minute per linear foot of tank or channel. When air for mechanical agitation (either with or without the use of chemicals) is used for additional purpose of obtaining increased reduction in BOD, the detention period should be at least 45 minutes at design flow. The agitation of sewage in the presence of air tends to collect or flocculate lighter suspended solids into heavier masses which settle more readily in the sedimentation tanks. It also helps to separate grease and oil from the sewage and sewage solids and to carry them to the surface. By the addition of air aerobic conditions are also restored in septic sewage to improve subsequent treatment.

The devices and equipment for introducing the air into the sewage are the same or similar to those used in the activated sludge process and are described under that heading in Chapter 6.

CHAPTER 5

PRIMARY TREATMENT

Primary treatment devices are designed to remove from the sewage organic and inorganic settleable solids, by the physical process of sedimentation. This is effected by reducing the velocity of flow. Sewers are designed to maintain a velocity of about two feet per second which is adequate to carry all solids with the sewage flow and prevent their deposition in the sewers. In preliminary treatment this velocity is lowered to about one foot per second for a very brief period during which the heavier inorganic solids are settled out as grit. In primary treatment the velocity of flow is reduced to a fraction of an *inch* per second in a settling or sedimentation tank for sufficient time to allow the major portion of the settleable solids, which are largely organic, to settle out of the sewage flow.

Principle primary treatment devices are sedimentation tanks, some of which have the further function of providing for the decomposition of the settled organic solids, known as sludge digestion. There are a number of types of tanks used.

SEPTIC TANKS

The septic tank was one of the earliest primary treatment devices developed. It is designed to hold the sewage at a very low velocity under anaerobic conditions for a period of 12 to 24 hours during which a high removal of the settleable solids in the sewage is effected. These solids decompose in the bottom of the tank with the formation of gas which, entrained in the solids, causes them to rise through the sewage to the surface and lie as a scum layer until the gas has escaped, after which they again settle. This continual floatation and resettling of solids carry them in the current of the sewage toward the outlet, with some eventually passing out with the effluent, thus partially defeating the purpose of the tank. Due to the long holding period and the mixing with decomposing solids, the sewage itself leaves the tank in a septic condition difficult to treat in secondary units.

Septic tanks are no longer used except for very small installations. They do, however, have common use for individual residences, small institutions or schools where the tank effluent can be disposed by by sub-surface methods or where the dilution factor in the receiving waters is high. In such situations they have the value of requiring a minimum of attention to operation which involves only occasional cleaning of the tank of sludge and scum accumulations.

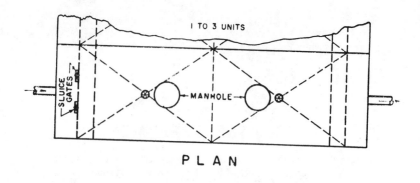

PLAN

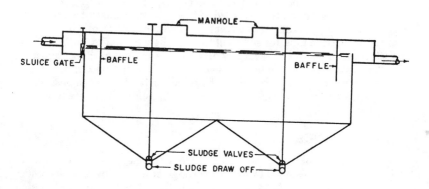

ELEVATION

SEPTIC TANK

FIGURE 5.

TWO-STORY TANKS

The two-story tank was developed to correct the two main defects of the septic tank.

(1) It prevents the solids once removed from the sewage from again being mixed with it though still providing for decomposition of these solids in the same unit and

(2) It provides an effluent amenable to further treatment.

Contact between the sewage and the anaerobic digesting sludge is practically eliminated and the holding period in the tank is reduced.

The best known and most used two-story tank was originally designed by Dr. Karl Imhoff and is known as the Imhoff tank. It may be either circular or rectangular and is divided into three compartments or chambers—(1) the upper section, called the flowing through chamber or sedimentation compartment; (2) the lower section known as sludge digestion chamber, and (3) the gas vent and scum chamber. Figure 6 shows a typical plan and cross section of an Imhoff tank. It is desirable

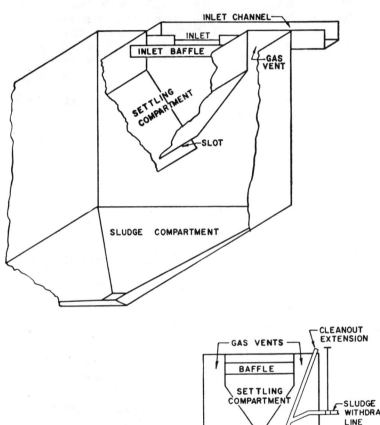

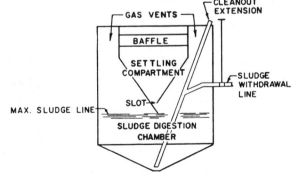

IMHOFF TANK
FIGURE 6

to be able to reverse the direction of flow to prevent excessive deposition of solids at one end of the flowing-through chamber. Reversing the flow every month will result in an even accumulation of sludge across the bottom of the tank.

In operation, all of the sewage flows through the upper compartment. Solids settle to the bottom of this compartment, which has slopes of about 1.4 vertical to one horizontal, slide down and pass through an opening or slot at the bottom. One of the bottom slopes extends at least six inches beyond the slot. This forms a trap to prevent gas or digesting sludge particles in the lower section from entering the sewage in the upper section. The gas and any rising sludge particles are diverted to the gas vent and scum chamber. This eliminates the main disadvantage of the septic tank. The gas vents should have a surface area of at least 20 per cent of the total area of the tank.

It is desirable to start the operation of an Imhoff tank in the spring or early summer when the temperature in the sludge compartment is high enough to promote rapid digestion. Seeding the tank with actively digesting sludge from a nearby Imhoff tank or separate sludge digester is advisable if it can be done conveniently. Otherwise the pH of the sludge in the sludge compartment should be controlled and maintained above 6.8 to prevent an acid condition unfavorable for proper digestion. This can be done by the addition of milk of lime gradually to the influent or by adding lime in the scum chamber. Care should be taken to prevent the addition of a large quantity of lime over a very short period of time as such sudden shocks of lime tend to upset digestion.

Imhoff tank operation. There are no mechanical parts in an Imhoff tank. Attention should, however, be given to the following:

(a) Daily removal of grease, scum and floating solids from the sedimentation compartment.

(b) Weekly scraping of the sides and sloping bottoms of the sedimentation compartment by a rubber squeegee to remove adhering solids which may decompose.

(c) Weekly cleaning the slot at the bottom of the sedimentation compartment. This can be done by use of a chain drag.

(d) At least monthly reversal of flow where this is provided for in the design of the tank.

(e) Control of the scum in the scum chamber, by breaking it up, hosing with water under pressure, keeping it wet with sewage from the sedimentation compartment and removal if the depth approaches two to three feet.

(f) Removal of sludge should be done before the sludge depth approaches within 18 inches of the slot in the sedimentation compartment. It is better to remove small amounts frequently than large amounts at long intervals. Sludge should be removed at a slow regular rate to avoid the formation of a channel through the sludge which would permit partially digested sludge and liquid held in storage above the digested sludge to be withdrawn from the tank. Before winter temperatures are expected, most of the digested sludge except that necessary for seeding (about 20 per cent) should be removed to provide space for winter accumulations when digestion is very slow. The height of the sludge in the sludge compartment should be determined at inlet and outlet ends of the tank at least once a month. The use of a pump for this purpose is the most desirable and satisfactory. The use of the plate or disc method is not usually satisfactory. The following are suitable methods for measuring the depth of sludge:

(1) One method involves the use of a pitcher pump provided with a rubber suction hose, weighted on the end and the length marked on the hose at intervals of two feet, measuring from the weighted end toward the pump. The hose is gradually lowered through the slot in the sedimentation compartment, meanwhile constantly pumping, and the length of immersed hose, when sludge first comes through the pump is determined. When the sludge elevation is reached, the pump will usually "choke" before sludge appears.

(2) A pitcher pump may also be used with a rubber suction hose, weighted on the end by a four foot length of steel pipe as an integral part of the pump suction line. This suction hose may be graduated and marked as above and the determination of sludge depth made in the same manner except that the hose is lowered through the gas vent instead of the sedimentation compartment slot.

(3) The sludge depth may also be determined by use of an iron plate or weighted wooden block, about 12-18 inches square, attached to a wire or chain lowered through the gas vent. The plate or block will stop when the sludge is reached and the distance from the surface to the sludge level is determined from the graduated wire or chain by which the device is lowered.

(4) Where the condition of gas vents will permit the use of a lighter implement, a modification of the above may be used. This consists of a wire loop, 12 or 15 inches in diameter, covered with a disc of a quarter inch mesh wire. A very light chain should be used with this disc suspended at three points.

(g) After each time that sludge is removed, the sludge pipes should be flushed and filled with water or sewage to prevent sludge from hardening in and clogging the pipes.

(h) Prevention of "Foaming." Every effort should be made to prevent "foaming" because correction after the condition arises is sometimes difficult. "Foaming" is usually associated with an acid condition of the sludge and in such cases may be prevented or corrected by treatment with lime to counteract the acidity of the sludge. When foaming occurs it is usually desirable to seek the advice of an expert sanitary engineer. There are, however, a few simple measures which may under certain circumstances remedy or improve the condition.

(1) The use of hydrated lime added to the gas vents of Imhoff tanks or to the sludge added to separate digesters will usually aid in correction. The pH value of the resulting sludge and lime mixture in the digestion compartment should not exceed 7.6.

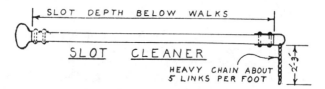

SLOT DEPTH BELOW WALKS

SLOT CLEANER

HEAVY CHAIN ABOUT 5 LINKS PER FOOT

2'-3"

ALL HANDLES ABOUT 1½" SQUARE WOOD OR ½" φ STEEL P PE. IRON HANDLE ENDS OPTIONAL.

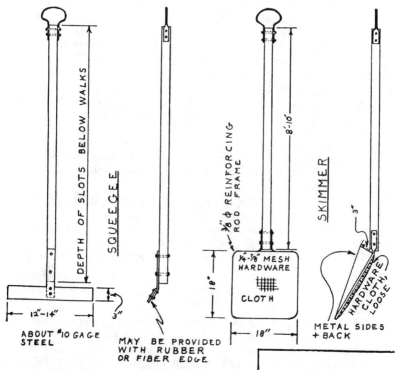

DEPTH OF SLOTS BELOW WALKS

SQUEEGEE

12"-14"

3"

ABOUT #10 GAGE STEEL

MAY BE PROVIDED WITH RUBBER OR FIBER EDGE

⅜" φ REINFORCING ROD FRAME

¼"-⅛" MESH HARDWARE

CLOTH

18"

18"

8'-16'

SKIMMER

3"

HARDWARE CLOTH, LOOSE

METAL SIDES + BACK

IMHOFF TANK - USEFUL EQUIPMENT
FIGURE 7

(2) Removing the tank from service where possible for a few days and allowing it to rest will sometimes improve conditions.

(3) In case of Imhoff tanks agitation of the gas vent area with a water hose or paddles will sometimes help.

(4) When foaming occurs in separate digestion tanks the gas line should be shut off or disconnected until the tank becomes normal again in order to protect the gas lines and gas control equipment from the foam solids.

(5) Lowering the temperature of the sludge in separate digesters for several days will reduce the foaming activity.

The Imhoff tank has no mechanical problems and is relatively easy and economical to operate. It provides sedimentation and sludge digestion in one unit and should produce a satisfactory primary effluent with a suspended solids removal of 40 to 60 per cent and a BOD reduction of 25 to 35 per cent. The two-story design requires a deep over-all tank. Other more recently developed types of tanks have largely replaced the Imhoff tank for large municipal installations. The Imhoff tank is best suited to small municipalities and large institutions where the tributary population is 5,000 or less.

Operators interested in operation and maintenance of Imhoff tanks will find an excellent article by L. W. VanKleeck in the February 1956 issue of *Wastes Engineering*, entitled, "Operation of Imhoff Tanks."

Other two-story tanks. A number of manufacturers have put on the market prefabricated parts to be installed in tanks constructed according to their designs to produce two-story tanks embodying the Imhoff tank principle. These are patented units with trade names and are classed as "package units."

They provide separate compartments for sedimentation and sludge digestion in one tank. Facilities for heating the digestion compartment can be installed, if desired. The units are circular in shape and made in sizes to serve populations up to 5.000.

Provision is made for the collection and utilization of digestion gas and there are special features such as radial, tangential and upward flow of the sewage. Some units have mechanical equipment for moving settled solids and sludge to outlets over relatively flat surfaces. This permits reduction in depth of the sedimentation and digestion compartments and lowers the cost of tank construction.

PLAIN SEDIMENTATION TANKS

These are tanks whose major function is to remove settleable solids from the sewage by the process of sedimentation. The settled solids are taken from the tanks continuously or at frequent intervals so that decomposition with gas formation does not have time to develop. The solids are then handled by other units which are discussed in Chapter 8. The solids may flow by gravity to a hopper or to a low point in the bottom of the tank from which they are pumped or removed by hydrostatic pressure. This method, however, has been replaced by the use of mechanical equipment for the collection of the solids in a hopper from which they are removed by pumps. Tanks with mechanical equipment for the collection of solids are known as mechanically cleaned plain sedimentation tanks.

Mechanically Cleaned Plain Sedimentation Tanks. These tanks may be rectangular, circular or square, but all operate on the same prinicple of collecting the settled solids by slow moving scrapers to the point of removal.

In the rectangular tanks the scrapers are attached near their ends to two endless chains which pass over sprockets driven by motors. The scrapers are dragged slowly along the tank floor pushing the settled solids to a sludge hopper located at the inlet end of the tank. The scrapers are then lifted by the chains to the surface of the tank where, partially submerged, they serve to push floating solids, grease and oil to a scum collector at the outlet end of the tank. Another type of mechanism consists of a traveling bridge spanning the tank from which is suspended a blade to push solids to the point of removal and a skimmer blade for floating solids, grease and oil. These blades operate when traveling in one direction and idle when traveling in the return direction.

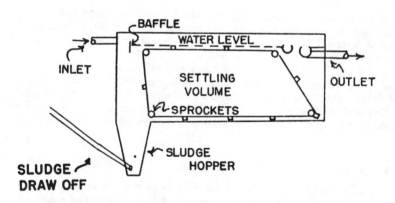

RECTANGULAR-PLAIN
SEDIMENTATION-TANK

FIGURE 8

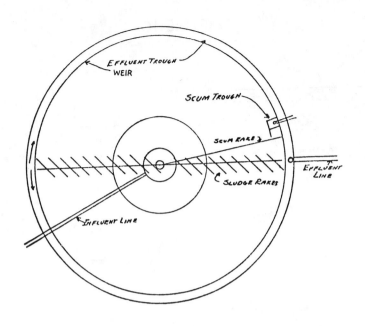

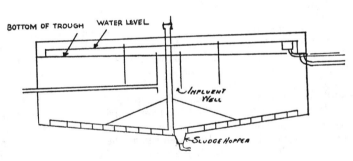

CIRCULAR-PLAIN SEDIMENTATION TANK
FIGURE 9

The circular tanks have scraper arms attached to a central motor-driven shaft. The bottom of the tanks are sloped toward the center and the scrapers move the settled solids to a sludge hopper at the center. Skimmer arms are attached to the central shaft at the surface for the collection of floating solids, greases and oils.

In the square tanks the mechanism is similar to that in the circular tanks. The major difference is that one or both of the rigid arms of the mechanism are equipped with pivoted corner blades which reach out into the four corners of the tank and move the solids in these areas to the path of the circular mechanism.

FIGURE 10
PRIMARY TREATMENT

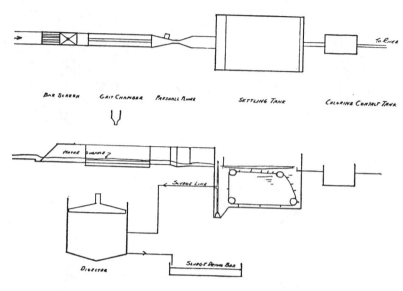

BAR SCREEN   GRIT CHAMBER   PARSHALL FLUME   SETTLING TANK   CHLORINE CONTACT TANK

To River

In the rectangular tanks the sewage enters at one end and flows horizontally to the other end. In the circular tanks sewage enters at the center and flows radially and generally horizontally to the periphery. In the square tanks the sewage may enter at the center and flow to the four sides or at one side and flow across the tank.

Several manufacturers have designed equipment to carry the incoming sewage close to the bottom of the tank from which it flows upward and radially through a sludge blanket to the outlet on the periphery. These are known as upward flow clarifiers and have the value of introducing the solids at the bottom where they are wanted instead of settling them from the upper layers.

Manufacturers of mechanical equipment have given trade names to tanks using equipment manufactured by them. This Manual cannot detail the different equipment or comment on the claims made by the manufacturers for their specific designs. There are, however, general features common to all primary settling tanks. New York State has adopted the standards of the Upper Mississippi River Board of Public Health Engineers and Great Lakes Board of Public Health Engineers which are commonly referred to as the Ten States Standards.

Inlets. Inlets should be designed to dissipate the inlet velocity, diffuse the flow equally across the entire cross section of the tank and prevent short-circuiting. They may be of the weir type but are more commonly a channel with spaced port openings.

Baffles. These are usually found at the inlet and outlet of a tank, the former to assist in diffusing the flow and the latter to hold back floating

40

material from the tank effluent. Mechanically cleaned tanks usually have a scum trough which serves the purpose of the outlet baffle and to which scum is brought by the skimmer. Scum baffles should be provided ahead of outlet weirs on all primary settling tanks, on all final settling tanks in plants not having primary settling facilities and on all non-mechanical final settling tanks.

Outlet Weirs. These vary greatly in design. They are for the purpose of removing the settled sewage as a thin sheet from the surface of the tank and are usually adjustable. It is important that they be kept level for uniform surface removal. The term *"weir loading"* is used to express the gallons per day passing over one foot of the weir. In plants of one mgd or less capacity this should not exceed 10,000 gallons per linear foot per day which may be increased to 15,000 for larger plants.

Surface Settling Rate. This is expressed in terms of gallons per square foot of tank area based on the sewage flow per day. For primary tanks not followed by secondary treatment this rate should not exceed 600 gallons per square foot per day for plants of one mgd or less capacity but may be higher for larger plants. This rate is an important factor and appears to affect directly the per cent removal of settleable solids and BOD.

Detention Period. This is the time in hours any sewage is held in the tank based on the sewage flow and tank volume, assuming total displacement and uniform flow through the settling compartment. This was at one time the commonly used factor of design. It has, however, been largely replaced by weir loading and surface settling rate. Based on design flow, detention periods should be at least 2.0 hours.

Overall Dimensions. Recent accepted standards are a minimum of 10.0 feet in length and a liquid depth (mechanically cleaned) of not less than 7.0 feet. The amount of sewage to be treated, the general layout of the sewage treatment plant, the surface settling rate and manufacturer's equipment determine the tank dimensions. Recent studies have indicated advantages in not making tanks too deep.

The following examples illustrate the use of the foregoing factors to evaluate the operating features of a sedimentation tank. Assume that one million gallons per day is being treated in a rectangular tank 70 feet long, 24 feet wide and 7 feet deep. The outlet weirs are "H" shaped with four approaches 24 feet long, and two approaches 2 feet long.

Weir Loading

$$4 \times 24 + 2 \times 2 = 100 \text{ ft. total weir length}$$

$$\frac{1,000,000 \text{ gal.}}{100 \text{ ft.}} = 10,000 \text{ gal./ft.}$$

Surface Settling Rate

$$24 \times 70 = 1,680 \text{ sq. ft. surface area}$$

$$\frac{1,000,000 \text{ gal./day}}{1,680 \text{ sq. ft.}} = 595 \text{ gal./sq. ft./day}$$

$$1,680 \times 7 \times 7.5 = 88,200 \text{ gal. tank volume}$$

$$\frac{88,200 \times 24}{1,000,000} = 2.12, \text{ or about two hours detention.}$$

Efficiency of Plain Sedimentation Tanks. Since the process of settling solids in plain sedimentation tanks is the same as in the sedimentation compartment of two-story tanks, similar results may be expected in their operation. About 90 to 95 per cent of the settleable solids, and 40 to 60 per cent of the total suspended solids, should be removed from the sewage. The BOD should be reduced by about 25 to 35 per cent. Such figures are, of course, general and may not apply to specific cases. Sewage with high suspended solids may have a higher percentage removed by sedimentation than sewage with a low suspended solids content, but the suspended solids in the tank effluent may still be greater in the former. A higher per cent removal can be expected in a tank treating fresh sewage than in one treating the same sewage after it has become septic because the solids in the septic sewage have been broken up or disintegrated by bacterial decomposition during their long travel in the sewer system. The amount and composition of industrial wastes are also an important factor affecting the percentage removal of suspended solids and BOD by primary settling tanks.

Operation of Mechanically Cleaned Plain Sedimentation Tanks. The establishment and maintenance of proper time schedules for operation of the mechanical cleaning equipment and for removal of sludge from the tank are most important factors in tank operation. They must be determined for each plant. At most plants the collecting mechanisms are run from two to eight hours a day depending on the size of the plant and the quantity of sludge produced. Very often circular tank mechanisms are run continuously. They should be run often enough to prevent a build-up of solids on the tank bottom. If the solids are allowed to build up in the tank, an undue load may be placed on the mechanism and cause damage to the equipment. Solids may also be decomposed with the resultant production of gas in the settling tank and some floating sludge. Before sludge is removed from the tank the mechanism should be run for a sufficient time to assure satisfactory collection of bottom solids in the sludge hopper.

Sludge should be removed from the tank at least daily. It is not good practice to remove sludge with an excessive amount of water as this water wastes storage space and heat in digestion tanks. Maintaining a sludge blanket of 12 to 18 inches in the sludge hopper and pumping small amounts at frequent intervals and at a low rate helps to obtain sludge of a higher solids concentration. The sludge pump should have a sampling tap. As a guide, if a sample of sludge in a test jar after settling for ten minutes shows more than a 50 per cent volume of sludge, pumping should be continued. If it shows less than 50 per cent, removal may be considered reasonably complete. A vacuum gauge on the suction side of the pump and a pressure gauge on the discharge line are valuable.

Should either gauge show zero the operator will know that the line is plugged. A decreasing reading on the pressure gauge shows that the sludge is getting thinner. The sludge removal schedule must be worked out for each plant by observation and tests, keeping in mind that the objective is not to see how fast sludge can be removed but to remove a concentrated sludge while it is still fresh and to have the floor of the tank clean after a removal cycle. Seasonal revision of the schedule will probably be necessary.

Scum and grease should be removed daily from the surface of the tank. Most mechanical collectors direct such material to a grease trough from which it flows to a grease well for disposal by pumping to the digestion tank or by other means.

Where there is more than one tank, poor flow distribution often accounts for poor operation. The operator should check his particular installation to be sure that each tank is receiving its share of the load. When it is found that one tank is receiving more or less than its share, the inlet arrangements should be checked to ascertain whether a manipulation can be made to equalize the flow to each tank. The elevation of all effluent weirs should be checked as uneven weirs can do a great deal to increase short circuiting and unequal flow distribution. When it is necessary to pump to a sedimentation tank the flow should be at as even a rate as possible to obtain the best possible results.

At all times the operator must be conscious that mechanical equipment requires attention and maintenance. Moving parts must be kept lubricated and weak or worn parts replaced. The best rule is to rigidly follow the instruction manual provided by the manufacturer of the equipment.

Advantages and Disadvantages of Mechanically Cleaned Plain Sedimentation Tanks with Separate Sludge Digestion. Except for relatively small installations this type of tank has almost universal use in this country and it is being used more and more in the smaller municipal and larger institutional plants.

There are two main reasons for this; (1) the treatment of sludge in separate tanks, especially heated tanks, provides more complete control of the digestion process. and (2) the cost of construction especially for large units is less.

These tanks do, however, require more time and competency in operation than the Imhoff tank, because of the operational requirement and the care and maintenance of mechanical equipment.

CHEMICAL TREATMENT

Chemical treatment has been conventionally classed as intermediate treatment, in that the results obtained by it are greater than with standard primary treatment but less than with secondary treatment. It is included in this Manual under primary treatment because it involves chemical and physical processes as distinct from the biological processes which are the basis of secondary treatment.

Chemical treatment is one of the older methods of sewage treatment which fell into discard but was reintroduced in the decade 1930-40. However, developments in secondary treatment methods, the supervision needed, the cost of chemicals and the excessive amounts of sludge requiring disposal have caused this method of treatment to be restricted to special conditions. It still has application in the treatment of industrial wastes which are not easily attacked biologically and where conditions in the receiving waters periodically require a higher degree of treatment than standard primary treatment, but do not warrant secondary treatment. Chemical treatment involves the addition of one or more chemicals to sewage to produce a floc which is an insoluble chemical compound that absorbs colloidal matter, enmeshes non-settleable suspended solids and settles readily. The precipitating chemical also dissociates or ionizes in the sewage and neutralizes the electric charges held by colloidal particles causing them to coalesce to form larger readily settleable solids. The chemicals most widely used are aluminum sulfate or alum, ferrous sulfate with lime, ferric sulfate and ferric chloride with or without lime.

A chemical treatment plant usually has the following features:

(1) Preliminary devices—screens, grit chambers etc. as described in Chapter 4

(2) Chemical feeders

(3) Mixing units

(4) Flocculation tanks

(5) Sedimentation tanks such as have already been described

(6) Increased facilities for the treatment and disposal of sludge

Chemical Feeders. A large variety of units to feed chemicals, either dry or in solution, in controlled amounts are made by a number of manufacturers. Details are not warranted in this Manual.

Mixing Units. The chemicals when added to sewage must be thoroughly and quickly mixed with it to provide complete and uniform reactions. This is accomplished by violent agitation for a short period of time either by mechanical or hydraulic methods. This agitation is carried on in special tanks, in sections of other tanks, or in the piping system. Mixing devices are made by a number of manufacturers.

Flocculators. After the chemical is mixed with sewage it is gently agitated for 15 to 30 minutes to foster the coagulation of particles. If BOD reduction is desired, the agitation time may be increased to 45 minutes. The colloidal and suspended solids meet and adhere together in large flocculant masses which settle readily in the sedimentation tank. Different types of equipment to accomplish this purpose are made by a number of manufacturers.

Sludge. The volume of sludge obtained by chemical treatment is greater than with standard primary treatment, necessitating a comparable increase in sludge handling facilities and cost of sludge treatment and disposal as described in Chapter 8.

Efficiency. Chemical treatment can effect a reduction up to 90 per cent in suspended solids and up to 70 per cent in the BOD. It is well adapted to intermittent operation and has value in sewage treatment to reduce pollution of streams during periods of low flow or to lessen pollution of bathing beaches and recreational waters during months when these facilities are in use. It is of value also for the treatment of sewage containing high concentrations of industrial wastes which will inhibit biological life and interfere with secondary treatment processes. Operation costs are high due to increase in operators time, chemicals and greater quantities of sludge to be treated and disposed of.

Operation. Because of its limited use in sewage treatment operation, details regarding the usage of chemicals in chemical precipitation are not included in this Manual.

SPECIAL REFERENCE FOR CHAPTER 5

Van Kleeck, L. W.—Wastes Engineering . . . . .January 1956
February 1956
March 1956
April 1956
May 1956

CHAPTER 6

SECONDARY TREATMENT

In many situations, primary treatment with the resulting removal of 40 to 60 per cent of the suspended solids and approximately 25 to 35 per cent of the BOD, together with the removal of floating material from the sewage, is adequate to meet requirements of the receiving water. However, if the accomplishment of primary treatment is not sufficient, there are two basic methods of secondary treatment available, trickling filters and activated sludge. Sand filters can be used when a high degree of treatment or a polishing effect is required. There are several other methods which are used to a limited extent. These types of treatment employ biological growths to effect aerobic decomposition or oxidation of organic material into more stable compounds and provide for a higher degree of treatment than that accomplished by primary sedimentation alone.

While trickling filters and activated sludge both depend on aerobic biological organisms to effect decomposition, there is an operational difference. In filters the organisms are attached to the filter medium and the organic material on which they do their work is brought to them. With activated sludge, however, the organisms are migrant and are carried to the organic matter in the sewage. In either case, successful operation involves the maintenance of aerobic environmental conditions favorable for the life cycle of the organisms, and control over the amount of organic matter which they decompose. The organic matter is the food upon which these organisms live. If they are either over-fed or under-fed their efficiency is reduced.

TRICKLING FILTERS

The word "filter" in this case is not correctly used, for there is no straining or filtering action involved. Actually, a trickling filter is a device for bringing settled sewage into contact with biological growths. A more applicable name would be "biological oxidizing bed," but time and usage have made the term trickling filter a popular one and it is used universally to described this type of unit.

Trickling filters are sturdy work units, not easily upset by shock loads, noted for their consistent performance, and capable of taking considerable abuse. Like all biological units they are affected by temperature; therefore, cold weather slows down biological activity in the filter. They occupy large areas and are expensive to construct.

For economy the filters should be preceded by primary sedimentation tanks equipped with scum collecting devices. Primary treatment ahead of filters makes available the full capacity of the filters for use in the conversion of non-settleable, colloidal and dissolved solids, to readily settleable solids. These solids which are largely organic, are not removed from the sewage but are converted to living microscopic organisms or stable organic matter temporarily attached to the filter medium and to inorganic matter carried off with the effluent. The attached material eventually sloughs off and is carried away in the filter effluent. For this reason, trickling filters should be followed by secondary sedimentation tanks to remove permanently the solids from the sewage.

Construction. A typical trickling filter consists of three parts, (a) the bed of filter medium, (b) an underdrainage system, and (c) mechanism for distributing the sewage evenly over the surface of the filter.

(a) The choice of filter media is often governed by the material locally available or the cost of bringing material in. Field stone, gravel, broken stone, blast furnace slag and anthracite coal have been used for this purpose. Redwood blocks and inert materials molded into appropriate shapes have also been employed. Whatever material is chosen, it is usually specified that it be sound, hard, clean and free of dust and insoluble in sewage constituents. The material should be approximately cubical in shape to prevent compacting, and of a size to pass a four and one-half inch square screen but be retained by a two inch square screen. The filter media should have a minimum depth of five feet and should not exceed seven feet in depth. The bed may be rectangular to circular. The former is common where distribution of sewage is by fixed spray nozzles, and the latter where rotating distributors are used as described under (c) below. The filter medium serves the dual purpose of providing a large surface area on which the slimes and gelatinous films produced by bacteria can develop yet leaving sufficient voids to permit free circulation of air throughout the filter.

(b) *Underdrain System.* The underdrains serve two purposes; (1) to carry the sewage passing through the filter away from it for subsequent treatment and disposal, and (2) to provide for ventilation of the filter and the maintenance of aerobic condition. The direction of air flow through the filter depends on the difference in temperature between the filter and the sewage being applied. When the filter stone is warmer than the sewage, the direction of air will generally be upwards through the filter. When the temperature of the filter is colder, the direction of the air will be downwards. The underdrain system consisting of precast filter blocks which are manufactured from vitrified clay or concrete, covers the entire bottom of the filter and leads to effluent channels. The blocks are usually rectangular in shape and have openings in the upper face equal to at least 20 per cent of the surface of the block.

(c) *Distributors.* Sewage is applied to the surface of the bed by fixed spray nozzles or rotary distributors. The fixed spray nozzles were used when trickling filters were first developed. The nozzles are

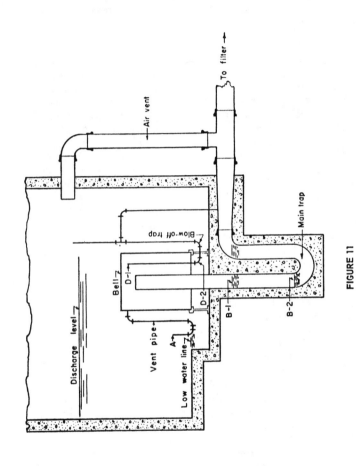

FIGURE 11

SEWAGE DOSING TANK WITH DEEP SEAL SIPHON
(COURTESY OF PACIFIC FLUSH TANK CO.)

49

attached to pipes laid in the filter medium and are fed intermittently from a siphon controlled dosing tank. By this method
sewage is applied to the filter for short periods of time. Between
applications the filter has rest periods while the dosing tank is
filling. Many types and shapes of nozzles have been developed
and the siphon dosing tank is designed to attain the best possible
even distribution of sewage over the entire surface of the filter.
At best, the distribution is not even and there are areas of the
filter on which very little sewage is sprayed.

Figure 11 shows diagrammatically a siphon controlled dosing tank.
When the dosing tank has finished discharging, the level of the sewage
is at the lower bend of the vent pipe. The sewage now stands at the level
B_1 in both legs of the main trap. The blowoff trap is filled with sewage
up to D_1 and the vent pipe is empty. As sewage rises in the dosing tank.
it seals the open end of the vent pipe at "A" and prevents the escape of
air from the bell. As the sewage continues to rise, the liquid level in the
bell also rises. The air in the long leg of the main trap and of the
blowoff trap is compressed and the surfaces of the sewage in these two
legs are forced downward. When the dosing tank is filled to a point just
below the discharge level, the surfaces of the sewage in the main trap
and in the blowoff trap are at B_2 and D_2. A further rise of sewage level
in the dosing tank causes the air in the bell to escape through the blowoff
trap. The release of air causes an inrush of sewage from the dosing tank
into the bell and down through the main trap, resulting in the dosing
apparatus going into full operation. The discharge continues until the
surface of the sewage reaches the lower elbow of the vent pipe. At this
point air enters the bell through the vent pipe and the siphonic action
is broken. The main trap and the blowoff trap remain filled with sewage.
The vent pipe is empty and the cycle of filling and discharge commences
again. The air vent in the discharge pipe allows escape of the air forced
out of the bell and traps. Twin dosing tanks are often so interlocked that
one may be filling while the other is discharging. There are many variations in design of dosing tanks. Some use mechanical devices to replace
the main trap shown here.

The fixed spray nozzles have been largely supplanted by rotary distributors which effect a more even dosage over the entire area of the
bed. With the rotary distributors, sewage is fed through a hollow vertical
center column to which are attached two or more arms. Each arm contains a number of nozzle openings, all of which point at right angles to
the arms and through which sewage is applied to the surface of the filter.
The central feed column and arms which revolve slowly over the surface
of the circular filter are usually driven by jet action of the sewage as it
discharges through the nozzles. Positive drive mechanisms also are
available.

Loading. Filter loadings are commonly expressed in terms of hydraulic
loading and organic load. The hydraulic load is the number of gallons
of sewage applied per acre of filter surface per day, or more accurately,
because of different depths of filters, per acre foot per day. The organic
loading is the number of pounds of BOD per 1000 cubic feet of filter

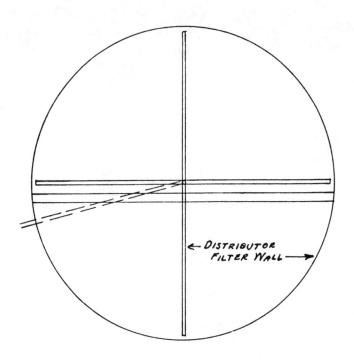

←DISTRIBUTOR
FILTER WALL →

TRICKLING FILTER

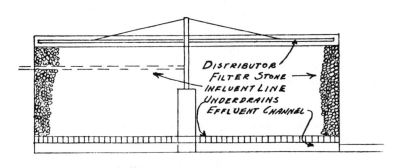

DISTRIBUTOR
FILTER STONE →
INFLUENT LINE
UNDERDRAINS
EFFLUENT CHANNEL

FIGURE 12

BAR SCREEN   GRIT CHAMBER   PARSHALL FLUME   DOSING TANK   PRIMARY TANK   TRICKLING FILTER   SECONDARY TANK

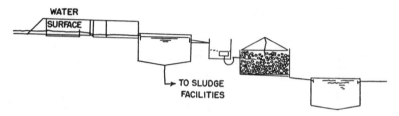

WATER SURFACE

TO SLUDGE FACILITIES

STANDARD RATE FILTER

FIGURE 13

medium. Pounds per acre foot or per cubic yard of filter medium also are used.

Based on hydraulic and BOD loadings trickling filters are classified as "Standard" and "High Rate."

Standard Trickling Filters. These are operated at a hydraulic loading of 1.1 to 4.4 million gallons per acre per day with an organic loading of 5.0 to 25.0 pounds per 1000 cubic feet of filter medium per day. The following example illustrates how the loadings of an operating filter are obtained:

Suppose a filter 100 feet in diameter and six feet deep is receiving 0.5 mgd of primary tank effluent with a BOD of 150 ppm.

$$\text{Area of filter (Acres)} = \frac{\Pi d^2}{4 \times 43,560} = 0.18 \text{ acres}$$

$$\text{The hydraulic loading} = \frac{0.5}{.18} = 2.8 \text{ mgad (Million gallons per acre per day)}$$

The pounds of BOD applied $= 0.5 \times 8.34 \times 150 = 625$ pounds per day

$$\text{The volume of filter medium} \frac{\Pi d^2}{4} \times 6 = 47,124 \text{ cubic feet}$$

$$\text{The BOD loading} = \frac{625}{47,124} \times 1000 = 13.3 \text{ pounds of BOD per 1000 cubic feet of filter medium per day}$$

52

Sewage is applied intermittently with rest periods which generally do not exceed five minutes at the designed rate of sewage flow. With proper loadings the standard trickling filter, including primary and secondary sedimentation units, should under normal operation remove from 80 to 85 per cent of the applied BOD. While there is some unloading of solids at all times, which has accumulated on the filter medium, the major unloading occurs severeal times a year for comparatively short periods of time.

High Rate Trickling Filters. These units are operated with hydraulic loadings of 8.7 to 44.0 million gallons per acre per day and organic loadings of 25.0 to 50.0 pounds per 1000 cubic feet of filter medium per day.

When trickling filters were first developed, it was believed that their successful operation required rest periods between dosing. The application of sewage was, therefore, intermittent. It later developed that the rest periods between doses were not essential and had some detrimental effects. This enabled a major increase in the hydraulic loadings and some, though not a proportional, increase in the BOD loadings. The higher hydraulic rate was attained by mixing filter effluent with the normal sewage flow in proportions of up to ten to one and recirculating it through the filter. The higher BOD load is attained by applying a larger volume per acre of the normal sewage flow to the filter. This effects a reduction in the BOD concentration of the sewage as applied to the filter, even though the total BOD load per day is higher. The various ways by which this recirculation is accomplished are patented processes and are identified by trade names, some of which are as follows:

Biofilter. In the biofilter, a process is used involving recirculation and a high rate of application to a shallow trickling filter. The recirculation in this case involves bringing the effluent of the filter or of the secondary sedimentation tank back through the primary settling tank. The secondary settling tank sludge is usually very light and can be continually fed back to the primary settling tank where the two types of sludges are collected together and pumped to the digester. See Figure 14a.

"Accelo" Filter. The accelo filter, another sewage treatment process, involves the recirculation of filter effluent directly back to the filter as shown in Figure 14b.

Aero-Filter. The aero-filter (Figure 14c) is still another process, which distributes the sewage by maintaining a continuous rain-like application of the sewage over the filter bed. For small beds, distribution is accomplished by a disk distributor revolving at a high speed of 260 to 369 rpm set 20″ above the surface of the filter to give a continuous rain-like distribution over the entire bed. For large beds a large number of revolving distributor arms, 10 or more, tend to give more uniform distribution. These filters are always operated at a rate in excess of 10 million gallons per acre of surface per day.

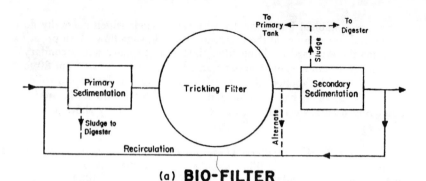

(a) **BIO-FILTER**

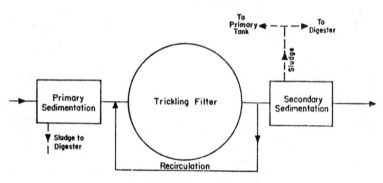

(b) **ACCELO-FILTER**

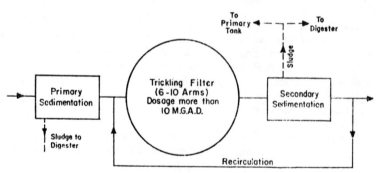

(c) **AERO-FILTER**

FIGURE 14

A typical computation for loadings of a high rate filter is as follows:

A filter 100 feet in diameter and six feet deep is receiving 1.0 mgd of normal settled sewage with a BOD of 150 ppm with recirculation at a rate of four to one or a total of 5 mgd.

Area of filter (acres) $= \dfrac{\Pi d^2}{4 \times 43,560} = 0.18$ acres

Hydraulic loading $= \dfrac{5.0}{.18} = 27.7$ mgad (million gallons per acre per day)

Pounds of BOD applied $= 1 \times 8.34 \times 150 = 1250$ pounds per day

Volume of filter medium $= \dfrac{\Pi d^2}{4} \times 6 = 47,124$ cubic feet

BOD loading $= \dfrac{1250}{47,124} \times 1000 = 26.6$ pounds of BOD per 1000 cubic feet of filter medium per day

High rate trickling filters including primary and secondary sedimentation should, under normal operation, remove from 65 to 80 per cent of the BOD of the sewage. Re-circulation should be adequate to provide continuous dosage at a rate equal to or in excess of 10 million gallons per acre per day with rest periods not more than 15 seconds. As a result of continuous dosing at such high rates some of the solids accumulated on the filter medium are washed off and carried away with the effluent continuously, and there are no intermittent unloading periods.

High rate trickling filters have been used advantageously for pre-treatment of industrial wastes and unusually strong sewage. When so used they are called *"roughing filters."* With these the BOD loading is usually in excess of 110 pounds of BOD per 1000 cubic feet of filter medium.

Two high rate filters in series have been used to effect a higher degree of treatment and produce a final settled effluent of less than 30 ppm of BOD.

The following table contains comparative data on a number of features of standard and high rate trickling filters.

TABLE 1

	Hydraulic Loading Mil. Gal. per acre per day	BOD Loading Pounds BOD per 1000 cu. ft. Filter Medium	Operation	Unloading	Per Cent BOD Removal including Primary and Secondary Sedimentation
Standard	1-4	Less than 15	Intermittent	Largely Periodic	80-85
High Rate	10-30	30-110	Continuous	Continuous	65-80

Operation: As both standard and high rate trickling filters are biological work shops, the principles of operation are the same, and the troubles encountered with their maintenance are similar.

The nozzles whether fixed spray or on rotators, should be inspected daily and all those found clogged or damaged should be cleaned or repaired.

During winter months careful attention is required to prevent freezing, especially with standard rate filters where intermittent operation causes periods of quiescence which are more conducive to freezing than with the continuous operation and constant motion of liquid in high rate filters. There is a tendency of some operators to by-pass the filters during the winter months. This practice should not be a general procedure. A trickling filter should be continued in operation except for brief periods when ice formation is sufficient to cause damage to the distribution system.

The distribution system whether fixed or moving should be flushed periodically, preferably daily, to remove any material which might cause clogging. If possible, the underdrains also should be hosed out occasionally.

Where the distribution system involves mehanical equipment with moving parts, the only safe rule is to know well and follow rigidly the instructions in the service manual which the manufacturer supplies for his particular equipment. It should be used, not filed or lost.

The surface of the filter must be kept free from weed growths and accumulation of leaves or other debris. Trees or shrubs in close proximity to a filter should be removed.

A number of chemicals may be received by a sewer system, generally in industrial wastes, which in appreciable concentration are toxic or poisonous to biological life. When the normal efficiency of a filter shows a somewhat sudden drop, immediate checks should be made at industrial plants tributary to the sewer system to determine if there has been a discharge of toxic material into the sewers and to arrange for its elimination or pre-treatment by the industry.

To provide uniform distribution of sewage over the bed practically all rotary distributors require periodic adjustment of the turnbuckles on the guy rods to the arms. This is needed in order to maintain the proper level of the arms and their distance from the surface of the filter. In hot weather the rods become longer and the turnbuckles should be taken up slightly to compensate for the mental expansion due to heat. In cold weather the condition is reversed and the turnbuckles should be let out.

Ponding of filters will occur if the voids in the filter medium become clogged and the free passage of liquid is prevented. This may be due to the use of too small filter medium or disintegrated filter medium. The only way to permanently correct this difficulty is to replace the filter medium with material of proper size and quality. If, however, the voids become filled by prolific growths of organisms and slimes on the surface of the filter medium, there are corrective measures available to the operator which should be employed as soon as ponding is evident. These measures include:

(1) Flushing the surface of the ponded area with a fire hose.
(2) Applying heavy doses of chlorine for short periods, either directly to the ponding area or to the sewage influent. The latter can best be done at night when the chlorine demand of the sewage is lowest.

Chlorine doses up to 5 ppm will kill the excessive growth in the filter.

(3) Flooding the entire filter and allowing it to stand full for 24 hours.

(4) Cutting the filter out of service and allowing it to stand unused for several days.

(5) Temporarily increasing the rate of recirculation. This can be done only where the filters are so designed to permit this method of operation.

Ponding is always an indication that something is wrong, and indicates to the operator not only to use the corrective measures outlined above, but to check the operation of the entire treatment plant for possible cause. If primary units are not properly removing grease or oils, the biological film on the filter medium will be coated, and the organisms will be deprived of oxygen and the sewage kept from contact with the organisms. It may be that the filter installation is inadequate for the plant load. This, of course, calls for the installation of additional units which should be constructed as soon as possible.

Another troublesome condition which frequently develops at trickling filter installations is the excessive production of the filter fly—the psychoda. These flies are so small that they can pass through an ordinary window screen and are very bothersome to the plant operator and nearby neighbors.

The larvae of the flies prefer a breeding place which is damp but not too wet and are, therefore, more prevalent in standard rate filters with intermittent dosages than in high rate filters with continuous dosing. Some of these insects may be present in a normal filter unit which is functioning properly, as the filter fly is one of the natural biological organisms which feeds on the sludge and film growth and assists in the decomposition of organic matter. However, excessive numbers indicate that the biological life in the filter is unbalanced, probably due to organic overloading.

The control of filter flies has proven to be very difficult. Keeping all parts of the filter wet, especially the edges, will discourage their breeding. Numerous insecticides such as D.D.T., chordane, lindane and others have been tried to rid an infested filter of these pests. None have been completely satisfactory except to give temporary relief. The use of any one insecticide seems to result in the development of resistant strains of the insect. It has been found that it is better to use several in rotation. This treatment is expensive and extreme caution is necessary as too heavy a dose may kill all the desirable and necessary biological life in the filter.

If duplicate filter units are available, one can be taken out of service for a day or two and either flooded or allowed to dry out to create conditions in the filter unfavorable for the fly development.

Although any one of the above may give temporary relief, the only permanent solution to the psychoda nuisance is, as in ponding control, to determine its cause and then to provide corrective action.

Since the operation of the trickling filter depends on biological life, it is evident that when one is first put into service it takes time to build up an adequate population of organisms on the filter medium. This is true not only of a new unit but also of one which has been idle long enough to have the organisms die for want of food and water. Bypassing a unit for any prolonged period should, if possible, be avoided.

Every trickling filter installation has its own particular characteristics. There appears to be no one method of operation best suited to all plants. Advantage should be taken of any provisions for flexible operation which are available, and different methods of operation such as parallel or series flow should be tried to determine the best conditions for the particular plant.

SECONDARY SEDIMENTATION TANKS

Since trickling filters merely alter the character but do not remove solids from the sewage, the effluent contains suspended solids which should be removed before disposal by discharge to receiving waters.

For this purpose secondary sedimentation tanks or final settling tanks are used. These tanks are similar in design to those described in Chapter 5 on Primary Treatment and should provide a surface settling rate not in excess of 800 gallons per square foot per day based on design flow.

ACTIVATED SLUDGE

The development of the activated sludge process marked an important advance in the secondary treatment of sewage. Like the trickling filter, it is a biological contact process where living aerobic organisms and the organic solids in the sewage are brought together in an environment favorable for the aerobic decomposition of the solids. Since the environment is the sewage itself, efficient operation of the process is dependent on the continual maintenance of dissolved oxygen at all times throughout the sewage being treated. The environment itself, however, accomplishes little unless it is inhabited by enough living workers.

Normal sewage contains some of these biological workers but the number is far too small to do the work at hand. It is necessary, therefore, to add many more organisms and to distribute them throughout the sewage before the activated sludge process can begin to function with any efficiency.

The activated sludge process is usually employed following plain sedimentation. The sewage contains some suspended and colloidal solids and, when agitated in the presence of air, the suspended solids form nuclei on which biological life develop and gradually build up to larger solids which are known as activated sludge.

Activated sludge is a brownish floc-like substance consisting largely of organic matter obtained from the sewage, and inhabited by myriads of bacteria and other forms of biological life. Activated sludge with its living organisms has the property of absorbing or adsorbing colloidal and dissolved organic matter including ammonia from sewage so that the suspended solids are reduced. The biologic organisms utilize the absorbed material as food and convert it into insoluble non-putrescible solids. Much of this conversion is a step-by-step process. Some bacteria attack the original complex substances to produce simpler compounds as

58

their waste products. Other bacteria use these waste products to produce still simpler compounds and the process continues until the final waste products can no longer be used as food for bacteria.

The generation of activated sludge or floc in sewage is a slow process, and the amount so formed from any volume of sewage during its period of treatment is small and inadequate for the rapid and effective treatment of the sewage which requires large concentrations of activated sludge. Such concentration is built up by collecting the sludge produced from each volume of sewage treated and re-using it in the treatment of subsequent sewage flows. The sludge so re-used is known as *returned sludge*. This is a cumulative process so that eventually more sludge has been produced and is available for re-use than is needed. The surplus, or *excess activated sludge*, is then permanently removed from the treatment process and conditioned for ultimate disposal as described in Chapter 8 on "Sludge Treatment and Disposal."

The activated sludge must be kept in suspension during its period of contact with the sewage being treated by some method of agitation. The activated sludge process, therefore, consists of the following steps:

(1) Mixing the activated sludge with the sewage to be treated.

(2) Aeration and agitation of this mixed liquor for the required length of time. to form nuclei for sew to build on

(3) Separation of the activated sludge from the mixed liquor.

(4) Return of the proper amount of activated sludge for mixture with the sewage.

(5) Disposal of the excess activated sludge.

A number of variations in carrying out the steps given above have been developed to meet different conditions. This has resulted in using the term "conventional activated sludge" for the original activated sludge process and giving specific names to the variations of the original process.

Before considering these variations, it is desirable to define two terms which are connonly used, and to consider the basic steps involved in the activated sludge process.

Sludge Volume Index is the volume in ml of one gram of activated sludge in the mixed liquor which has settled for thirty minutes. The procedure and computations involved in determining it are give in Chapter 11 on "Sampling and Procedures in Testing." The best sludge volume index must be determined for each plant and slight variations from day to day are to be expected, but a rising sludge volume index indicates that the volume occupied by one gram of sludge is increasing, causing a loss in density and a tendency towards bulking which is discussed later.

Sludge Age is the average time in days a particle of suspended solids remains under aeration in the activated sludge sewage treatment process. It is calculated from the weight of activated sludge in the aeration tank and the suspended solids in the sewage entering the aeration tank using the formula:

$$\text{Sludge age} = \frac{V \times A}{Q \times C}$$

V = volume of aeration tank in mg

A = concentration of suspended solids in the aeration tank in ppm

Q = sewage flow in mgd

C = concentration of suspended solids in the sewage entering the aeration tank in ppm exclusive of returned sludge.

The sludge age must be kept within certain limits for satisfactory operation depending on the character of the sewage being treated and must be determined for each plant. For an average domestic sewage a sludge age of three to four days is generally satisfactory.

Mixing the Activated Sludge with the Sewage to be Treated. It is very important that the returned activated sludge be thoroughly mixed with the sewage. This is generally accomplished by adding the return sludge to the settled sewage at the inlet end of the aeration tank in which the agitation provides rapid and satisfactory mixing. In some cases small mixing chambers with agitation are provided, but this is not common practice.

Aeration and Agitation of Mixed Liquor. Aeration accomplishes three objectives; mixing the returned activated sludge with the sewage, keeping the sludge in suspension by agitation of the mixture, and supplying the oxygen required for biological oxidation. Air is generally added by one of two methods known as "diffused air" or "pressure aeration" system or by mechanical aeration.

In the *diffused air system,* air under low pressure, generally not more than eight to ten pounds, is supplied by blowers and forced through various types of porous material in plates or tubes which break up the air into fine bubbles. These plates or tubes are so located in the aeration tank that a rotary motion is imparted to the sewage mixture resulting in a considerable amount of air being absorbed from the atmosphere. Diffuser plates are composed of fused crystalline alumina or a high-silica sand. They are set in containers usually made of reinforced concrete. Diffuser tubes are made of similar material or, more recently, of corrugated stainless steel pipe with multiple outlets and wrapped with saran twisted cord. These are suspended in the aeration tank in sections and can be disconnected above the sewage surface and removed for cleaning or renewal. When installed on swing joint connections so that they may be brought to the surface of the tank, they are known as "Swing Diffusers."

To prevent clogging of the diffuser plates or tubes, the air to them should be filtered to remove dust, oil or other impurities, and the piping should be of non-corrosive material. There are a number of types of filters available based on different principles which may be used alone or in combination.

Mechanical aerators are of two general types—paddle and vertical draft tube. The paddle type consists of a paddle wheel or brush partly submerged in the sewage revolving on a horizontal axis. Air is absorbed by surface contact and by droplets thrown through the air by the paddle mechanism. With the vertical draft tube sewage is drawn up or down through a central vertical tube by a revolving impeller. There are a number of types of the vertical draft tube aerator made by different manufacturers each with special patented features.

In addition to the above two methods, there are several other types of aerators on the market using different devices to introduce or entrain air and provide agitation.

Air Requirements are governed by:

(1) The BOD loading
(2) The quality of the activated sludge
(3) The solids concentration
(4) The desired efficiency in BOD removal

The basic air requirement is that there shall be sufficient air added to the sewage to maintain in it at least two ppm of dissolved oxygen under all conditions of loading in all parts of the aeration tanks except immediately beyond the inlets. Tests for dissolved oxygen should be made in different sections of the tank to assure that this value is maintained.

In the diffused air systems, the amount of air added is often stated in terms of the cubic feet of air per gallon of sewage, usually ranging from one-half to one and one-half. A preferable method of expression, now more commonly used, is in terms of cubic feet of air per pound of BOD to be removed from the primary tank effluent. Normal requirements are assumed to be 1000 cu. ft. per pound of BOD, and the air system should be capable of delivering 150 per cent of this figure.

The above figures apply generally to a normal domestic sewage in a conventional type activated sludge plant as defined later. Where industrial wastes are involved or the plant is one of the modified types (also defined later), major variation from these figures may occur and must be determined by operating experience at each plant. Insufficient air will result in a deterioration of the quality of the activated sludge and a serious breakdown of plant efficiency. The use of excessive amounts of air is not only wasteful but may result in a sludge so finely dispersed that it becomes difficult to settle.

Aeration Time. In the activated sludge process, the sludge accomplishes the major part of the removal of BOD and solids from the sewage being treated in a relatively short period of aeration. It takes, however, a much longer time for the sludge to assimilate the organic matter which it has absorbed. During this time an aerobic environment must be maintained. To effect the most complete treatment of sewage and most economical operation in the conventional activated sludge process, an aeration time of six to eight hours has been found to be adequate for diffused air aeration and nine to twelve hours for mechanical aeration. Materially shorter periods are used in some of the modifications of the conventional process. These shorter aeration periods generally result in a lowering of the quality of the plant effluents. This is described later under the various types of activated sludge plants.

Separation of Activated Sludge from the Mixed Liquor. Before the sewage treated in the aeration tank can be disposed of by discharging into receiving waters, the activated sludge must be removed. This is done in secondary or final settling tanks. These tanks are similar in design to the mechanically cleaned primary sedimentation tanks described in Chapter 5. Surface settling rates should not exceed 800 gallons per square foot per day.

The cycle of sludge removal from the secondary tanks is much more important than with primary tanks. Some sludge is being removed continuously to be used as returned sludge in the aeration tanks. The excess sludge must be removed before it loses its activity because of the death of the aerobic organism resulting from lack of oxygen at the bottom of the tank. It is possible, where facilities are available, to reactivate return sludge in separate reaeration tanks before addition to the sewage. However, it is much wiser to retain the activity of the sludge by prompt withdrawal from the tank.

Return of the Proper Amount of Activated Sludge for Mixture with the Sewage. The amount of sludge returned to the aeration tank must be sufficient to produce the desired purification in the available aeration time and yet low enough to give economical air utilization. Because of variations in the character and concentration of the sewage and the type of plant, the amount of returned sludge may range from 10 to 50 per cent of the volume of sewage being treated. This will be further discussed in connection with the various types of plants. For a conventional plant, the percentage is usually between 20 and 30 per cent. This will result in a concentration of solids in the mixed liquor of from 1000 to 2500 ppm in diffused air plants, and 500 to 1500 ppm in mechanical aeration plants. The best concentration must be determined for each plant by trial operation and should be carefully maintained by controlling the proportion of return sludge. The maximum concentration is limited by the air supply and sewage load. If solids are allowed to build up, the air and food requirements will exceed those available and an upset will occur.

Treatment and Disposal of Excess Activated Sludge. Ultimately excess activated sludge is treated and disposed of with the sludge from primary sedimentation tanks. Chapter 8, which deals with sludge treatment and disposal, applies to sludges from both primary and secondary treatment. However, there are several methods by which excess activated sludge is combined with sludge from primary devices.

Probably the most common practice is to pump excess sludge to the influent end of the primary sedimentation tank where it is settled with the solids in the raw sewage. The activated sludge settles readily and, because of the large flocculent character of the sludge particles, it tends to strain out some of the non-settleable solids in the sewage, thus reducing the organic and solids load on the aeration tank.

Where the above procedure is not followed, the excess activated sludge is transferred to the sludge digestion tanks either directly or through thickeners as described in Chapter 8 or by other procedures outlined in that chapter.

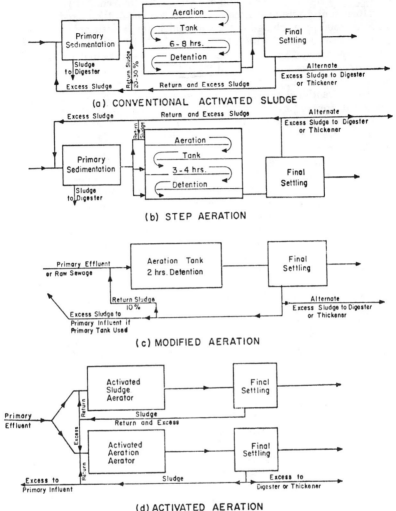

(a) CONVENTIONAL ACTIVATED SLUDGE

(b) STEP AERATION

(c) MODIFIED AERATION

(d) ACTIVATED AERATION

FIGURE 15

Conventional Activated Sludge Process. The flow diagram of a conventional activated sludge plant for domestic sewage using the diffused air system of aeration is shown in Figure 15(a). All of the settled sewage is mixed with the returned activated sludge at the head of the areation tank. With average domestic sewage, the volume of returned sludge is 20 to 30 per cent of the volume of the sewage to be treated. The aeration tanks are designed to provide an aeration time of six to eight hours with diffused air aeration and nine to twelve hours for mechanical aeration. The longer times are used for the lower sewage flows. Air is applied at the rate of one to one and one-half cubic feet per gallon of sewage or

63

900 to 1100 cubic feet per pound of BOD to be removed. Activated sludge is returned at a rate to maintain a solids content in the mixed liquor of 1000 to 2500 ppm. Sludge index and sludge age, as determined for each plant, will usually fall within the range of 200 to 300 and three to four days respectively. An overall plant efficiency, as measured by reduction in BOD and suspended solids, of 80 to 95 per cent can be expected with efficiencies in the upper part of this range predominating.

The conventional activated sludge process is capable of effecting the highest degree of purification yet attained by sewage treatment methods that are in general use with the exception of that obtained by intermittent sand filtration. Although the activated sludge is similar in composition and biochemical reactions to the slime formed on trickling filter medium, it is somewhat more effective. The activated sludge floc moves through the sewage flow and, in effect, goes searching for food. Consequently the decomposition of the organic matter in the sewage can be more complete than that which can be attained by trickling filters. Since the biological contact process takes place under water, fly breeding is eliminated and odors can be greatly reduced. The space required for activated sludge units is much less than needed for trickling filters used to treat the same volume of flow.

The activated sludge process is not as rugged, however, as the trickling filter process. It is complex and presents many technical problems requiring more operating skill and time. While the activated sludge process can be adapted to treat sewage and wastes of widely varying strengths and composition, it is sensitive to shock loads and toxic substances which may be discharged into sewers especially from industrial plants. These industrial wastes may destroy or inhibit the activity of the microorganism essential for the decomposition of organic matter.

MODIFICATIONS OF THE CONVENTIONAL ACTIVATED SLUDGE PROCESS

Mention has already been made of modifications of the conventional activated sludge plant. These have been developed to meet local conditions or to effect economies in construction and operation. Several of these modifications are described below.

Step Aeration. In this process, Figure 15(b), sewage enters the aeration tank at a number of different points but all of the return sludge is introduced at the first point of entry with, or without, a portion of the sewage. The sludge solids concentration in the mixed liquor is, therefore, greatest at the first step or point of entry and decreases as more sewage is introduced at subsequent steps. This provides a means of ready regulation of the total amount of solids held under aeration. In this process, treatment practically equivalent to the conventional activated sludge process can be attained in about half the aeration time while maintaining the sludge age within proper limits of three to four days.

By using an aeration tank of only half the capacity needed in the conventional process construction costs and the area required for step aeration are less. Operation costs are about the same for the conventional and step processes.

Tapered Aeration. This process was developed on the theory that the greatest amount of air is needed during the early part of the aeration period. Air is, therefore, introduced into the sewage at a higher rate in the inlet section of the aeration tank than in subsequent sections to roughly approximate the oxygen utilization in the various sections or stages of aeration in the tank.

The advantages claimed for this modification of the conventional activated sludge process are a better control of the process in meeting shock loads and a reduction in the cost of operation.

Modified Aeration. This modification of the conventional activated sludge process, Figure 15(c), is also known as high-rate activated sludge treatment. It is applicable where the receiving waters require a degree of treatment greater than that obtained by primary treatment but not the suspended solids and BOD removals that can be obtained by the conventional activated sludge process.

In modified aeration either raw or settled sewage mixed with about 10 per cent of return sludge is aerated for a period of only one or two hours. The suspended solids of the mixed liquor are reduced to below 1000 ppm resulting in a reduction in air requirements. By controlling the air supply, the aeration period, and the per cent of return sludge, almost any degree of treatment between primary sedimentation and the conventional activated sludge process can be effected.

This process effects savings in construction and operating costs and takes less area than the conventional plant. The sludge produced is dense, more nearly resembling primary tank sludge than activated sludge, and is not subject to bulking as described later.

Activated Aeration. This process was recently developed in New York City, Figure 15(d), and is a conventional or step-activated sludge treatment with a reduced aeration period. The culture which is produced in the activated sludge section and which is ordinarily wasted as excess sludge, is transferred to an activated aeration section which also receives a portion of the settled sewage flow. In the activated aeration section, that portion of settled sewage sent to it is aerated with a low solids concentration of 200 to 400 ppm. Final settling tanks are provided for both sections with effluents to the receiving waters.

By varying the proportion of the total sewage flow between the two sections of the plant and other operating factors, the activated aeration process affords great flexibility and a wide range of treatment efficiency, depending on the requirement of the receiving waters. Reductions in BOD of 80 to 85 per cent can be attained along with savings in air costs as compared with the conventional process.

Contact Stabilization is another modification of the conventional activated sludge process. In this method the biologically active sludge is brought into intimate contact with the sewage for only 15 to 30 minutes during which time the activated sludge absorbs and adsorbs a high percentage of the suspended, colloidal and dissolved pollutional matter from the sewage. The mixture then flows to the settling tank from which the sludge is removed to a regenerating tank where it is stabilized and regenerated by aeration. This modification is especially applicable in treating industrial wastes as the entire supply of seed sludge is not vulnerable to shock loads because the majority of the seed is kept under separate aeration. A slug of wastes would only affect that small portion of the sludge being mixed with the sewage.

Aerobic Digestion (Total Oxidation). In this process a continuous flow of raw sewage or wastes and its mascerated solids are aerated vigorously in a tank designed to detain an entire day's flow. The aerated sewage then passes to a conventional settling tank where two functions occur—clarified effluent overflows to the receiving waters and settled sludge is recirculated back to the aeration compartment at a high rate.

This relatively simple process depends upon practically complete stabilization of the putrescible fraction of the sewage by biological oxidation in a single compartment. Experience indicates that this process is sensitive to sudden changes in volume and/or character of the waste. Sludge should be wasted periodically from the system in order to maintain equilibrium and consistently produce a high quality effluent.

This process has been applied at moderately small installations thus far, and experience indicates that the resultant degree of treatment realized compares favorably with other highly efficient secondary processes.

OPERATION OF ACTIVATED SLUDGE PROCESS

Details of operating procedure will vary at different activated sludge plants, depending on a number of factors, such as the type of facilities available, strength and character of the sewage, temperatures, requirements of receiving waters, and others. Best operating procedure for each plant must be determined by experience. With this qualification, the following will generally apply for a conventional type of plant treating an average domestic sewage. For modified type plants see the sections on these various units.

(1) There must be sufficient aeration to maintain a dissolved oxygen content of at least two ppm at all times throughout the aeration tanks, except immediately beyond the inlet. This can be expected when an aeration time of six to eight hours for diffused air and nine to twelve hours with mechanical aeration is provided and when about 1000 cubic feet of air is supplied for each pound of BOD to be removed.

(2) Dissolved oxygen should be present at all times in the treated sewage in the final settling tanks.

(3) Activated sludge must be returned continuously from the final settling tanks to the aeration tanks.

(4) Optimum rate of returning activated sludge will vary with each installation and with different load factors. In general, it will range from 20 to 30 per cent of the sewage flow for diffused air and 10 to 20 per cent for mechanical aeration units.

(5) The optimum suspended solids content in the aeration tanks may vary considerably but usually in the range of 1000 to 2500 ppm with diffused air and 600 to 1200 ppm with mechanical aeration.

(6) A sludge volume index of about 100 and a sludge age of three to four days are normal for most plants. When the optimum sludge volume index is established for a plant, it should be maintained within a reasonably narrow range. A material increase is a warning of trouble ahead as discussed below under sludge bulking.

(7) The suspended solids content in the aeration tanks may be controlled by the amount of sludge returned to them. All sludge in excess of that needed in the aeration tanks must be removed from the system. It should be removed in small amounts continuously or at frequent intervals rather than in large amounts at any one time. Sludge held too long in the final settling tank will become septic, lose its activity and deplete the necessary dissolved oxygen content in the tank. (See 2 above).

(8) Septic conditions in the primary sedimentation tanks will adversely affect the functioning of the activated sludge process. Pre-chlorination or pre-aeration as described under preliminary treatment in Chapter 4 may be used to forestall septic conditions in the sewage entering the aeration tanks.

(9) Periodic or sudden organic overloads such as may result from large amounts of sludge digester overflow to the primary tanks or from doses of industrial wastes having an excessive BOD or containing toxic chemicals will usually cause operating difficulties. Whenever possible overloading should be minimized by controlling the discharge or by pretreatment of such deleterious wastes. It may even be preferable to bypass the activated sludge units at the plant than to knock out the whole activated sludge process. This procedure must be used with caution and, if it must become a frequent practice or involves large volumes, the plant facilities are probably inadequate and additional units must be installed.

Sludge Bulking. The most common problem encountered in the operation of activated sludge plants is sludge bulking. A desirable activated sludge is one which settles rapidly leaving a clear, odorless and stable supernatant. The floc is granular in appearance, with sharp defined edges, is golden brown in color and has a musty odor. When the character of the activated sludge changes so that its settleability decreases, as measured by a significant rise in the sludge volume index, a condition known as sludge bulking develops in the final settling tank. As a portion of the sludge does not settle in the tank, it is carried away in the effluent. This results in a serious impairment in the quality of the plant effluent and places an added organic load on the receiving waters.

As always, it is better, where possible, to prevent trouble than to correct it, and knowledge of its possible source is the first step in prevention. There are a number of causes for sludge bulking, some of which are given below.

(1) Excessive or storm flow resulting in shortened aeration periods.

(2) Short circuiting of aeration tanks.

(3) Industrial wastes with high organic content or containing chemicals having toxic effects on bacterial development.

(4) Solids content in aeration tanks either too high or too low.

(5) Insufficient aeration with failure to maintain dissolved oxygen throughout the system or possibly the use of too much air tending to break up the floc.

(6) Septic sewage in the primary sedimentation.

(7) Interruption in the continuity of returning of sludge to the aeration tank or too long intervals in removing excess sludge from the process units.

(8) A preponderance of fungi forming thread-like filaments in the sludge.

All of these can be pretty well summed up by saying that sludge bulking results from overloading or the improper balance between the three variable—BOD loading, suspended solids concentration of the mixed liquor, and the amount of air used in aeration.

There are no infallible rules for either the prevention or control of sludge bulking. If the condition does develop, the ultimate solution is to determine the cause and then either correct or eliminate it or take compensatory steps in operation control. There are some remedial steps which can be taken where facilities are available, and which may help to bring the process back to normal operation. Among these are:

(1) Addition of hydrated lime to the aeration tanks to raise the pH value to not exceeding 7.1. This was formerly used more than at present. It has been largely replaced by the use of chlorine as noted under (4) below.

(2) Reduction of the solids content carried in aeration tanks by removal of some of the activated sludge as excess.

(3) Re-aeration of returned activated sludge before entering aeration tanks.

(4) Chlorination of returned activated sludge. This is further discussed in Chapter 7 on chlorination. This must be carefully controlled to avoid killing the organisms in the sludge.

(5) Increase aeration in time and rate.

It is sometimes desirable or necessary to remove as much of the sludge as possible from the system and then develop fresh and properly activated sludge.

Frothing. The formation of a thick layer of froth over the surface of aeration tanks is becoming a more common and more serious problem for the operators of activated sludge plants. The cause (or causes) are not definitely known, though it is frequently attributed to the increasing use in industry and homes of synthetic detergent compounds. Whatever the cause, there are several methods of control available. One method is the use of defoamants which tend to reduce surface tension and are quite effective. These materials are expensive and cost may prevent their use when large quantities are required. Another method is the application to the foam of fine sprays of water or plant effluent. The installation and operation of a satisfactory spray system may also involve considerable expenditures. At some plants a combination of these two methods has been used by adding a defoamant to the spray. The necessity for foam control and the control method used depend on the seriousness of the problem and the relative costs of the various control methods at any specific plant.

CONTACT AERATION

The contact aeration process is covered by several patents. Like all secondary treatment processes, it depends on aerobic biological organisms to break down the complex putrescible organic material in sewage into simpler, more stable forms. The organisms are, like those in a trickling filter, stationary and attached to a fixed medium. They are, however, continually submerged and supplied with air by means similar to the diffused air system in the activated sludge process.

A typical contact aeration plant consists of five tanks in series to provide for primary settling, first stage aeration, intermediate settling, second stage aeration and final settling. In addition, facilities for sludge treatment and disposal must be provided.

The aeration units consist of tanks which contain a number of thin plates made of a variety of materials such as corrugated aluminum sheets or corrugated asbestos sheets. These are suspended vertically and spaced about one and one-half inch center to center. The necessary biological life develops on these sheets. Sewage is carried to the bottom of the tank and passes upward between the plates mixed with air from a diffuser system at the bottom. Aerobic conditions are thus maintained for the biological life on the submerged plates. Growths with organic solids are continually breaking away from the plates. Those from first stage aeration are removed in the intermediate settling tanks and those from second stage aeration in the final settling tank.

The process is quite rugged and can, like the trickling filter, withstand shock loads. The units are adaptable to manufacture and installation as "package" units with automatic controls to reduce, but not eliminate, the time and attention given to operation. A removal of BOD and suspended solids of 90 per cent or more can be attained with plants correctly designed and operated. To date, the use of this process has been restricted to plants serving small villages, realty developments or similar small groups. However, with multiple units, larger installations would appear to be practical.

INTERMITTENT SAND FILTERS

The intermittent sand filter is a specially prepared bed of sand on which effluents from primary treatment or from trickling filters or secondary settling tanks may be applied intermittently by using troughs or perforated pipe distributors. The effluent from the filter is removed by an underdrainage system.

Bed construction. The filter bed should have a depth of clean sand of at least 24 inches overlying clean, graded gravel. The gravel should be placed in at least three layers around the underdrains and to a depth of at least six inches over the top of the underdrains. The sand itself should have an effective size of 0.3 to 0.6 millimeters and have a uniformity coefficient of not more than 3.5. The center to center spacing of underdrains should not be more than 10 feet.

Capacity. When treating a primary effluent from normal sewage, the rate of application on the filter should not exceed 125,000 gallons per acre per day, which should be reduced if the sewage is strong. With trickling filter and secondary settling tank effluent, the loading should not exceed 500,000 gallons per acre per day.

The intermittent sand filter is a true filter which strains out and retains fine suspended solids and also acts as an oxidizing unit. The major portion of the straining and oxidation is effected at or near the surface of the sand. Straining results from the fine nature of the sand medium with small voids and from a biological slime growth of organisms which develops on the surface of the sand. Oxidation is effected, as in all secondary treatment devices, by the living aerobic microorganisms which develop primarily at the surface, forming a slime layer, but also extending into the sand medium.

Operation. It is important that the filter be allowed to empty itself and obtain a fresh air supply at intervals. This is accomplished by intermittent dosing of the sewage onto the filter. Sewage is applied from two to six times a day in quantities sufficient to cover the surface of the filter to a depth of two to three inches, and as the sewage passes down through the sand, air is drawn in from the surface. Sand filters are constructed in two or more units which are used in rotation. Eventually the slime layer on the surface causes the top layer of sand to become clogged and necessitates the removal of the top layer of sand in order to put the unit back into efficient operation.

Pooling should not be allowed to develop on the beds as this tends to produce septic action, obnoxious odors and an effluent of poor quality. Pooling indicates that cleaning is necessary. The surface of the beds should be kept level to afford uniform distribution of the sewage and weeds, grass, etc., should not be allowed to grow on the beds.

For winter use, the open air beds in the northern part of the State should be ridged every two feet in order to hold the ice off the main body of sand. An alternate method is that of raking up small four to six inch piles of the top surface every three feet over the surface of the bed. The bed should be cleaned and leveled as early as possible in the spring. Where natural sand percolation beds are used it is sometimes advisable to shallow harrow the beds after careful removal of all organic deposits. Such harrowing is not advisable with underdrained beds because of possible damage to the underdrainage system.

Efficiency and Use. A well operated intermittent sand filter plant will give a clear, sparkling stable effluent almost completely oxidized and nitrified. Over-all plant removals of 95 per cent or more of the BOD and suspended solids in the raw sewage can be expected. This exceeds other accepted secondary treatment processes.

When compared with other sewage treatment processes, large areas of land are needed, construction costs per unit of sewage treated are high, and maintenance in keeping the filters clean is considerable. The use of filters of this type is restricted to situations where the volume of sewage to be treated is small, or where an exceptionally high grade of plant effluent is necessary. They have been used effectively for the additional treatment of secondary treatment effluents. Modification of the sand filters have been proposed in the past but, in general, have not proven practical for treatment of large volumes of sewage.

STABILIZATION PONDS ~ Same as aerated lagoon process?

In recent years there has developed a system of sewage treatment which depends on the use of specially prepared ponds which are termed stabilization ponds. These ponds were first used in areas where warm climates and sunny days are prevalent, but have been found to operate with satisfactory results in colder climates and where there is considerable cloudiness. Stabilization ponds might be used most anywhere. The rate at which they could be operated would vary with temperature, light energy, and other local conditions.

The process involves two steps in the decomposition of organic matter in sewage. The carbonaceous matter in sewage is first broken down by the aerobic organisms with the formation of carbon dioxide. The carbon dioxide so formed is used by algae in their photosynthesis. *Photosynthesis* is a natural process carried on in green plant tissue under the influence of light and in the presence of chlorophyll which is the green coloring substance of plant life. In this process, the oxygen in the carbon dioxide is liberated and dissolved by the liquid in which the algae grow. As a result the organic matter in sewage is converted into algae and the sewage is supplied with oxygen to support further aerobic decomposition. The sewage solids enter the pond in a highly putrescible state and leave in the form of highly stable algae cells which, within certain limitations, can be discharged to receiving waters without deleterious effect.

Oxidation ponds can be used as a complete treatment receiving raw sewage, or as a secondary treatment for settled sewage, or as a further treatment for effluents from secondary processes. They have been used most commonly as a secondary treatment for primary effluents.

Most stabilization ponds are two to four feet in depth with continuous flow through the pond. They have been designed for loadings of one acre per 400 persons, 50 pounds of BOD per acre per day or 15 pounds of BOD per acre foot per day with detention periods generally greater than 30 days. The natural soil in which they are located should be fairly impervious, so that seepage will not materially affect the surface level of the sewage in the pond.

These ponds are low cost in construction, and require a minimum of operation. The requirement that large, fairly isolated areas be provided limits their use to relatively small populations in areas where land is available.

SPECIAL REFERENCES FOR CHAPTER 6

Torpy, W. N.—"Step Aeration for Activated Sludge"—Sewage Works Journal 20, 5 September, 1948

Torpy, W. N. and Chasic, A. H.—"Activated Sludge Principles"—Sewage and Industrial Wastes, 27, 11—November, 1955

Wilford, John and Conlon, T. P.—"Contact Aeration Sewage Treatment Plants in New Jersey"—Sewage and Industrial Wastes, 29, 8—August, 1957

"Operation and Control of Sewage Treatment Plants"—Bulletin 25, New York State Department of Health (out of print)

CHAPTER 7

CHLORINATION OF SEWAGE

Chlorination of sewage is the application of chlorine to sewage to accomplish some definite purpose. The chlorine may be applied as a gas, as a gas dissolved in water, or in the form of a hypochlorite obtained from salts such as sodium or calcium hypochlorite which, when dissolved in water, releases chlorine. As chlorine gas costs much less than that obtained from the hypochlorites, it is generally used in sewage treatment except where, in rare instances, only a relatively small amount of chlorine is needed. Regardless of its source, the chlorine is the same and its application to sewage is usually controlled by special devices which are known as chlorinators, chlorinizers or similar names.

REACTION OF CHLORINE IN SEWAGE

In order to determine at what points in the treatment process, and how much chlorine should be applied to accomplish the purpose desired, it is necessary to know the action of chlorine when added to sewage.

Chlorine is an extremely active chemical that will react with many compounds to produce many different products. If a small amount of chlorine is added to sewage it will react rapidly with such substances as hydrogen sulfide and ferrous iron and be destroyed. Under these conditions no disinfection will result. If enough chlorine is added to react with all these substances, called reducing compounds, then a little more chlorine added will react with organic matter present and form chloro-organic compounds, which have slight disinfecting action. Again, if enough chlorine is added to react with all the reducing compounds and all the organic matter, then a little more chlorine added will react with ammonia or other nitrogenous compounds to produce chloramines or other combined forms of chlorine, which do have disinfecting action.

The exact mechanism of this disinfecting action is not fully known. In some theories the chlorine is considered to exert a direct action against the bacterial cell, thus destroying it. A more recent theory is that the toxic character of chlorine inactivate the enzymes upon which the living microorganisms are dependent for utilizing their food supply. As a result, the organisms die of staravation. From the point of view of sewage treatment, the mechanism of the action of chlorine is much less important than its effects as a disinfecting agent.

The quantity of reducing substances, both organic and inorganic, in sewage varies, so that the amount of chlorine that has to be added to sewage for different purposes will vary. The chlorine used by these organic and inorganic reducing substances is defined as the chlorine demand. It is equal to the amount added minus that remaining as combined chlorine after a period of time, which is generally 15 minutes.

Disinfection is caused only by that amount remaining after the chlorine demand has been satisfied. This quantity of chlorine in excess of the chlorine demand is defined as residual chlorine and expressed as parts per million. For example: A chlorinator is set to feed 50 lbs. of chlorine per 24 hours; the sewage flow is at a rate of 0.85 mgd and the chlorine as measured by the OT (Orthotolidine) test after 15 minutes contact is 0.5 ppm.

$$\left.\begin{array}{c} \text{chlorine feed} \\ \text{or} \\ \text{chlorine dose} \end{array}\right\} = \frac{50}{0.85} = 59 \text{ lbs./mg} = \frac{59}{8.33} = 7.1 \text{ ppm}$$

Chlorine dose in ppm	7.1
Chlorine residual in ppm	0.5
Chlorine demand	6.6 ppm

PURPOSES OF CHLORINATION

Chlorine is added to sewage for a number of different purposes; these include:

1. *Disinfection.* Neither primary nor secondary methods of sewage treatment can remove completely from the sewage the pathogenic bacteria which are always potentially present. When sewage or treated effluents are discharged to bodies of water which are, or may be used as a soucrce of public water supply, or for recreational purposes, treatment for the destruction of pathogenic organisms is required to minimize the health hazards of pollution of these receiving waters. Such treatment is known as disinfection.

Chlorination for disinfection requires that essentially all of the pathogens in the sewage plant effluent be destroyed. Incidentally, many but not all of the saprophytic organisms are also destroyed. No attempt is made to sterilize sewage. *Sterilization* is the destruction of *all* living organisms which is not only unnecessary but impractical. In some instances this might be detrimental where other treatment dependent upon the activity of the saprophytes may follow chlorination. Fortunately the pathogenic organisms are less resistant to chlorine than most saprophytes so that disinfection can be effected without sterilization. It is not believed that chlorination as commonly practiced in sewage treatment is adequate to inactivate all of the enteric (intestinal) viruses which may be present in sewage.

To accomplish disinfection, sufficient chlorine must be added to satisfy the chlorine demand and leave a residual chlorine that will destroy bacteria. Special laboratory equipment is necessary to measure the destruction of bacteria and the tests require several days to complete. Thus, bacteriological examinations are not practical for the day-to-day control of the application of chlorine. Laboratory experiments and actual plant experience have shown that if sufficient chlorine is added to sewage so that 15 minutes after the chlorine has been added a residual chlorine concentration of 0.5 ppm is present in the sewage, disinfection will be accomplished. This is similar to any toxic action. There must be a concentration of toxic material acting over a period of time. A small concentration acting over a long period of time would have the same effect as a large concentration acting over a short period of time. Thus, disinfection of sewage is arbitrarily defined as the addition of sufficient chlorine so that a chlorine residual of 0.5 ppm is present 15 minutes after the chlorine is applied. Therefore, the practical control of chlorination for disinfection is by measurement of the residual chlorine using the orthotolidine test described in Chapter 11. By this means, test results can be obtained in a few minutes and the chlorine machine adjusted to the proper feed.

In the metropolitan area of the state under the jurisdiction of the Interstate Sanitation Commission, disinfection of sewage is defined as reduction in the concentration of coliform organisms so that not more than 50 per cent of a series of samples of effluent shall contain more than one coliform organism per ml. In effect this is a mpn (most probable number) of 100 per 100 ml. It may be that a 0.5 ppm residual after 15 minutes will not meet this bacteriological standard at all sewage treatment plants. In that case experiments can be made to determine the residual chlorine value that must be obtained to comply with the standard if it is applicable, and then this determined residual is used for control of chlorine application.

Disinfection must be a continuous process as it would be hazardous to discharge untreated effluent even for a short period of time. The point of chlorine application must be at a place where the chlorine feed can be rapidly mixed with the entire flow of sewage and where the mixture of chlorine and sewage can be held for a minimum of 15 minutes before discharge into the receiving stream.

Where the outfall sewer is long enough to require at least 15 minutes for the effluent to flow from the plant to the stream, chlorination of the effluent as it leaves the plant can be used. Control, in this case, should be by measurement of the residual chlorine in the sewage at the end of the outfall. Many times the end of the outfall is under water or at an inconvenient distance from the plant. It is advisable under such conditions to collect a sample of the chlorinated sewage, making sure it is taken at a place where the chlorine is completely mixed with the sewage, and hold the sample for 15 minutes before measuring the residual chlorine.

If the chlorine residual is greater or less than 0.5 ppm, the chlorine feed is decreased or increased until the proper residual is obtained. As the chlorine demand of sewage varies during the day, the chlorine feed required to maintain 0.5 ppm will vary. In a small sewage plant (less than 1 mgd), the operator does not have time to check the residual chlorine repeatedly, and repeatedly adjust the rate of chlorine application. The chlorine feed is adjusted once daily to give the required residual at the time of maximum sewage flow, which generally coincides with the time of maximum chlorine demand and in most plants occurs about 10:00 a.m. Then at all other times during the day the chlorine residual should be greater than 0.5 ppm. This means that chlorine is being wasted, but the operator is sure that disinfection is being accomplished.

The amount of chlorine required to produce 0.5 ppm residual in most primary effluents will be between 100 and 200 lbs. per million gallons. By frequent adjustment of the chlorine feed it might be possible to save about five to ten lbs. of chlorine per mg. Chlorine costs about $0.15 per lb. so only about $1.00 a day would be saved in a small plant. This saving is not enough to pay for the time spent by the operator to effect it and it is better to waste a little chlorine than try to make adjustments more often than once a day. In a larger plant (10 mgd) the waste of chlorine would amount to about $10 per day and this is worth trying to save. Therefore, residual chlorine values are measured possibly three or four times a day and the chlorinator adjusted each time. In still larger plants, it pays to make measurements frequently and it is often the practice to adjust the chlorine feed hourly.

A refinement of this method is to determine a program for the chlorine dosage at various periods of the day which will assure the required residual at all times. The chlorine machine can then be set manually or automatically to adjust the chlorine dosage to follow the program. In many of the larger plants mechanisms are provided to adjust the chlorine rate automatically in proportion to the sewage flow so that manual adjustment is necessary only for changes in the chlorine demand.

Where the outlet sewer does not provide 15 minutes holding time at peak hourly flow, at maximum rate of pumping or 30 minutes holding at average rate of flow, a chlorine contact tank is built and so designed as to give 15 minutes contact. In this case, chlorine is applied to the influent of the contact tank and the residual measured in the effluent. Where only primary treatment is provided, it is common practice to use the sedimentation tank as the contact chamber and chlorinate the influent. This has the added advantage of obtaining all the operating benefits of pre-chlorination, but it must be remembered that the primary object is disinfection, and chlorination must be sufficient to produce residual chlorine in the effluent. A similar practice is sometimes used with secondary treatment where chlorination prior to settling in the final clarifier is used to provide the necessary contact time.

The object of disinfection is destruction of pathogenic bacteria, and the ultimate measure of effectiveness is the bacteriological result. The measurement of residual chlorine does supply a tool for practical control. If the residual chlorine value commonly effective in most sewage plants does not yield satisfactory bacteriologic kills in a particular plant, then the residual chlorine that does must be determined and used as control in that plant. In other words, the 0.5 ppm residual chlorine, while generally effective, is not a rigid standard but a guide that may be changed to meet local requirements. One special case would be the use of chlorine in the effluent from a plant serving a tuberculosis hospital. Studies have indicated that a residual of at least 2.0 ppm should be maintained in the effluent from this type institution and that the detention period should be at least two hours at the average rate of flow instead of the 30 minutes which is normally used for basis of design.

It will generally be found that in a normal domestic sewage the following doses of chlorine will be sufficient to produce chlorine residual adequate for disinfection.

Type Treatment	Dosage (Based on Design Average Flow)
Primary plant effluent	20-25 ppm (mg/liter)

Trickling filter plant effluent	15 ppm (mg/liter)
Activated sludge plant effluent	8 ppm (mg/liter)
Sand filter effluent	6 ppm (mg/liter)

2. *Prevention of Sewage Decomposition.* a. Odor Control: The decomposition of sewage starts in sewers and becomes objectionable only after anaerobic decomposition has taken over. The degree of putrefaction that occurs is related to the time sewage is in the sewers which, in turn, depends on the length and grades of the sewers. Odor problems, therefore, develop where the sewers are long or where it is necessary to collect sewage in pump sumps and subsequently pump the sewage to a treatment plant. There are few places in this state where the sewers are so long that putrefaction occurs to such a degree that offensive odors rise from the sewers before the sewage reaches the sewage treatment plant. If such a condition occurs it is possible to chlorinate the sewage at a manhole on a trunk sewer. The amount of chlorine required varies depending on how long the decomposition of the sewage must be delayed. It is not necessary to add sufficient chlorine to satisfy the chlorine demand but merely sufficient to destroy odors and slow bacterial decomposition. Thus, no residual chlorine is produced. Doses of four to six ppm are generally sufficient to control odors. Chlorine may be applied up sewer from plant, to foremains, pump suction wells, screen chambers, grit chambers, trickling filter influent, settling tanks or wherever there is a sewage odor problem. Normally, the practice is to start with a fairly high dose of chlorine (10 ppm) to quickly control the odors and gradually reduce the dose over a period of time to determine the minimum that will satisfy the local condition.

The production of offensive odors at pumping stations is a fairly common occurrence. Chlorination of the sewage as it enters the pump sump or in the pump sump is effective as a preventative. The amount of chlorine required varies with the different situations but is less than that required to produce a residual. Generally it is about 50 per cent of the chlorine demand or 25 to 50 lbs. per million gallons, but the minimum dose effective must be found by trail and error for each installation.

Another common occurrence is for sewage to be septic, or a source of odor, as it is received at the sewage plant. To prevent the emanation of disagreeable odors during treatment, chlorination of the influent of the primary sedimentation tank is practiced. This is called pre-chlorination. If the purpose is only odor control and not disinfection, the chlorination need not be sufficient to produce a residual. Generally, a dose that will destroy all the reducing substances and thus slow the rate of decomposition is used. How great this dose must be depends to a large extent on how far putrefaction proceeded before the sewage reached the plant. When putrefaction is far advanced, the chlorine dose may be equal to or greater than the dose which would produce a residual if the sewage were fresh.

A similar situation may develop when the sewage is received fresh but becomes septic during the treatment process. This often occurs in a new plant where the initial sewage flow is far less than the design flow and the detention period in the primary tanks is greatly prolonged. Again pre-chlorination of the tank influent is used to delay putrefaction and resulting odors. In this case the chlorine dose will be much less than that required if the sewage were septic. The amount of reducing substances in the sewage will be low and a dose of two to five ppm of chlorine may be sufficient to prevent odors. When only primary treatment is provided, odor prevention and disinfection are often combined and the pre-chlorination dose is sufficient to produce a residual for disinfection.

b. Protection of Plant Structures: Decomposition of sewage can proceed to the point of hydrogen sulfied production but, owing to location or low concentration, odors are not a problem. If this occurs in a pumping station, intercepting sewers or treatment plant, there may be serious corrosion. The remedy is similar to that for odor control—chlorination sufficient to prevent hydrogen sulfide formation or to destroy hydrogen sulfide if it has been produced. The points of application are similar to those used for odor control but the quantity of chlorine may be less because only hydrogen sulfide has to be controlled. Without extensive laboratory control the dose of chlorine can be found only by trial and error in an endeavor to use as little chlorine as is necessary for the local problem. It may not be necessary to destroy all the hydrogen sulfide but only to reduce the concentration to one or two ppm so that the amount evolved will be a minimum. Hydrogen sulfide causes structures to be damaged and weakened due to corrosion, resulting in shut-down of the plant for repair. Generally it is an economic problem, but factors other than cost must be considered. One such factor is the toxic nature of hydrogen sulfide as discussed in Chapter 14.

c. Sludge Thickening: Excess activated sludge or raw sludge may be concentrated in holding tanks or thickeners prior to pumping to the digester. The maintenance of a chlorine residual of 1.0 mg per liter in the supernatant liquor of the concentrator appears to prevent the sludge from becoming septic during the holding period. Chlorine is applied to the incoming sludge to provide for thorough contact with the tank contents.

3. *Aid in Plant Operation.* a. Sedimentation: Pre-chlorination at the influent of a settling tank is seldom practical for the benefits obtained in improved settling. Generally, such benefits are incidental to the use of pre-chlorination for some other purpose. However, when there is a choice of the point of chlorine application, it is well to bear in mind that improved sedimentation and heavier sludge are generally obtained when chlorination of the influent is practiced.

b. Trickling Filters: Offensive odors released during the distribution of sewage over a trickling filter are generally controlled by pre-chlorination at the primary tank influent. Where this is not possible, chlorination at the dosing tank will control odors. The dose used is not sufficient to produce residual chlorine but only to destroy the odors. Chlorination to a residual less than 0.5 ppm does not interfere with the activity of the living organisms and thus does not affect the purification obtained by the operation of a trickling filter. However, chlorination of a trickling filter influent cannot be used until after the filter has been in active operation. Except in a large plant, the chlorine dose is generally set at about half the chlorine demand and not adjusted for moderate variations in flow or strength.

To induce unloading of a trickling filter, a shock dose of chlorine that will produce a residual of about 10 ppm in the filter influent may be applied. It requires a fairly large dose of chlorine to produce this amount of residual. As it is only to be maintained for a short period of time, it is most economical to apply during the night when the flow is low and the chlorine demand at a minimum. The chlorine is applied at the dosing tank, generally by making a slurry of one of the hypochlorites and pouring it into the dosing tank. Two dosing tank discharges containing 10 ppm residual are generally enough to cause the filter to unload the next day. A word of caution—when a filter is made to unload it does so quickly if at all and a very large volume of secondary sludge is produced in one or two days. Addition of this large quantity of sludge to the digesters has caused foaming on occasions.

When ponding on a filter is caused by an excessive growth of filamentous organisms, continuous chlorination of the filter influent may be used for control. If the ponding is caused by overloading, chlorination may be a temporary benefit but it will not offer a cure. Obviously, if ponding is caused by fine material from disintegration of stone, chlorination will be of no benefit. It is customary to apply chlorine to a ponding filter by chlorinating at the dosing tank to produce a residual of about one to two ppm at the nozzles. This is continued until the filters are free. There may be some deterioration of the purification accomplished by the filters during chlorination. Consequently, when the filters are free, chlorination is stopped. Often, the clogging will not return until the conditions, such as temperature, that caused the excessive growth are repeated. At some filters intermittent chlorination of two weeks per month during warm weather is required to keep the filters free and in others continuous chlorination is practiced.

c. Activated Sludge Bulking: When bulking of activated sludge is caused by overloading, pre-chlorination to reduce the load on the aeration process has been tried with some success. Pre-chlorination of the primary tank influent to produce a residual of about 0.1 ppm in the primary tank effluent is used. Much better control is obtained by chlorination of the return activated sludge. The point of application should be where the return sludge will be in contact with the chlorine solution for about one minute before the sludge is mixed with the aerator influent. The chlorine dose is varied according to the variations in the sludge volume index and may be calculated as follows:

S.V.I. $\times$ F $\times$ W $\times$ 0.0000834 = pounds of chlorine per day.
where

S.V.I. = Sludge volume index

F = Return sludge rate in mgd

W = Suspended solids in return sludge in ppm

In general, chlorination of a bulking sludge will reduce the sludge volume index, thus the dose is reduced daily until bulking is corrected. In some plants intermittent chlorination will maintain a low sludge volume index, and in others continuous chlorination of the return sludge has proven more satisfactory. Generally, when chlorination of the return sludge is started, the turbidity of the plant effluent will increase but after a few days of operation the turbidity will again decrease to that of normal conditions.

d. Imhoff Tank Foaming: The continuous addition of 3 to 15 mg per liter of chlorine to the raw sewage entering an Imhoff tank has been used on occasions to aid in control of foaming.

4. *Reduction or Delay of Biochemical Oxygen Demand.* Chlorination of raw sewage to produce a residual of 0.2 to 0.5 ppm after 15 minutes contact may cause a reduction of 15 to 35 per cent in the BOD of the sewage. Generally, a reduction of at least 2 ppm of 5 day BOD is obtained for each ppm of chlorine absorbed up to the point at which ortholodine residual is produced. When units of a plant become overloaded, use is made of chlorination to reduce the load until additional treatment facilities can be provided as the use of chlorine for BOD reduction is usually not economical. Chlorine is also used when the load is intermittent, such as when supernatant is returned from sludge digesters and when a plant receives intermittent discharges of industrial wastes.

Occasionally, chlorination of plant effluent to a residual is practiced to delay or reduce the BOD load on receiving waters during short periods of extremely low stream flow. This is only an emergency procedure but does offer some aid under such conditions. Generally, the higher the residual carried the more the load is reduced, but care must be taken to prevent fish kills by chlorine, although were the procedure is used it would be likely that fish had disappeared due to low dissolved oxygen concentrations.

CHLORINE HAZARDS

As stated in the chapter on safety, chlorine gas is extremely toxic and corrosive in moist atmospheres. Dry chlorine gas can be safely handled in steel containers and piping, but with moisture must be handled in corrosion resisting materials such as silver, glass, rubber and certain plastics. The gas is very irritating to mucous membranes and a very small percentage in air causes severe coughing. Heavy exposure can be fatal. Thus, it is important that one or more of several types of gas masks be provided and that persons handling chlorine be properly instructed in safety procedures and be constantly alert for leakage. The chlorine gas mask should be properly stored and ready for instant use at a convenient location outside of the chlorinator room.

OPERATION AND MAINTENANCE OF CHLORINATORS

a. *Types of Equipment*

Dry (direct) feed gas chlorinators	Application of dry chlorine gas to the sewage. Used only where water under pressure is not available; care in selecting point of application is required.

Solution feed gas chlorinators	Solution feed—Chlorine gas mixed with auxiliary supply of water and solution applied to sewage to be treated. Vacuum chlorinators of this type are preferable.
Electrolytic cell— gas chlorinator	Generation of chlorine at point of use. For special applications. Of little value in sewage works practice.
Hypochlorinators— chlorine compounds	For relatively low flows, or for intermittent, steady, or emergency use. May be electric or water meter driven; or by gravity or displacement.

All chlorinators should be installed for continuous trouble free operation. Chlorine gas will dissolve in water to form a solution having a maximum concentration of 0.3 per cent or 3000 mg/1.

b. *Types of Control for Chlorinators*

(A) Manual	Rate of feed varied by hand. Only suitable at points where flow of sewage to be treated is constant or flow is varied by hand at which time of feed can be set.
(B) Semi-automatic	Feed started or stopped automatically by electric or hydraulic means.
(C) Fully automatic	Flow meter control with proportional displacement.

c. *Selection of Point of Chlorination* should be based on:

1. Moderate pressure at point of chlorination.
2. Minimum variation in rates of flow (chlorinator capacity and range).
3. Best facilities for securing rapid and thorough dispersion of chlorine throughout sewage treated.
4. Accessibility of chlorination equipment for inspection.
5. Minimum damage caused by high chlorine residuals.
6. Availability of suitably heated building, water supply and cylinder storage.
7. Available power—electricity; auxiliary power.

d. *Installation Features of Importance*

1. Chlorinators located near point of application.
2. Separate room for chlorinators if possible (above ground).
3. Ample working space around equipment and storage space for spare parts.
4. Ample supply of water under pressure of at least 15 lbs. per square inch and three times back pressure of point of treatment.

Booster pumps may be necessary. In general a minimum of 40 to 50 gallons per day is required per pound of chlorinator capacity. Failure of water supply means failure of chlorination. The supply must be clear enough not to clog strainers. Minimum water pressure should be 10 to 15 lbs.

5. Adequate heated building. The chlorinator temperature should be above 50°F. to avoid clogging by chlorine ice. Chlorine cylinders must be kept at reasonable temperature and chlorine piping and chlorinator must be at higher temperature to prevent condensing of gas into liquid in pipe lines and chlorinator. The maximum temperature at which a chlorine cylinder is stored should not exceed 140°F.

6. It is not advisable to draw more than 40 pounds of chlorine from any one cylinder in a 24 hour period because of the danger of "freezing" and slowing up the chlorine flow. If more chlorine is necessary, two or more tanks should be connected and used in parallel. With ton cylinders, the limit of chlorine gas is about 400 pounds per day.

7. Adequate light.

8. Adequate ventilation. Continuous ventilation is desirable to remove leaking chlorine gas. Forced ventilation must be provided to remove gas if large leak develops. Inlet of forced ventilation system must be near floor.

9. Convenient handling and storage of chlorine containers. It is dangerous and expensive to handle cylinders up and downstairs and through narrow doors or passageways.

10. Adequate measuring and controlling chlorine dosage is required. Scales and loss-in-weight recorders are desirable as a continuous check on and as a record of the continuity of chlorination.

e. *Continuity of Chlorination*

When chlorination is practiced for disinfection, it is needed continuously. Therefore, arrange that chlorination will function for 1440 minutes or 86,400 seconds per day. To secure continuous chlorination the chlorine gas lines from cylinders should feed to a manifold so that cylinders can be removed without interrupting feed of gas. Duplicate units or an emergency hypochlorinator provided—Adequate supply of spare parts on hand—Adequate number of cylinders connected to manifold to supply gas at the maximum rate of feed. The maximum amount of chlorine feed per 100 lb. or 150 lb. cylinder, should never be greater than at a rate of 35 lb. per day.

f. *Chlorine Containers*

1. Capacity, Handling and Storage.
   Cylinders—100 lb.; 150 lb.; 1 ton.
   Tank cars—16, 30 and 55 tons.
   Cylinders provided with fusible plugs—melts 157°F. to 162°F.

Cylinders will not explode when handling.

Cylinders provided with protective cap for draw off valve.

Cylinder pressure varies with temperature (40°F. to 150°F.).

Liquid chlorine fills about 80 per cent of cylinder capacity as a safety measure.

Chlorine cylinders can be handled with complete safety.

Where large cylinders used, a device such as block and tackle is desirable.

Cylinders can be rolled in a vertical position.

Protective cap should always be replaced when moving cylinder.

Cylinders should be stored at temperatures above 50°F. and kept away from direct heat (steam pipes, radiators, etc.).

Cylinders should be stored upright.

Ton containers can be stored horizontally.

2. Safety precautions.
   A. Keep cylinders away from excessive heat.
   B. Handle so there will be no danger of their falling.
   C. Follow manufacturer's instructions on care and operation of valves.
   D. Repair leaks at once—locate by ammonia, not smell.
   E. Keep gas mask for prompt use outside the chlorine room and use it.
   F. Have first aid equipment available and be sure men are properly instructed in what to do with persons overcome by gas.

g. *First Aid in Case of Chlorine Inhalation*

Remove patient to a place where the air is warm and fresh.

Keep patient quiet and warm.

Do not give alcohol.

If conscious, give black coffee or essence of peppermint.

Warm milk or cream will relieve throat irritation.

Steam inhalations with Tincture of Benzoin compound help relieve cough and difficulty in breathing.

When not breathing use artificial respiration.

Do not use Pulmotor or other mechanical means of resuscitation.

Call or consult physician and in case of serious exposure, the patient should be removed to a hospital.

SPECIAL REFERENCES FOR CHAPTER 7

"Chlorination of Sewage and Industrial Wastes"—Federation of Sewage and Industrial Wastes Associations, Manual of Practice No. 4

CHAPTER 8

SLUDGE TREATMENT AND DISPOSAL

Sewage sludge is the mixture of sewage and settled solids. Descriptive of its source, it may be termed primary, secondary, excess activated, or chemical sludge. From its state, or treatment received, it may be called raw or fresh, digested, elutriated, dewatered or dried. These are the most common descriptive terms and may be used in combination. Other descriptive terms are Imhoff and septic-tank sludge.

As with the liquid portion of sewage, disposal of the solids contained in the sludge must be accomplished. Also, like the liquid portion, the sludge must generally be subjected to some treatment to so alter its character that it may be disposed of without endangering heath or creating nuisances.

Reasons for sludge treatment. Sludge is treated to facilitate its disposal. The various treatment processes have two objectives: (1) to reduce the volume of material to be handled by removal of some or all of the liquid portion, and (2) to decompose the highly putrescible organic matter to relatively stable or inert organic and inorganic compounds from which water will separate more readily. This is called digestion which causes a reduction in the total solids.

Composition of sludge. The quantity and composition of sludge varies with the character of the sewage from which it is removed and depends upon the treatment process by which it is obtained. The following table contains data applicable to a normal domestic sewage.

TABLE 2

NOMINAL QUANTITIES AND CHARACTERISTICS OF SLUDGE PRODUCED BY DIFFERENT TREATMENT PROCESSES

	Treatment Process					
	Plain Sedimentation	Secondary Settling Tanks		Single Story Septic Tanks	Two Story Settling or Separate Sludge Digestion Tanks	Chemical Precipitation
		Trickling Filters	Activated Sludge			
Normal volume of sludge-gal. per million gal. of sewage	2,500	500	13,500	900	500	5,000
Moisture, per cent	95	92.5	98	90	85.	92.5
Dry solids, pounds per million gal.	1,080	320	2,250	810	690	3,300

(Note: The above data taken from "Sewerage and Sewage Disposal," by Metcalf and Eddy)

The sludge obtained from plain sedimentation tanks is essentially the settleable solids in the raw sewage and is termed raw sludge. It has undergone practically no decomposition and is, therefore, highly unstable and putrescible. Such sludge is usually gray in color, disagreeable in appearance, contains bits of garbage, fecal solids, sticks and other debris, and has a foul odor.

The sludge from the secondary settling tank following a trickling filter consists of partially decomposed organic matter. It is usually dark brown and flocculent, more homogeneous in appearane, and has less odor than raw sludge. The excess sludge withdrawn from the activated sludge process is also partically decomposed, is golden brown and flocculent, and has a rather pleasant earthy odor. Both will, with further decomposition, become septic, with offensive odors.

As already noted in Chapter 5, on primary treatment, septic and two story tanks provide for the decomposition of sludge within the unit. The sludge from both is black and, if well digested by long storage, not offensive, with an odor of hot tar, burnt rubber or sealing wax. If withdrawn from the tanks without adequate holding, further decomposition will produce offensive odors.

Sludge from the chemical precipitation process is usually black in color. The odor may be objectionable, but not so bad as sludge from plain sedimentation. It will decompose or digest, but more slowly than sludges from other processes. This is not of much importance as the volume of sludge produced by this process is so great it is not practical to provide digestion facilities, therefore, other treatments are used in preparing it for disposal.

SLUDGE TREATMENT

Any treatment of sludge must have either one or both of the following objectives. It must reduce, by removing water, the volume for subsequent treatment and disposal or change the putrescible organic solids to more stable or inert organic and inorganic solids.

The proportion of solids and water in liquid sludge depends on the nature of the solids, its source, whether from primary or secondary settling tanks and the frequency of removal from these tanks. It may vary from one per cent in a watery activated sludge to ten per cent or more in a concentrated raw or a digested sludge. Concentration is important because the volume occupied is inversely proportional to the solids content. This is well illustrated by the following computations showing 100 pounds of two per cent sludge concentrated to five and ten per cent sludge by the removal of water:

Weight of solids in sludge—lbs.	2	2	2
Per cent of solids	2	5	10
Weight of water—lbs.	98	38	18
Water removed—lbs.		60	80
Gallons of sludge (approx.)	11.7	4.7	2.2
Volume of sludge—cu. ft. (approx.)	1.6	0.6	0.3

It is desirable to handle the most concentrated sludge possible for the following reasons: To save storage space in a digester or to provide a longer digestion period for solids; to save pumping capacity; to reduce heat requirements in heated digesters because there is less water to be heated; and to reduce heat and power requirements for other types of sludge treatment.

SLUDGE TREATMENT METHODS

This manual includes under sludge treatment the methods or processes employed at a plant up to the point of final disposal of the products of the treatment processes. These include:

(1) Thickening
(2) Digestion with or without heat
(3) Drying on sand bed—open or covered
(4) Chemical conditioning
(5) Elutriation
(6) Vacuum filtration
(7) Heat drying
(8) Incineration
(9) Wet oxidation

Thickening. This process involves the concentration of thin sludges to more dense sludge in special tanks designed for this purpose. Its use is largely restricted to the watery excess sludge from the activated sludge process, and in large plants of this type where the sludge is sent direct to digesters instead of to the primary tanks. It may also be used to concentrate sludge from primary tanks or a mixture of primary and excess activated sludge prior to high rate digestion.

The thickening tank is equipped with slowly moving vertical paddles built like a picket fence. Sludge is pumped continuously from the settling tank to the thickener which has a low overflow rate so that the excess water overflows and the sludge solids concentrate in the bottom. A blanket of sludge is maintained by controlled removal which may be continuous at a low rate. A sludge with a solids content of ten per cent or more can be produced by this method. This means that with an original sludge of two per cent, about four-fifths of the water has been removed, and one of the objectives in sludge treatment has been attained. This results in smaller digestion units for the sludge solids and savings in heat required to maintain temperature in heated sludge digesters.

Digestion. The purpose of digestion is to attain both of the objectives of sludge treatment—a reduction in volume and the decomposition of highly putrescible organic matter to relatively stable or inert organic and inorganic compounds. Except with the septic and two story tanks digestion is carried out in separate tanks used only for this purpose.

Digestion Process. Sludge digestion is carried out in the absence of free oxygen by anaerobic organisms. It is, therefore, anaerobic decomposition. The solid matter in raw sludge is about 70 per cent organic and 30 per cent inorganic or mineral. Much of the water in sewage sludge is "bound" water which will not separate from the sludge solids. The living organisms break down the complex molecular structure of these solids setting free the "bound" water and obtaining oxygen and food for their growth.

The microorganisms—bacteria and other forms—first attack the soluble or dissolved solids, such as the sugars. From these reactions organic acids, at times up to several thousand ppm, and gases, such as carbon dioxide and hydrogen sulfide are formed. The pH value of the sludge decreases to a range of from 6.8 to 5.1. This is known as the stage of acid fermentation and proceeds rapidly. It is followed by a second stage carried on by organisms to which an acid environment is favorable and is known as a period of acid digestion in which the organic acids and nitrogenous compounds are attacked and liquified at a much slower rate. During this stage the pH value increases to a range from 5.1 to 6.8.

In the third stage of digestion, known as the period of intensive digestion, stabilization and gasification, the more resistent nitrogenous materials, such as the proteins, amino-acids and others, are attacked. The volatile acid content is reduced to less than 500 ppm. The pH value increases to the range from 6.8 to 7.4. Large volumes of gases with a 65 or higher percentage of methane (CH_4) are produced. Methane is an odorless, highly inflammable gas which can be used as a fuel, as described in Chapter 9. The solids still remaining are relatively stable or only slowly putrescible, can be disposed of without creating objectionable conditions and have value in agriculture as discussed later in this Chapter.

The whole process of sludge digestion may be likened to a factory production line where one group of workers takes the raw material and conditions it for a second group with different "skills" who further convert the material for the specialized work of the third group to turn out the end products.

Where sludge digestion is carried on in a single tank as with the septic, two-story and single separate sludge digestion tank, all of the above stages are taking place continuously and at the same time. Fresh sewage solids are being added at frequent intervals with the stabilized solids being removed for further treatment or disposal at less frequent intervals. The supernatant digester liquor, the product of liquefaction and mechanical separation is removed frequently to make room for the added fresh solids and the gas is, of course, being removed continuously.

While all stages of digestion may be proceeding in a tank at the same time with the acids produced in the first stage being neutralized by the ammonia produced in subsequent stages, best and quickest results are obtained when the over-all pH value of the third stage (6.8 to 7.4) predominates. The first two stages of acid formation and acid regression should be evident only in starting up digestion units. Once good alkaline digestion is established, the acid stages are not apparent unless the normal digestion becomes upset by overloading, poisonous chemicals or for other reasons.

The progress of digestion can be measured by destruction of organic matter (volatile solids) or by the volume and composition of gases produced, with the pH or volatile acid content used as an indicator of the stage.

The reduction of organic matter as measured by the volatile solids indicates the completeness of digestion. Raw sludge usually contains from 60 to 70 per cent volatile solids while a well digested sludge may have as little as 50 per cent. This would represent a reduction of about 50 per cent. Imhoff and Fair indicate that the reduction of organic matter in primary sludge may be as much as 66 per cent with a slight increase in the dissolved mineral content.

A well digested sludge should be black in color, have a not unpleasant tarry odor and, when collected in a glass cylinder, should appear granular in structure and show definite channels caused by water rising to the top as the solids settle to the bottom.

For domestic sewage in a normally operating digestion tank, gas production should be in the vicinity of 12 cu. ft. of gas per day per pound of volatile matter destroyed. This would indicate that for a 50 per cent reduction of volatile matter, a gas yield of six cu. ft. per pound of volatile matter added should be attained. A popular figure for sludge from average domestic sewage is an expected gas yield of one cu. ft. per capita per day. Industrial wastes, depending on their character, may raise or lower this figure materially. The gas is usually about 70 per cent methane, about 30 per cent carbon dioxide and inert gases such as nitrogen. Carbon dioxide in excess of 35 per cent may be an indication that the digestion process is not proceeding properly.

Many sewage treatment plants have only one digestion unit in which all stages of digestion take place, while others have multiple units. In the latter case, it is often desirable to operate the tanks in series as primary and secondary digesters. Raw sludge is pumped to the primary digester displacing partially digested sludge or liquor to the secondary digester. The major portion of the digestion with the greatest gas yield is effected in the primary unit. The secondary tank may be heated, as discussed later under temperature control, to a lower temperature or not at all, and less agitation due to gas production occurs so that a clearer supernatant liquor can be obtained than from a single unit or from the primary digester. The disposition of this liquor presents its own problem which will be noted later. Digested sludge for further treatment and disposal is drawn only from the secondary digester.

The digestion process is seldom carried to full completion but only to a degree where the resulting solids, although still organic in composition, have been sufficiently decomposed to become relatively stable or inert, in the nature of humus material.

Since digestion is accomplished by living organisms, it is desirable to provide an environment in which they are most active and carry on their work in the shortest time. The environmental factors involved are moisture, temperature, availability of proper food supply, and alkalinity. To these might be added the absence of chemicals toxic to the organisms. Moisture is always adequate in sewage sludge. The other three merit discussion.

Temperature. It has been found that sludge digestion proceeds in almost any range of temperature likely to be encountered, but the time taken to complete digestion varies greatly with the temperature. Also rapid changes in temperature are detrimental. At a temperature of 55°F., about 90 per cent of the desired digestion is completed in about 55 days. As the temperature increases, the time decreases, so that at 75° the time is cut to 35 days, at 85° to 26 days, and at 95° to 24 days. The theoretical time for sludge digestion at 95°F. is one half that at 60°. Of course the figures are average, not exact figures for all sludges of varying composition. These digestion times may be materially reduced in digesters provided with efficient mixing of thickened sludge.

Digestion in the temperature range between 80° and 100°F. is called *mesophilic* digestion and is most favorable for some organisms. Others work better at temperatures above 100 causing *thermophilic* digestion. Both types yield satisfactory results but in practice the latter is generally restricted to the digestion of certain kinds of organic solids. The most common range used for best digester operation is between 85° and 95°F. but regardless of the temperature selected in this range it must be maintained consistently within a narrow range of two to three degrees. The working organisms don't like sudden or wide changes in temperature in their workshop and they slow down if it occurs.

Not all plants have facilities to heat sludge for digestion. Where the primary settling unit is a septic tank, heating facilities are never provided. They are seldom available in the Imhoff tank, and may or may not be in other two story tanks. Separate sludge digestion tanks are generally heated but not always.

One important reason for using heated digestion tanks is the extra capital cost of building storage space to hold sludge over a long digestion period as compared with a shorter one. Where the composition of the sewage has been established, tank capacity should be computed from the volume and character of the sludge to be digested with due allowance made for sludge storage and supernatant. Where such data are not available the following table should be used for conventional tanks treating domestic sewage.

TABLE 3

DIGESTER CAPACITIES FOR VARIOUS TYPES OF
TREATMENT PLANTS

Type of Plant	Recommended Digester Capacity Cubic Feet per Capita	
	Heated	Unheated
Imhoff tanks		3 to 4*
Imhoff tank and trickling filter		4 to 6*
Primary ....2 to 3		4 to 6*
Primary and trickling filter ....4 to 5		8 to 10*
Activated sludge ....4 to 6		8 to 12*

*These are figures generally applicable in the Middle Atlantic States area. Different climatic conditions in other areas should be considered in the use of these figures.

The above figures are for a domestic sewage, and should be increased by allowing for suspended solids in industrial wastes, or where appreciable amounts of garbage solids are anticipated from extensive use of household garbage grinders. They may be decreased where mechanical sludge thickeners, as already described, are used. The higher values should be used for plants serving a population of 5,000 or less.

Another important reason for heating digesters is that gas production is at a faster rate at higher temperatures. Thus in an unheated tank, with a digestion temperature of 50°F. about seven cu. ft. of gas per pound of volatile matter destroyed will be produced in 90 days, while 12 cu. ft. will be produced from the same amount of volatile matter in 25 days with a digestion temperature of 86°F. Since this gas is a valuable fuel by-product of sludge digestion, the amount and continuity of production regardless of climatic condition are important.

In heating digesters enough heat must be supplied to:

(1) Heat the raw sludge to the desired uniform tank temperature.

(2) Overcome all heat losses through walls, top and bottom of the tank.

A number of methods have been used to supply the heat. They include:

(1) Circulation of hot water (120°F.) through pipes or coils hung inside the tank walls.

(2) Circulation of mixed sludge from the digestion tank, or raw sludge through a heat exchanger outside the tank.

(3) Burning sludge gas in a submerged or underwater heater.

(4) Injection of steam into the bottom of the tank.

(5) Introduction of hot water or steam into the raw sludge before it enters the tank.

Of the above, the first method is the one most commonly used in older plants but the second is gaining in popularity for new installations.

Food Supply. The proper amount of food must be provided for the digester organisms. This is in the form of raw sludge solids from the various sewage treatment units. The total volume of raw sludge pumped to the digester, the rate at which it is pumped, and the degree to which it is made available to all of the different groups of organisms are vital factors in efficient digester operation. If too much sludge is added to a digester, the first, or acid stage, predominates to such an extent that the environment becomes unfavorable for the organisms responsible for the second and third stages of digestion, the balance of the whole digestion process is upset, and the digester is said to be overloaded. If this is due to unbalanced plant design whereby the digester capacity is too small in relation to the sludge producing units, about the only solution is to provide additional digester capacity. There are, however, other factors which can upset the balance of the digestion process and which are under the control of the operator. In heated digesters failure to maintain uniform temperatures in the digester within the proper range will upset the digestion process. Adding fresh solids in large volumes at widely separated intervals or removing too much digested sludge at one time will result in temporary overloading. In unheated digestion tanks similar conditions are to be expected seasonly and during winter months digester organisms are almost dormant, so that with the advent of warm weather there is in the digester an excessive accumulation of almost raw sludge solids. This, together with the normally slower digestion in unheated tanks, necessitates storage capacity twice that needed in heated digesters.

The organisms in a digester are most efficient when food is furnished them in small volumes at frequent intervals. Fresh sludge solids should, therefore, be pumped to the digester as often as practical, at least twice a day for the smallest plants and more frequently where facilities and operators' attention are available. This, of course, fits in with the proper schedule of removing sludge from settling units before it becomes septic in them.

Mixing and Seeding. In starting a digester unit, quickest results can be obtained by putting in it at the start some digested sludge if this is obtainable from another digester or a nearby plant. In this way all stages of digestion can be started almost simultaneously instead of by successive stages. This seeding supplies an adequate number of organisms of the second and third stage to consume the end products of the first stage and in this way the unit will "ripen" in the shortest time.

After normal operation has been established, seeding of the fresh solids as added to the digester by mixing them with the digesting sludge greatly improves the rate of digestion. This mixing serves several purposes:

(1) The incoming raw solids are intimately mixed with the actively digesting sludge.

(2) Scum formation is prevented.

(3) The transmission of heat from internal coils or other heating devices to the sludge is improved.

There are a number of methods whereby proper mixing is attained. These include:

(1) Stirring by rotating paddles and scum breaker arms.

(2) Forced circulation of sludge and/or supernatant by pumps or by draft tubes with impeller.

(3) Discharge of compressed sludge gas from diffusers at the bottom of the digestion tank.

Mixing may be either intermittent or continuous, but however effected it provides all working organisms their proper food requirements and helps maintain uniform temperature so that all can work together throughout the whole contents of the digester to accomplish the desired results. Intermittent mixing allows separation and removal of supernatant from a single digester. With continuous mixing the digestion proceeds at a higher rate throughout the entire tank thus reducing the tank capacity needed. Such continuous mixing requires a second digester or storage tank into which digesting sludge may be moved to make room for fresh sludge in the first digester and to make possible separation and removal of supernatant in the second tank.

92

pH Control. The optimum pH value of the sludge in a digester is close to the neutral reading of 7.0 lying within a range of 6.8 and 7.4 with values of 7.0 to 7.2 most common. In this range all the groups of organisms can perform their functions. Ordinarily in a well designed and operated digester it is possible to maintain a balance between fresh and digesting solids so that the reaction will remain within these favorable limits, the acids produced in the first stage being neutralized by the alkaline production in the second stage, and the material in the third providing a buffer (cushioning against change in pH) action. Marked variations from the pH range of 6.8 to 7.4 means that the digestion process is out of balance.

Types of Sludge Digesters. There are many types of units used for sludge digestion, the difference between them being in construction and operation facilities. Thus there are:

(1) Digestion units as part of the sedimentation tank as in the septic tank and two story tank. In the former, digesting sludge is in contact with the settling sewage, while in the latter the two functions are in separate compartments.

(2) Separate tanks used only for digestion. These may be subdivided into:

    (a) Open or covered. In the open tanks gas escapes directly to the atmosphere, while with covered tanks, gas is collected to be used as a fuel for gas engines or heat. The covers may be stationary or "fixed" or they may be "floating," rising or falling with the amount of sludge and gas accumulated.

    (b) Unheated or heated.

    (c) With or without stirring or mixing devices.

Operating Procedures and Controls for Separate Sludge Digestion Tanks. It is not practical to cover all of the special problems which may develop in the operation of sludge digestion units. There are, however, many routine procedures which usually give the best results with heated separate sludge digestion tanks, which are most common. A number of them are listed below.

(1) *Sludge Pumping.* Sludge should be drawn from sedimentation units before it has become septic, and should be as dense as possible and still handled satisfactorily through the pumps and piping. A thin sludge contains needless water which occupies storage space and will have to be heated.

Sludge should be added to the digester at frequent intervals—at least twice a day and oftener if practical. Small additions at frequent intervals assures a more constant food supply to the organisms and a more uniform digestion rate. With fixed cover digesters, the rate of addition should be low to minimize disturbing the supernatant which is discharged from the digester at the same rate as sludge is added. This is not so important with digesters with floating covers as the supernatant is not necessarily discharged at the same time. In general, fresh solids (dry basis) added daily should not exceed five per cent of the solids (dry basis) already in the digester.

The selection of pumps for pumping sludge depends on many factors such as size of plant, economy, and maintenance. Types of pumps used have been plunger, diaphragm, centrifugal and modification of the centrifugal. Air lifts and ejectors have also been utilized and recently positive displacement rotary pumps have been installed in some plants to pump thickened sludge.

(2) *Two-Stage Digester Operation.* Two-stage digestion uses two compartments or two tanks and separates the violent initial digestion period from the slower final one. In the primary digester, incoming raw sludge is well mixed with seeding material and the tank contents are kept well mixed by use of mechanical stirrers or recirculation if necessary. Some sludge separation normally occurs in spite of the mixing, with the heavier material settling to the bottom of the tank. The digestion process is completed in the secondary tank where there is lower gas production which causes less mixing and produces a much clearer supernatant than can be produced in a single-stage digester.

In using two-stage digestion with a fixed cover primary digester the supernatant or lighter sludge is normally transferred while raw sludge is being pumped to the primary digester, causing the overflow of this material to the secondary digester through the supernatant transfer line. The supernatant and digested sludge is withdrawn from the secondary digester in the same manner as it is done with a single digester. If the primary digester tends to become upset and the pH drops, sludge may be pumped from the bottom of the secondary digester to the primary to provide additional seed to maintain alkaline digestion. Supernatant must be transferred from the primary to the secondary digester simultaneously. The temperature in the secondary digester is normally maintained 5°F. to 10°F. below that of the primary digester so as to improve supernatant separation. Under normal conditions this makes heating of the secondary digester unnecessary, except during the coldest part of the year. However, if complete digestion is not being obtained, the temperature should be increased to 90°F. or 95°F.

In using two-stage digestion with a floating cover the primary digester may be operated the same as the fixed cover type with automatic supernatant or light-sludge transfer through the overflow piping. As an alternate the transfer may be made every two or three days. In other respects operation is similar to that with a fixed cover primary digester.

(3) *Temperature Control.* The temperature in the digester should be maintained within a range of two to three degrees of that selected which is usually somewhere between 85°F. and 95°F. With heating coils in the digester, the temperature of the water in the coils should be high enough to maintain sludge temperature, but not over 130°F. (At temperatures of 140° or over the sludge will cake on the coils and form an insulating layer reducing the efficiency of heat exchange.)

(4) *pH Control.* The reaction of the sludge should be kept close to neutral within the pH range of 6.8 to 7.4. Some claim that adding lime will neutralize a too acid sludge, while others say that lime has no place

in a digester. The addition of lime certainly is not a cure-all for acid sludge. This condition can, under normal operation, be prevented or corrected by proper control over the fresh solids input.

(5) *Stirring.* Where available, stirring devices should be used at intervals frequent enough to assure adequate seeding of fresh solids with sludge in advanced stages of digestion. This will give more rapid and uniform digestion, help to prevent scum formation, and lessen the possibility of foaming difficulties.

(6) *Withdrawal of Supernatant.* The supernatant is the digester liquor lying above the sludge solids in the digester. It is the liquor which has been separated from the sludge solids. While it should contain few suspended solids, it is high in dissolved organic matter which decomposes rapidly with the development of foul odors and is generally subjected to some treatment before disposal.

Supernatant is withdrawn from the digester to reduce the volume of sludge remaining by concentrating the solids content and to provide storage space for the addition of fresh solids.

With fixed cover digesters supernatant is withdrawn at the same time and same rate raw sludge is added. This is a further reason why raw sludge should be pumped for short periods at frequent intervals. It prevents the discharge of large volumes of supernatant in a short period of time. It is most important that the supernatant outlet be kept clean. If clogged, the addition of fresh sludge can increase the internal pressure to a point where it may lift or crack the cover.

With floating cover digesters the safety of the cover is not a factor and it is possible to withdraw supernatant at a low rate over a long period of time. Where the sludge is agitated by stirring devices or recirculation it is desirable to allow a quiescent period of several hours before withdrawing supernatant to allow for its separation from the rest of the digester contents.

There are a number of methods used for the disposition of supernatant. Probably the most common procedure is to return it to the influent of the primary sedimentation tanks. This may cause difficulties by causing the tank to become septic. At some plants it has been found advantageous to return the supernatant to the influent of an activated sludge aeration tank or trickling filter. Where primary and secondary sewage treatment units are not able to accept this additional load without detriment, sludge beds, as described later, or lagoons have been used. Even with these, it is customary to return the clarified supernatant to the treatment process. Lagoons may create objectionable odors and their location should be carefully selected.

Withdrawal of Digested Sludge. The type of digester, subsequent sludge treatment, season of the year, and need for storage space for fresh sludge normally govern the withdrawal of digested sludge. It is important to always leave enough digested sludge to seed the raw sludge and maintain balanced digestion near neutral reaction. In heated digesters the same amount of sludge may be left in the tank regardless of season. In unheated digesters about twice the normal digested sludge should be retained as cold weather approaches. Normally it is wise to leave about four feet of digested sludge above the hopper. Withdrawal of proper amounts at regular intervals is better than large withdrawals, as the digester then becomes overloaded. This generally aggravates conditions by upsetting the reaction balance.

Only well digested sludge should be normally withdrawn. Gray or light brown streaks in the dark color of well digested sludge are signs that undigested material is being withdrawn.

It is of the utmost importance with covered digesters to be sure that no air is being drawn into the tank during sludge withdrawal. In the withdrawal of sludge, care must be exercised to avoid negative pressure in a fixed cover digester. This can be done by adding raw sludge, sewage, gas or water from a make-up tank at the same rate that sludge is withdrawn from the digestion tank. The addition of air to digester gasses produces a highly explosive and dangerous mixture. It is equally important to see that safeguards provided to prevent build-up of excessive hydrostatic pressure under a fixed cover are functioning. The most common provision is an unvalved supernatant overflow line which must be kept open at all times.

Drying Sand Beds. Even the best, most concentrated sludge from a digester contains too much water to permit, under most conditions, satisfactory and economical disposal. The sand drying bed is a device to remove enough water so that the remainder can be handled as solid material with a moisture content below 70 per cent.

*Construction.** Sludge drying beds consist of a layer of graded gravel 12 inches deep under a layer of clean sand six to nine inches deep. Open joint tile underdrains are laid in the gravel layer with at least six inch gravel cover and spaced not more than 20 feet apart. The sludge pipe to the bed should terminate at least 12 inches above the sand surface. Concrete splash plates should be provided at sludge discharge points. The beds may be open or uncovered, or they may be covered with a glass, greenhouse type cover. The open beds are more common.

*Area.** The following table gives the area required for the two types of beds with different sewage treatment processes. The figures are for locations between 40° and 45° N. Latitude and should be increased or decreased by 25 per cent for latitudes north of 45° or south of 40° respectively.

TABLE 4

SLUDGE BED AREAS FOR VARIOUS TYPES OF TREATMENT

Type of Treatment	Area in Square Feet per Capita	
	Open Beds	Covered Beds
Primary	1.00	0.75
Trickling Filter	1.50	1.25
Activated Sludge	1.75	1.35
Chemical Precipitation	2.00	1.50

*Standard for the ten states of the Upper Mississippi and Great Lakes Boards of Public Health Engineers.

The purpose of the glass cover is, of course, to permit operation of the beds throughout the cold winter months when the sludge on open beds would freeze and not dry, and to prevent wetting partially dry sludge on the beds by rain. As evidenced by the above table, less area is required for covered than open but construction costs are much higher.

Operation. The drying of the sludge on the beds is a combination of two factors—first, drainage, and second, evaporation. When sludge is applied the release of entrained and dissolved gases tend to float the solids, leaving a layer of liquor at the bottom which drains away through the sand. Gas release may be increased by dosing the sludge with one pound of alum per 100 to 300 gallons of sludge. The major portion of this drainage occurs in the first 12 to 18 hours. Further drying is due to evaporation of water. As this takes place the sludge layer cracks open at the surface, permitting further evaporation from lower layers as the cracks deepen.

The sludge applied should be as dense as possible. Experience is the best guide in determining the depth of sludge applied. It generally ranges from eight to twelve inches. The condition and moisture content of the sludge, the bed area available, and the need for storage space in the digesters are factors. The thinner layer will dry more rapidly, permitting quicker removal and re-use of the bed. An eight inch layer should dry in about three weeks, while a ten inch layer of the same sludge will take four weeks, so that 25 per cent more sludge takes 33 per cent more time. If alum is used. as noted above. the drying time may be cut to as much as one half, from an average of three weeks to ten days. This may be important where more sludge should be drawn from the digester than there is bed area available. If this is a common situation, more sludge beds should be provided.

The surface of drying bed should be kept clean and free from all previously discharged sludge. Never discharge wet sludge on dried or partially dried sludge.

Under favorable weather conditions evaporation is more rapid with open than with covered beds. With covered beds it is advantageous to keep the ventilators closed to maintain temperature during the drainage stage and open for air exchange during the evaporation stage.

After sludge has been drawn from a digester, the sludge lines should be well drained and flushed with water. This not only prevents plugging of the lines, but also the development of quite heavy pressures in them from gases generated in the sludge left in the lines. Always remember that these gases, when mixed with air are highly explosive. Matches. lighted cigarettes or pipes or fire should be avoided when opening sludge valves.

Cleaning Beds. The best time to remove sludge from the drying beds depends on a number of factors such as subsequent treatment by grinding or shredding. the need to remove sludge from digesters and, of course. the moisture content of the sludge on the beds. Sludge cake can be removed by shovel or forks at a moisture content of 60 to 70 per cent. but if it is allowed to dry to 40 per cent, it will weigh only half as much. At the other end of the scale a dried sludge with ten per cent moisture is dusty.

A few large plants have mechanical elevators, conveyor belts and loaders, but most operators have to use hand tools to lift the sludge from the sand surface. One of the best tools is a shovel-like fork having several tines, or long teeth an inch or so apart, such as an ensilage fork or coal or stone fork. With a fork, sludge can be removed with much less sand loss than with a shovel. At best some sand will hang to the bottom of the sludge cake and eventually this sand will have to be replaced.

Many small plant operators use wheelbarrows to haul the sludge from the bed. Planks are laid on the bed for a runway. Wheelbarrows can be placed close to the worker so that the shoveling distance is not great. More and more plants use pickup trucks or dual-wheeled dump trucks. The dump truck has the advantage of quick unloading and most municipalities have them for other purposes.

Where trucks are used, it is best to have concrete treadways in the bed wide enough to carry dual wheels as the bed would be damaged if the trucks were driven directly onto the sand. The treadways should be spaced close enough together so that there is not a long carry from any part of the bed to the truck. If there are no permanent treadways, heavy planks may be placed on the sand.

The crawler trailer with side bins is very popular in larger plants because it can operate on any shape or size of bed without treadways. Less commonly, industrial railways with small dump carts are used.

After sludge has been removed, the bed should be prepared for the next drawing. It may be necessary to replace sand which has been lost by previous cleanings. Abount an inch of sand is lost each year so that the sand layer should be built up to proper depth about once every three years. Any clean course sand is satisfactory. If beds are idle for a long period, they should be kept free from excessive weed growth.

The sludge removed from the bed may be finally disposed of as discussed later or it may be stockpiled and allowed to weather over winter or for several months before disposal. Weathering takes the heat from the sludge and it falls apart into smooth small particles very much like soft earth and is in good condition for disposal by agricultural uses as described later.

Sludge Lagoons. The considerable labor involved in sludge drying bed operation may be avoided by the use of sludge lagoons. These lagoons are nothing but excavated areas in which digested sludge is allowed to drain and dry over a period of months or even a year or more. They are usually dug out by bulldozers, or other dirt-moving equipment, with the excavated material used for building up the sides to confine the sludge. Depths may range from two to six feet. Areas vary, and although drainage is desirable, it is not usually provided.

Digested sludge is drawn as frequently as needed, with successive drawings on top of the previous ones until the lagoon is filled. A second lagoon may then be operated while the filled one is drying. After the sludge has dried enough to be moved, a bulldozer, or a tractor with an end-loader, may be used to scoop out the sludge. In some locations it may be pushed from the lagoon by dozers into low ground for fill.

Lagoons may be used for regular drying of sludge, re-used after emptying, or allowed to fill and dry, then leveled and developed into lawn. They can also be used as emergency storage when the sludge beds are full or when the digester must be emptied for repair. In the latter case it should be treated with some odor control chemicals, such as hydrated or chlorinated lime.

The size of the lagoon depends upon the use to which it will be put. For example, a town of 5000 could operate with two lagoons, say 25 feet by 100 feet (or 50 by 50 feet) each, and three feet deep, for a considerable time. This example is based on a capacity of three cubic feet per capita but more or less volume may be desired.

Lagoons may take the place of sludge beds or provide a place for emergency drawings of sludge, but they may be unsightly and even unwanted on a small plant site. However, they are becoming more popular because they are inexpensive to build and operate.

Chemical Conditioning. Chemical conditioning (sludge conditioning) prepares the sludge for better and more economical further treatment with vacuum filters or centrifuges. Many chemicals have been used such as sulfuric acid, alum, chlorinated copperas, ferrous sulfate, and ferric chloride with or without lime, and others. The local cost of the various chemicals is usually the determining factor. In recent years the price of ferric chloride has been reduced to a point where it is the one most commonly used.

The addition of the chemical to the sludge lowers its pH value to a point where small particles coagulate into larger ones and the water in the sludge solids is given up most readily. There is not one pH value best for all sludges. Different sludges such as primary, various secondary, and digested sludge and different sludges of the same type have different optimum pH values which must be determined for each sludge by trial and error.

Tanks for dissolving acid salts, such as ferric chloride, are lined with rubber or other acid-proof material. Intimate mixing of sludge and coagulant is essential for proper conditioning. Feeders are also necessary for applying the chemicals needed for proper chemical conditioning.

Elutriation. The word "elutriation" means to purify by washing. In sludge treatment it means washing out of the sludge by water or treatment plant effluents excessive amounts of amino and ammonia compounds to reduce the coagulant demand. It is, therefore, used as a pre-treatment before chemical coagulation. It is accomplished by mixing the sludge with water or plant effluent for a very short period, often less than 20 seconds, using mechanical, or diffused air agitation. The mixture is then settled and the supernatant returned to the sewage treatment process.

The process is carried out in tanks similar to sedimentation tanks, usually in pairs, in which sludge and wash water enter at opposite ends. Piping and channels are so arranged that wash water entering the second stage tank comes first into contact with sludge already washed in the first stage tank with wash water from the second stage. The volume of wash water required is from two to three times the volume of the sludge being elutriated. Figure 16 shows a flow diagram and plan of tanks for elutriation.

The advantages claimed for elutriation include (1) a reduction by 65 to 80 per cent of the amount of conditioning chemical required, (2) a lower ash content in the filter cake, and (3) little or no lime is required as a conditioning chemical. As is always the case, costs enter the picture. The cost of the equipment, its operation and disposal of the wash water must be balanced against savings in chemicals.

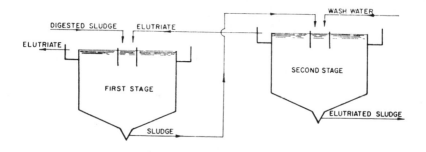

FLOW SHEET

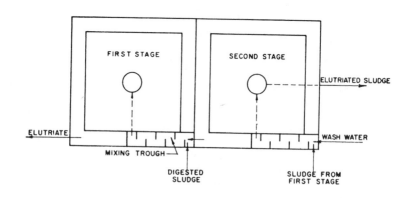

PLAN

TWO-STAGE COUNTERCURRENT ELUTRIATION
FIGURE 16

Vacuum Filtration. The vacuum filter for dewatering sludge is a drum over which is laid the filtering medium consisting of a cloth of cotton, wool, nylon, dynel, fiber glass or plastic, or a stainless steel mesh, or a double layer of stainless steel coil springs. The drum with horizontal axis is set in a tank with about one quarter of the drum submerged in conditioned sludge. Valves and piping are so arranged that, as a portion of the drum rotates slowly in the sludge, a vacuum is applied on the inner side of the filter medium, drawing out water from the sludge and holding the sludge against it. The application of the vacuum is continued as the drum rotates out of the sludge and into the atmosphere. This pulls water away from the sludge, leaving a moist mat or cake on the outer surface. This mat is scraped, blown or lifted away from the drum just before it enters the sludge tank again.

The common measure of performance of vacuum filters is the rate in pounds per hour of dry solids filtered per square foot of filter surface. For various sludges this rate may vary from a low of 2.5 for activated sludge to a high of 6 to 11 for the best digested primary sludge. The moisture content in the sludge cake also varies with the type of sludge from 80 to 84 per cent, for raw activated sludge to 60 to 68 per cent for well digested primary sludge.

While operating costs, including conditioning of sludge for vacuum filtration, are usually higher than with sludge beds, filtration has the advantage of requiring much less area, is independent of seasons and weather conditions, and can eliminate necessity for digestion since raw sludge can be dewatered sufficiently to be incinerated. The details of operation of a vacuum filter vary somewhat, depending on the make of filter, the chemicals used for conditioning and the type of sludge to be handled. There are, however, a few general suggestions on operation which should be considered such as:

Conditioned sludge should be filtered as quickly as possible after the addition of the chemicals and adequate mixing. Continuous feeding is preferable to batch conditioning.

In raw sludge filtration, fresh sewage solids and sludge filter more readily than stale or septic sludge. This applies to raw sludge filtration.

Completely digested sludge usually filters more readily than partially digested sludge.

Concentration of sludge to be filtered is desirable as sludge with the higher solid content usually filters more readily than that with a lower solid content.

The presence of mineral oils and wastes from dry cleaning establishments makes sludge filtration difficult. Such wastes should, therefore, be kept out of the sewer system and disposed of separately.

Prolongation of the life of the material used as the filter may be effected by proper care. Such care includes washing of the filter material with the spray jets after every period of use, removal of grease and fats with warm soap solution if clogged, treatment with diluted hydrochloric acid for removal of lime encrustations, maintenance of scraper blade in careful adjustment to filter drum to prevent tearing of the filter material.

Diluted ferric chloride solutions (10% to 20%) usually give better results in the conditioning of the sludge.

A high calcium lime is preferable for sludge filtration work.

The maintenance of a uniform vacuum is necessary for satisfactory operation. Loss or fluctuations in vacuum usually indicate a break in the filter material, poorly conditioned sludge or uneven distribution of the sludge solids in the filter pan.

Avoid excessive use of chemicals. The quantities of chemicals used for conditioning can be frequently reduced by careful control of the mixing and flocculation equipment.

After every use the vauum filter should be cleaned, and all sludge drained from the unit. This sludge and wash water should not be returned to the sludge storage tank but to the raw sewage channel or to a digester.

Heat Drying. Where sludge is to be used in the manufacture of fertilizers, the moisture content must be reduced to about 10 per cent which is much less than is normally attained on sludge beds or by vacuum filtration. Where sludge is to be incinerated, it must be dried to a point where it will ignite and burn. For such purposes heat drying is used. There are about four commonly used units for heat drying: (1) the rotary kiln dryer, (2) the flash dryer, (3) the spray dryer, and (4) the multiple-hearth furnace.

The *rotary kiln dryer* is a cylinder four to eight feet in diameter with the length eight to ten times the diameter. The cylinder revolves four to eight rpm on an inclined axis. The sludge to be dried enters at one end and is carried to the discharge and by gravity, breaking and mixing over flights set in the wall of the cylinder. Heated gases are introduced to the cylinder with the hotter gases coming in contact with the cold sludge. Rotary driers are generally used with dewatered sludge from a vacuum filter. As sludge with a moisture content of over 50 per cent tends to form balls which will dry on the outside, leaving a moist center, it is customary to return and mix with the entering sludge enough dried sludge to reduce the moisture content of the mixture to a proper value. The average drying temperature should not exceed 700°F. The gases from the dryer contain dust which must be removed before discharge to the atmosphere. They can also create serious odor nuisances unless deodorized by washing, by chlorination, or by incinerating them at a temperature of 1200° to 1400°F.

With the *flash dryer*, sludge cake mixed with previously dried sludge is fed to a cage type mill where the sludge particles are dried almost instantly as they are dispersed and held in suspension in a stream of hot gases. The gas-borne sludge particles pass to a separator where the dried sludge is removed from the moisture ladened gases. The dried sludge may either be burned or used as a fertilizer.

The *spray dryer* consists of a vertical "hot-tower" down which a current of hot gases is passing. Wet sludge is sprayed into this tower. The water is evaporated from the atomized particles and passes off with the hot gases and the dried solids drop to the bottom of the tower. Dust carried with the hot gases is removed from them by a dust catcher or separator. As with the flash dryer, the dried solids can be burned or used as fertilizer.

Dried sludge from the rotary kiln is granular and may contain large clinker-like masses which require grinding for further use. but that resulting from flash or spray is a fluffy material suitable for fertilizer use or for burning in a manner used for powdered fuel.

Care must be observed in the handling of very dry pulverized sludge that it does not accumulate as dust which may later be disturbed and ignited to cause a dust explosion.

The *multiple-hearth furnace* is considered under heat drying as well as under incineration, because part of the unit is used for heat drying of the sludge which is necessary before it can be incinerated. The multiple-hearth furnace consists of a vertical cylinder lined with fire brick or other refractory material and containing a series of four or more hearths one above the other. As generally used, partially dewatered sludge such as the cake from a vacuum filter, is fed to the upper hearth, and partially dried by the hot gases from the lower hearths. It is moved successively down to the next lower hearth by rotating plows or mechanical rakes until dried to a point where it will ignite and burn.

Incineration. Incineration of sludge is quite commonly considered a method of sludge disposal. It is, however, included in this manual under sludge treatment because the end product of the process is an ash which requires disposal.

There are two general types of sludge incinerators, the flash and the multiple-hearth incinerators. The flash type is designed to burn the dried sludge from the flash or spray driers. This is a fluffy material which can be blown into the fire box in a manner similar to that used for powdered fuel. The heat of combustion is used for the driers.

The multiple-hearth type has been described above under heat treatment.

In all types of incinerators, the gases from combustion must be brought to and kept at a temperature of 1250° to 1400°F. until they are completely burned. This is essential to prevent odor nuisance from stack discharge. It is also necessary to maintain effective removal of dust. fly ash and soot from the stack discharge. This may be done by a settling chamber, by a centrifugal separator, or by a Cottrell electrical precipitator. The selection depends on the degree of removal efficiency required for the plant location.

All types of sludges, primary, secondary, raw or digested sludge may be dried and burned. Raw primary sludge with about 70 per cent volatile solids contains about 7800 BTU per pound of dry solids and when combustion is once started will burn without supplementary fuel, in fact an excess of heat is usually available. Digested sludge may or may not require supplementary fuel, depending on the moisture content of the cake and per cent volatile solids or degree of digestion. Raw activated sludge generally requires supplementary fuel for drying and burning. In all cases supplementary fuel is necessary to start operation and until combustion of the solids has been established.

Incineration of sludge appears to be gaining popularity, especially at large plants. It has the advantages of economy, freedom from odor. independence of weather and the great reduction in the volume and weight of end product to be disposed of. There is a minimum size of sewage treatment plant below which incineration is not economical. There must be enough sludge to necessitate reasonable use of costly equipment. One of the difficulties in operating an incinerator is variations in tonnage and moisture of sludge handled.

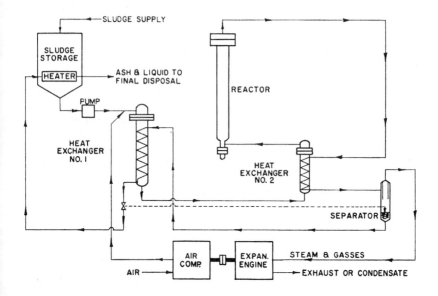

WET SLUDGE OXIDATION
(ZIMMERMAN PROCESS)

FIGURE 17

Wet oxidation (Zimmermann Process). In this process, as shown by Figure 17, sewage sludge, comminuted to pass one-quarter inch openings, is pre-heated in a storage-mixing tank to about 180°F. and then fed by a rotary pump to a high pressure pump capable of discharging into a pipe line into which air is introduced at 1200 to 1800 psi. The warm air-sludge mixture is then passed through heat exchangers which raise the temperature to about 400°F. before the mixture enters a vertical reactor for upward flow. Within the reactor oxygen from the air combines with organic matter in the sludge oxidizing it to an ash with the liberation of heat. The temperature in the reactor becomes about 500°F. Effluent from the reactor passes through the heat exchangers giving up much of its heat to the incoming sludge. The liquid portion of the effluent carries the ash which may be removed by sedimentation in tanks or lagoons, or in some cases discharged with plant effluent. The hot gases and steam when of sufficient quantity may be utilized in a turbine or engine to produce power for compressing the necessary air. Other products of the wet oxidation of sewage sludge are ammonia, volatile acids and some residual BOD. The completeness of oxidation depends mainly upon the temperature in the reactor. Air requirements of the process are determined by: the heat value of the sludge being oxidized (BTU per pound of air), the moisture content of the sludge, and reactor conditions as to temperature and pressure. Whether or not the process at any particular plant will be self-sustaining depends largely upon moisture content of the sludge and its heat value, which in turn depends upon the organic or volatile content.

Successful operation of the wet oxidation process depends upon maintaining a supply of homogenous sludge of fairly uniform solids content, and maintaining a proper ratio of air to sludge. The latter may be accomplished by controlling the rate of sludge pumping or the discharge volume of the air compressor to maintain the amount of oxygen in the exhaust gases at a given figure, generally about two per cent by volume as indicated by a stack-gas analyzer. This control may be manual or automatic. Other operations in connection with this process will consist of sampling for laboratory control, adjustment of instruments and a few operating controls, and the usual proper maintenance of mechanical equipment such as pumps, compressors, motors and valves.

SLUDGE DISPOSAL

All the sewage sludge produced at a treatment plant must be disposed of ultimately. Treatment processes such as have been described may reduce its volume or so change its character as to facilitate its disposal, but still leave a residue which in most cases must be removed from the plant site.

Like the liquid effluent from the treatment plant, there are two broad methods for the disposal of sludge—(1) disposal in water, and (2) disposal on land. This applies regardless of whether or not the sludge is treated to facilitate or permit the selected method of disposal.

Disposal in Water. This is an economical but not common method because it is contingent on the availability of bodies of water adequate to permit it. At some seacoast cities sludge either raw or digested is pumped to barges and carried to sea to be dumped in deep water far enough off shore to provide huge dilution factors and prevent any ill effects along shore.

Where barged to sea, the value of some treatment such as thickening or digestion depends on the relative cost of the treatment and savings in cost by barging smaller volumes, or the value of gas produced by digestion.

Disposal on land. Under land disposal the following may be included:

(1) Burial

(2) Fill

(3) Application as fertilizer or soil conditioner

Burial. This method is used principally for raw sludge where, unless covered by earth, serious odor nuisances are created. The sludge is run into trenches two to three feet wide and about two feet deep. The raw sludge in the trenches should be covered by at least 12 inches of earth. Where large areas of land are available, burial of raw sludge is probably the most economical method of sludge disposal as it eliminates the costs of all sludge treatment processes. It is, however, rarely used and even then as a temporary makeshift because of the land area required. The sludge in the trenches may remain moist and malodorous for years so that an area once used cannot be re-used for the same purpose or for any other purpose for a long period of time.

Fill. Use of sludge for fill is confined almost entirely to digested sludge which can be exposed to the atmosphere without creating serious or widespread odor nuisances. The sludge should be well digested without any appreciable amount of raw or undigested mixed with it.

Either wet or partially dewatered sludge such as obtained from drying beds or vacuum filters can be used to fill low areas. Where wet sludge is used the area becomes a sludge lagoon, which has been discussed also under sludge treatment. When used as a method of disposal, the lagoon area is used only until filled, and then abandoned. When used, as a method of treatment, the sludge after some drying is removed for final disposal and the lagoon re-used. Lagoons used for disposal are usually fairly deep. Sludge is added in successive layers until the lagoon is completely filled. Final disposal of digested sludge by lagoons is economical, as it eliminates all dewatering treatments. It is applicable, however, only where low waste areas are available on the plant site or within reasonable piping distance. They are frequently used to supplement inadequate drying bed facilities.

Dewatered digested sludge from drying beds and vacuum filters can be disposed of by filling low areas at the plant site or hauled to similar areas elsewhere without creating nuisances.

The ash from sludge incinerators is usually disposed of by using it for fill. Where fill area is available close to the incinerator, the ash can be made into a slurry with water when removed from the ash hopper and pumped to the point of disposal. If the fill area is remote, the ash should be wet sufficiently to surpress the dust and transported by truck or railroad cars to the point of disposal.

For fertilizer or soil conditioner. Sewage sludge contains many elements essential to plant life, such as nitrogen, phosphorus, potassium and in addition at least traces of minor nutrients which are considered more or less indispensable for plant growth, such as boron, calcium, copper, iron, magnesium, manganese, sulfur and zinc. In fact, sometimes these trace elements are found in concentrations, perhaps from industrial wastes, which may be detrimental. The sludge humus, besides furnishing plant food, benefits the soil by increasing the water holding capacity and improving the tilth, thus making possible the working of heavy soils into satisfactory seed beds. It also reduces soil erosion.

Soils vary in their requirements for fertilizer, but it appears that the elements essential for plant growth may be divided into two groups: those which come from the air and water freely and those which are found in the soil or have to be added at certain intervals. In the first group are hydrogen, oxygen and carbon. In the second group are nitrogen, phosphorus and potassium and several miscellaneous elements usually found in sufficient quantities in the average soil such as calcium, magnesium, sulfur, iron, manganese and others. The major fertilizing elements are nitrogen, phosphorus and potassium, and the amount of each required depends on the soil, climatic conditions and crop.

Nitrogen is required by all plants, particularly where leaf development is required. Thus, it is of great value in fertilizing grass, radishes, lettuce, spinach and celery. It stimulates growth of leaf and stem.

Phosphorus is essential in many phases of plant growth. It hastens ripening, encourages root growth and increases resistance to disease.

Potassium is an important factor in vigorous growth. It develops the woody parts of stems and pulps of fruits. It increases resistence to disease, but delays ripening, and is needed in the formation of chlorophyl.

The Federation of Sewage and Industrial Wastes Association Manual of Practice No. 2 gives the following data of sludge analyses:

TABLE 5

ANALYSIS OF VARIOUS TYPES OF SLUDGE

PER CENT DRY BASIS

| | *TYPES OF SLUDGE* | | | | |
| | | | | *Filter Cake* | |
CONSTITUENT	*Raw*	*Digested*	*Activated*	*Raw*	*Digested*
Volatile Material	60–80	45–60	62–75	55–75	40–60
Ash	20–40	40–45	25–38	25–45	40–60
Insoluable Ash	17–35	35–50	22–30	15–30	30–45
Greases and Fats	7–35	3–17	5–12	5–30	2–15
Protein	22–28	16–21	32–41	20–25	14–30
Ammonium Nitrate	1–3.5	1–4	4–7	1.3	1.3–1.6
P_2O_5 (Phosphoric Acid)	1–1.5	0.5–3.7	3–4	1.4	0.5–3.5
K_2O (Potash)		0–4	0.86		
Cellulose, etc.	10–13	10–13	7.8	8–10	8–12
Si 0		15–16	8.5		
Iron		5.4	7.1		

Dried or dewatered sewage sludge makes an excellent soil conditioner and a good, though incomplete fertilizer unless fortified with nitrogen, phosphorus and potassium. Heat-dried, raw activated sludge is the best sludge product, both chemically and hygienically, although some odor may result from its use. Heat-dried, digested sludge contains much less nitrogen and is more valuable for its soil conditioning and building qualities than for its fertilizer content. For some crops it is deleterious. It is practically odorless when well digested.

The "growth producing" factor of sludge as a soil conditioner is now thought to be its vitamin content as well as its soil conditioning value.

Air-dried sludge varies greatly in moisture content and physical appearance. The large hunks which are usually removed from either open or glass covered beds need to be broken up or disintegrated if the material is to be readily applied with any uniformity to turf, fields or gardens. At some plants sludge has been air-dried to only ten per cent moisture and then broken up by hammer mills. A more common method has been to use a "Royer" disintegrator which can effectively shred a sludge cake dry enough so that it is not sticky or gummy in the disintegrator, which has spring steel fingers on an endless belt running under fixed fingers. Sludge is fed on to the belt through a hopper.

Sludge cake from vacuum filters, because of its pasty nature, cannot be readily spread on land as a fertilizer or soil conditioner. It must be further air-dried. At some plants the sludge cake is stockpiled on the plant site over winter. Freezing, thawing and air drying result in a material which breaks up readily.

Numerous studies, both laboratory and field that is, actual growing tests under controlled conditions, have been made to evaluate sewage sludge as a fertilizer.

Most authorities, for many reasons, have agreed that heat-dried, activated sludge is a different material from digested sludge and that it has considerable value in agriculture. This is borne out by the fact that "Milorganite" from the activated sludge plant of Milwaukee has been marketed successfully with a guaranteed analysis over a period of thirty years.

Digested sludge has been said to be somewhat comparable to farm manure in its content of fertilizer constituents, their relative availability and the physical nature of the material. It has been further said that the more important differences in the two materials are that the more easily decomposable nitrogen compounds of the sludge have been more completely removed by the digestion process than is the case with manure. leaving a nitrogenous residue of lower availability, and that the potash. being mostly water-soluble, has been largely washed out of the sludge, while it is retained in the manure. The following table shows comparative analyses of sludge and manures:

TABLE 6

FERTILIZING INGREDIENTS IN SLUDGE AND VARIOUS MANURES

PER CENT DRY BASIS

	Nitrogen as (N)	Phosphoric Acid	Pota.
Digested Settled Sludge	0.8–3.5	1.6**	
Digested Activated Sludge	2.0–4.8	1.6*	
Heat-dried Activated Sludge	4.0–7.0	1.7–2.5	0.13
Commercial Pulverized:			
Sheep Manure	1.2–2.5	1.0–2.0	2.0–4.0
Cattle Manure	1.6–2.1	1.0	1.0–2.2
Poultry Manure	1.9–4.0	2.5–3.7	0.8–1.3

*Digested mixed fresh and activated
**By Rudolphs

Before sludge digestion was so widely adopted, the application of raw sludge to fields was sometimes detrimental because the grease content was difficult for the soil to absorb and caused it to become impervious. In digested sludge, however, fat has been reduced and become so finely divided that it does not adversely affect the porosity of the soil.

The continued use of digested sludge tends to lower the pH value of soil and it is recommended that either lime or ground limestone be applied occasionally.

In some tests it has been found that activated sludge used as an organic carrier for added inorganic forms of nitrogen has given better results for crops with a short growing season than activated sludge alone. The inorganic nitrogen is quickly available while that from the organic portion is available more slowly and lasts over a period of time.

At a few plants efforts have been made to sell or dispose of undewatered sludge by applying it directly to land from tank carts. This has not become very popular because of the large volume required to be transported. New York City, however, has recently developed a procedure of applying liquid sludge to sandy soil containing some clay, allowing the sludge to drain and dry, then mechanically mixing the top layer and repeating the procedure several times until a top-soil is produced which will grow and maintain a satisfactory turf. By this method, large unfertile areas are being developed into satisfactory park areas.

Considerable attention has been given to the question of health hazards from the use of sludge on land. Van Kleeck states, "Reports of sickness traceable to use of digested sludges, either vacuum-filtered or air-dried, continue to be negative." Cram and Gilcreas have pointed out the potential hazard of transmission of parasitic infections with air-dried digested sludges as a result of handling the sludge or from sludge contaminated vegetables eaten raw. Spreading of digested sludge in the fall and allowing it to freeze in cold climates in the winter is believed helpful in killing these organisms. Experience with actual parasitic infections is negative to date. Heat-dried sludge is considered safe for use under all conditions because of the destructive action of heat upon bacteria.

In summary, it may be well to quote from Van Kleeck who has worked personally with sewage sludges and who has studied and written much on the subject:

"Raw primary sludge, unless composted, is unsatisfactory as a soil conditioner because of its effect on the soil and on growing plants, and because of the health hazards involved.

"Raw activated sludge, after heat drying, is established as a superior sludge product. Such sludge retains most of its organic solids and it contains more nitrogen than other sludges.

"Digested sludges from all sewage treatment processes are materials of moderate but definite value as a source of slowly available nitrogen and some phosphate. They are comparable with farm yard manure except for a deficiency of potash. Their principal value is the humus content resulting in increased moisture-holding capacity of the soil and a change in soil structure which results in a greater friability."

SPECIAL REFERENCES FOR CHAPTER 8

Van Kleeck, LeRoy—"Control of Sludge Quality"—Wastes Engineering, December 1952 and January 1953

Van Kleeck, LeRoy—"Utilization of Sewage Sludge"—Water and Sewage Works, Reference and Data 1953, page R-203

Van Kleeck, LeRoy—"This is the Lot that Sludge Nourished"—Water and Sewage Works, June 1952

Van Kleeck, LeRoy—"Fertilizer Value in Waste Disposal Methods"—American Journal of Public Health, Vol. 44, page 349 (1954)

Niles, A. H.—"Sludge as a Fertilizer"—Water and Sewage Works, Reference and Data 1954

Lunt, H. A.—"Sludge as a Soil Producer"—Water and Sewage Works, Reference and Data Edition, June 1955, page R-304. Also Water and Sewage Works, August 1953, page 295

"Utilization of Sewage Sludge"—Water and Sewage Works, Reference and Data Edition, June 1955, page R-302

"Utilization of Sewage Sludge as Fertilizer"—Federation of Sewage and Industrial Wastes Associations, Manual of Practice No. 2

"Sludge Treatment and Disposal by the Zimmermann Process"—ASCE Journal of the Sanitary Engineering Division, July 1959

CHAPTER 9

GAS FROM SLUDGE DIGESTION

Gas produced by the digestion of sewage solids has become the most valuable by-product of sewage treatment. Its utilization can reduce the overall cost of sewage treatment and has, in a number of installations, been utilized to furnish all the power needed for a complete treatment plant, including sizeable pumping installations. In fact, the larger plants can probably make better use economically of the gas than can a small installation.

COMPOSITION AND QUANTITY OF SLUDGE GAS

In Chapter 8 on Sludge Treatment, it was pointed out that when a digestion tank is put into service without the benefit of seeding material from an established tank, the first gas resulting from the acid digestion phase was largely carbon dioxide and not combustible. When alkaline digestion is established and maintained, the composition of the gas will depend on the processes of sewage and sludge treatment and may be affected by industrial wastes. The combustible gases (principally methane) will ordinarily constitute from 65 to 70 per cent of the total volume, and inert gases (mostly carbon dioxide) from 25 to 30 per cent. Other combustible gases which may be present are hydrogen and hydrogen sulfide, and other non-combustibles may be present such as nitrogen and oxygen.

Digestion of trickling filter humus with the primary sludge improves the gas yield and fuel value from 10, to less than 25 per cent, while the digestion of excess activated sludge can be expected to increase the gas yield and fuel value about 25 per cent. It can be shown that about one-half of the fuel value of fresh sludge can be recovered by digestion and utilization of the gas, the other half being retained in the digested sludge.

Some figures to keep in mind which may be expected from well established and properly operated digestion are:

    12 cu. ft. of gas per lb. of volatile matter destroyed
    70 per cent methane
    30 per cent non-combustibles (CO_2, etc.)
    650 BTU per cu. ft.
    7,800 BTU per lb. of volatile matter destroyed

A popular figure to keep in mind is that approximately one cubic foot of gas is obtained per capita per day, and that the heat value is 500 to 700 BTU per cubic foot. Manufactured city gas is about 500 BTU and natural gas 1000 BTU per cubic foot. Studies of the average yield of gas in the United States from the digestion of sludge from primary sedimentation tanks have indicated the average to be 0.8 cubic feet per capita with a range of from 0.5 to 1.3 cubic feet.

COLLECTION AND STORAGE OF SLUDGE GAS

There are three general types of tank covers provided to collect gas, known as fixed covers, floating covers, and a combination of floating covers and gas holder.

The fixed covers are often part of the reinforced concrete structures, but they may be of steel sealed to concrete side walls. They, of course, definitely set the internal capacity of the tank so that when fresh sludge is added a compensating volume of sludge, or supernatant, or gas must be removed to keep from building up too much pressure in the tank. When sludge is withdrawn a compensating volume of fresh sludge, or water, or gas from storage must be put into the tank to prevent the development of negative pressures. In large installations the latter can be attained by withdrawal of sludge at a controlled rate somewhat less than the displacement rate of gas production.

Floating and gas storage covers are similar to inverted shallow kitchen pots or deep pans with the edges sealed in the liquid. These are free to move up and down through a considerable range, thus changing the total internal capacity of the tank to compensate for sludge additions and withdrawals.

With all types of covers, the gas is usually kept at a low pressure of 6 to 10 inches of water or about 3 to 5 ounces of gauge pressure.

Where the rate of gas production is not sufficient to meet peak requirements of gas usage, such as for the start-up of an incinerator or peak power demand, gas storage can be provided. This may be in the digestion tank itself by using a combination floating and storage cover, or by separate gas holding tanks. Separate gas holding tanks may be of the low pressure gasometer type where the pressure is close to that in the digester or of the pressure type, usually a steel sphere, which is the strongest structural shape and thus most economical to build. In the pressure type, gas is held under pressures of 25 to 50 psi at which the volume is reduced from one-third to one-quarter that at digester pressure.

Where the rate of gas utilization is fairly uniform, and at no time exceeds the rate of production, the gas from the digester may be compressed for better transmission in pipe lines or better operation at the gas using units, but storage is not necessary. Any excess gas production is automatically wasted to a gas burner or to the atmosphere.

Waste gas burners should be located at least 25 feet from any plant structure if placed at ground level, or may be on the roof of the control building if sufficiently removed from the digesters. They must be provided with a pilot light and a flame trap located near the point of combustion. In remote locations gas may be wasted to the atmosphere through a return-bend screened vent terminating at least 10 feet above the walking surface. It, too, must be protected by a flame trap.

Pipe lines for sludge gas should be of ample size to keep down friction loss in the lines which is often increased by collection of moisture, slimy deposits, and even corrosion brought about by the saturated gas, and often the presence of hydrogen sulfide which results in acid conditions. The pipe lines should be provided with ample slope for drainage, means for collecting condensation, and for flushing to maintain capacity.

It is essential for good plant operation to know the rate of gas production and the volume produced in a given time. This is accomplished in the smaller plants by orifice measuring devices, and by the bellows type of displacement meters; while in the larger plants measurement is usually by rotary meters. Both types of meters require maintenance, and this is particularly true of the bellows type which must be drained and cleaned frequently. Corrosion of the moving parts is often a problem. A recent adaptation of a velocity type steam flow meter to sludge gas measurement may result in less maintenance.

UTILIZATION OF SLUDGE GAS

The two principal uses of sludge gas are for heating purposes and for power production, or for a combination of the two. Recently a further use has been made of the sludge gas to agitate and mix the digestion tank contents to improve the efficiency of the digestion tank by keeping the contents well mixed and homogenous. This use in no way affects the burning of the gas for heat or power, except to increase the rate of production.

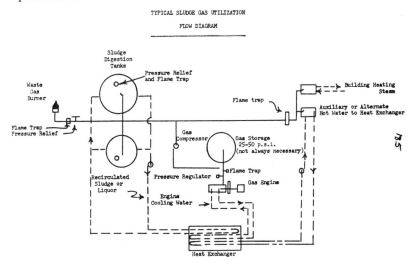

TYPICAL SLUDGE GAS UTILIZATION

FLOW DIAGRAM

FIGURE 18

Sludge gas utilized for heating buildings or digestion tanks can be burned in low pressure grid type burners under cast iron boilers, or in industrial type burners, at somewhat higher gas pressures, in regular or package type steel boilers. Industrial type burners can be obtained to burn gas from a ring concentric with an oil burning nozzle. This is convenient and economical arrangement in plants where gas production is not adequate for all requirements and an auxiliary fuel is necessary. There are several types of external type sludge heaters being used. They are especially designed to burn sludge gas to heat sewage sludge circulated through them, or they can be heated by hot water from the cooling system of gas engines.

Where sludge gas is used for power production, it is desirable to provide for an auxiliary fuel in case of digestion difficulties and at times when gas production or storage is inadequate.

For small plants where relatively small amounts of power are produced, but the load is uniform, spark ignition engines are often used with gasoline as a stand by fuel.

Where plants are larger and can afford the capital outlay for heavy duty, slow speed engines, the so-called dual fuel engine can be used. These can operate on oil fuel alone on the Diesel principle, on almost any ratio of fuel oil and sludge gas, or almost entirely with sludge gas and only a minimum amount of pilot oil-fuel (about 5 per cent) to produce ignition which will not occur with gas alone in these engines. This type of engine operates more economically than the spark ignition engine. It does, however, require a minimum amount of fuel oil constantly which is not needed with the spark ignition gas engine. Where the gas supply is ample, the indicated economy of the dual fuel engine may not be true economy. Gas engines of the heavy duty type with dual fuel require approximately 6,500 BTU, including that of the oil, per brake horsepower per hour, as compared with 9,500 for the spark ignition type, equivalent to 10 and 15 cubic feet of sludge gas per brake horsepower per hour, respectively.

The use of power varies at different plants. Gas engines may be directly connected to drive pumps or blowers or they may be used to drive generators which in turn supply electric power for all requirements of the plant, including sewage pumping. At some plants there are no outside sources of power. The power requirements of the plant, and the amount of gas produced, are factors determining the extent of gas utilization and the need for auxiliary fuel or outside power.

HAZARDS AND SAFETY MEASURES IN SLUDGE GAS UTILIZATION

The danger to life and property in the use of sludge gas comes from its inherent characteristics. Sludge gas may contain toxic concentration of hydrogen sulfide, can cause asphyxiation from lack of oxygen, is flammable and violently explosive when mixed with air.

It may be odorless and not readily detected by smell. If it contains hydrogen sulfide it has the characteristic odor of "rotten eggs" sensed at concentrations of .001 per cent. However, at high concentrations, the sense of smell will be dulled and brief exposure to concentrations as low as 0.1 per cent may be fatal. Hydrogen sulfide in moisture ladened gas is corrosive and damaging to metal. Where its concentration in the gas is more than 0.25 to 1.0 per cent provisions are sometimes made to remove or scrub it out.

Sludge gas, over a range of mixtures of one part gas with 10 to 15 parts of air, is violently explosive. Methane is lighter than air, but hydrogen sulfide is heavier. It is, thus, desirable to provide ventilation, natural or forced, for both high and low areas where gas might accumulate. Gas collectors are provided with relief pressure valves protected by flame

114

traps. These are subject to corrosion and clogging and should be inspected and cleaned periodically. As stated elsewhere, gas lines must drain to a low point where condensate may be removed. Drainage should be through a two-way valve so that gas may not escape. All open-ended "U" tubes for manometers or water seals and vents above diaphragms of regulating or pressure reducing valves should be vented to the outside atmosphere. A positive pressure must be maintained at all times in gas collectors and pipe lines. Low pressure cut outs, alarms, and back pressure regulators are used to insure this, but much often depends upon the operator to prevent a situation where negative pressures might occur.

When pressure type gas holders are provided in cold climates, problems arise from the freezing of condensate within the holders and the operator must see that provisions are made to overcome any effect of slush ice.

In enclosed areas where there is any possibility of gas-air mixtures from leaks or otherwise, there is usually provided an explosion-proof electrical installation. This must be complete or else it is useless. Installations have been seen where everything in a given area was explosion-proof except for one thing—such as an ordinary light switch. The operator should be certain that this situation does not exist in his plant and that he does not create it by improper repair or maintenance.

One other safety precaution, now provided on modern heating installations but neglected on earlier designs, is a means for automatically purging the combustion chamber of the heating unit thoroughly with air after a shut-down or pilot light failure, and before it can be again ignited to be certain that no explosive mixture exists within the unit.

Because of their great importance from a safety angle some operating hints are given here even if they may be repeated in Chapter 14 on Safety About the Treatment Plant.

1. Allow no smoking, sparks or open flames in areas where gas may be present from leaks or from exposed digesting sludge.

2. Check up condensate traps frequently and set up a regular schedule for draining them.

3. Check safety devices, such as high pressure reliefs, low pressure cut outs or alarms for such situations by artifically setting up a situation to make them function. See that pressure gauges operate properly.

4. Inspect flame traps periodically in accordance with manufacturers instructions to see that they are not clogged with debris.

5. In hazardous areas where explosion proof wiring and electrical fixtures have been provided, see that such protection is properly maintained by making proper replacements of gaskets and sealing devices when necessary.

6. Test hazardous areas periodically for presence of inflammable or explosive mixtures. Don't rely on the nose to always detect gas leaks.

SPECIAL REFERENCES FOR CHAPTER 9

"The Dual-Fuel Engine and Its Application to Sewage Treatment Plants," Sewage Works Journal, November 1949, p. 957

"Dual-Fuel Engine Economy," Sewage and Industrial Wastes, June 1954, p. 800

"Dual-Fuel Engine Operating and Maintenance Experience at Owl's Head Plant of New York City," Kass and Lino, Water and Sewage Works, June 1956, p. 231

CHAPTER 10

INDUSTRIAL WASTES

The term industrial wastes is a broad and all inclusive one. It includes the solid, liquid and gaseous wastes produced by manufacturing and other industrial operations.

These wastes will vary in both quantity and composition with the type of industry and with the processes used in the same industry. In many communities, the quantity of liquid waste exceeds that of the sewage and the polluting power of the waste is often much higher than that of the sewage. The problem is universal but wastes having the same characteristics are not widespread. Industries whose wastes present difficult problems in treatment and disposal are numerous and widespread. They are also increasing in both number and size.

From the viewpoint of the industry, the waste it produces is a liability. As such, it must be disposed of as quickly as possible and at a minimum cost. To the public, industrial wastes are also a liability in that they may cause damage to sewers and to treatment plant facilities, increase the cost of treatment and disposal of municipal wastes and contribute to stream pollution.

Regulations relative to the treatment and disposal of industrial wastes are issued by local, state and by certain branches of the federal government. State and federal regulations are primarily directed toward the control of stream pollution. Local and municipal ordinances usually regulate the type of wastes which may be discharged into the sewerage system. In general, municipal ordinances will permit only such wastes that are not injurious to the sewer system and treatment plant facilities, and which will not interfere with the methods of sewage treatment being used.

It is readily seen that the important problem of industrial waste collection, treatment and disposal is one of both great magnitude and complexity. It cannot be adequately solved unless all aspects of the problem are considered. The U. S. National Resources Committee has emphasized "that the essential approach to the problem of ridding stream waters of undesirable industrial wastes lies in the active cooperation of the industries involved; always assuming, however, flexible and reasonably administered water pollution regulation. The problem cannot be settled by abstract studies on the part of the government, nor by inflexible and arbitrary state and federal legislation. Waste materials are so diverse and so complex that each industry and possibly each plant presents a special problem."

From the above, it is obvious that a complete analysis of industrial wastes is far beyond the scope of this chapter. Further information and detailed consideration of the many and varied problems associated with treatment and disposal may be found in the current literature. Several new and excellent texts on this subject are now available.

The reader of this chapter will have a particular interest in the liquid wastes which enter the sewer system and must be treated with the municipal sewage. After a brief consideration of solid and gaseous wastes, the quantity, characteristics and problems associated with the treatment of the liquid wastes will be considered.

SOLID AND GASEOUS WASTES

Solid Wastes should not generally be discharged into the sewer system. They produce a needless load upon grit chambers, sedimentation and digestion tanks. Typical of such wastes are mine tailings, slag, sawdust, ashes, and waste materials from canneries. These solids should, insofar as possible, be kept out of the liquid waste because their removal from the plant site and their ultimate disposal are generally easier and cheaper in their original solid form.

The proper decision relative to the separation of solids from the liquid waste is one which requires careful economic consideration at each plant. In cases where the solids are wet or already in suspension the liquid may be economically transferred to a separation plant before final disposal. This condition may be true in the case of coal and gravel washing, sludges from the chemical and mining industries, and the sludge produced in a water softening plant.

Gaseous Wastes containing nuisance gases and dusts are produced in many industries. Usually these wastes are dispersed directly into the atmosphere unless special treatment processes are required.

In the past decade much attention has been given to the problem of air pollution. It has, in this short time, become a major field of practice in the area of engineering in public health. The control of air pollution usually requires the washing or scrubbing of waste gases with water or other liquid which in turn results in a liquid waste treatment and disposal problem.

Occasionally atmospheric pollution may result from certain liquid waste treatment processes. The treatment of cyanide wastes by the use of acid and air converts the cyanide to hydrogen cyanide gas which is discharged into the atmosphere. Ammonia, cyanides, phenols and other waste gases may be carried to the atmosphere by the steam and vapor created when coke and gas plant waters are used in quenching coke. Atmospheric pollution may also result from the incineration of highly concentrated organic wastes. This is especially true where the wastes contain sulfur compounds.

INDUSTRIAL WASTE WATER

Liquid wastes are produced by all wet-process industries. The waste waters from such industries vary so greatly in both quantity and pollutional capacity that it is impossible to assign fixed values to their common constituents. These wastes may be discharged into the sewer system, provided the volume is small with respect to the normal sewage flow, or when they are sufficiently pretreated.

In general, industrial waste waters contain suspended, colloidal and dissolved mineral and organic solids. In addition they may be either excessively acid or alkaline and may contain high or low concentrations of coloring matter.

These wastes may contain inert, organic or toxic materials and possibly pathogenic bacteria.

Inert wastes are those which are not changed by chemical or biological processes. Typical of such wastes are those from stone quarry operation, the washing of sands and gravels, the blow down from boilers and certain types of sludges produced in precipitation plants.

Most oragnic wastes are amenable to biologic treatment, such as the liquid wastes from the dairy, canning, packing house, textile, and paper industries.

Toxic wastes are those which may produce poisonous gases or vapors, or those containing chemicals and metals which may destroy the biological processes used in sewage treatment. This type of waste may also interfere with the biological activity in receiving streams and may persist for great distances. Such wastes can be tolerated provided the concentrations are so low that no hazard to treatment plant personnel or interference with the normal operation of the plant, or with biological activity of the stream results. Wastes containing such constituents should be carefully studied with respect to the above restrictions before permission to discharge them into the sewer system is granted.

TREATMENT AND DISPOSAL

The degree of treatment required for any industrial waste depends on the dilution and stabilizing characteristics of the receiving stream. The quantity and concentration of pollutants should be reduced to a minimum at the industrial plant.

The treatment processes used depend on the character of the waste. These processes have been adopted from sewage treatment practice and are often modified to produce the most effective results for a given individual situation.

The organic load placed upon the sewage treatment plant is expressed in terms of its "population equivalent." This term is evaluated as the ratio of the BOD demand of the waste in pounds per day to the average BOD contributed by each person using the sewer system. This daily per capita demand has been accepted as .17 lb. For example, an industrial waste having a daily BOD demand of 17,000 lb. would have a population equivalent of 100,000.

It should be emphasized that population equivalent refers only to oxidizable organic content of the waste. It does not evaluate other important pollutional characteristics of the waste.

A summary of combinations of treatment processes commonly used in treating industrial wastes is given herewith.

1. Remove sizeable suspended solids by screening or settling.
2. Remove fats, oils, and greasy solids by flotation and skimming procedures, aided in some cases by chemical treatment.

3. Remove colloidal solids by flocculation with chemical coagulants and electrolytes, followed by settling and possible filtration.

4. Neutralize excessive acidity or alkalinity by addition of chemicals.

5. Remove or stabilize dissolved solids by chemical precipitation, ion exchange or biological processes or a combination of these.

6. Decolorize by chemical treatment, with settling or filtration, singly or in combination.

7. Re-oxygenate the wastes by suitable aeration methods.

8. Lower the temperature of excessively hot wastes by suitable cooling processes.

Dairies. Wastes from the dairy industry result chiefly from receiving stations, bottling plants, creameries, condensing plants and cheese manufacturing plants. They consist of the washings from cans, bottles, pipe lines, equipment such as separators and churns, the leakage from poorly made up joints in the pipe lines and the washing of floors and equipment.

The industry is wide spread and has done much toward the control of both quantity and quality of its wastes at the processing plants.

The BOD of milk plant waste is high and the decomposition is rapid. Eldridge reports that the five-day BOD for whey, buttermilk, skim milk and whole milk ranges from 32,000 to 102,500 ppm and the organic solids from 6.4 to 11.7 per cent.

These wastes may be treated with domestic sewage but since most of the solids are either in the dissolved or colloidal state primary treatment is ineffective and the chlorine demand of the sewage may be excessive. Chemical precipitation, activated sludge, trickling filters and broad irrigation have been successfully used.

Meat Packing Industries. These wastes include those from stockyards, slaughter houses and meat packing establishments. The wastes from stockyards include manure, hay, straw, dirt and fibrous material. Slaughter and packing house wastes usually contain blood, grease, paunch manure, dirt, hair, and particles of flesh.

All these wastes contain both suspended and dissolved materials and the BOD varies in the range of 350 to 2000 ppm. Blood and paunch manure should not be discharged to sanitary sewers.

Treatment of meat packing wastes with the sewage is practical in large city systems. They may also be so treated in smaller communities provided the treatment plant capacity is adequate. Processes involved in treatment usually are screening, sedimentation, trickling filters, activated sludge and anaerobic digestion. Chemical coagulants are sometimes used. BOD reductions as high as 95 per cent have been reported.

Fermentation Industries. Breweries, distilleries, alcohol and other organic chemical manufacturing plants, and certain parts of the pharmaceutical industry are representative of the fermentation industries.

Most of their wastes have a high pollutional potential. However, a major reduction in the pollutional load of these wastes has been accomplished by treatment to recover by-products.

120

The principal waste from breweries and distilleries is the spent grain, sometimes termed stillage. With no treatment for recovery, the BOD of this material is very high. Population equivalents as high as 50,000 per 1,000 bushels of grain processed have been reported.

These industries usually treat the waste for recovery of the spent grain which is used for animal feed or in the manufacture of certain chemical products. The residual waste is usually large in volume but may be low in BOD. This may be disposed of by dilution or on trickling filters. Should the final wastes contain high dissolved solids they may be evaporated and treated biologically.

The wastes from the manufacture of penicillin and other antibiotics have a high BOD. The average BOD value of wash waters is reported to range from 2,000 to 5,000 ppm. These wastes are not usually treated with municipal sewage. Where the BOD is extremely high (14,000 ppm or more) anaerobic digestion may provide an 80 per cent reduction. This may also be accomplished by controlled aeration. The effluents from these processes may be further treated on sand-filters which usually reduce the BOD to about 40 ppm. In some cases evaporation followed by incineration is used.

Fruit and Vegetable Processing Industries. The manufacture of sugar from sugar beets and the production of corn products, together with the commercial canning of fruits, fruit juices and vegetables represents a widespread and diversified industry. The canning industry has expanded to include the dehydration, pickling and freezing processes of food preservation.

The wastes from all these processes are troublesome. In general they are high in volume, consisting of both solid and liquid. They are high in both total organic solids and BOD. Plants are usually located in rural areas or small towns and the operation is seasonal.

About 350 to 850 gallons of liquid waste are produced per ton of beets processed for sugar manufacturing. These wastes are high in both suspended and dissolved solids and in BOD. Less waste results in the manufacturing of cane sugar because the pressed cane may be used as fuel. Also, the sugar produced requires less purification.

Methods used for treatment include ponding, fine screens, grit chambers, sedimentation, lime treatment followed by coagulation and sedimentation. The later treatment may reduce suspended solids by about 90 per cent and the BOD by about 40 per cent. Ponding is usually not satisfactory because of anaerobic decomposition. This method can be improved by use of lime and is considered practical if the sludge is removed annually. The sludge is sometimes used as fertilizer.

Corn products wastes result from the wet-milling of shelled corn in the production of starch, oil, sugar and syrup. The remaining material is used as cattle feed.

The mixed liquid waste from these processes is usually warm, acid and highly putrescible. As produced it is almost neutral but decomposes very rapidly and has a high BOD. It is both a concentrated and seasonal operation.

Much has been accomplished in reducing the pollutional load by the practice of maximum recovery of material at the plant. This can usually be accomplished because there are relatively few plants and they are of large capacity. When the loss of material is kept low, these wastes may be satisfactorily treated with municipal sewage. However, pretreatment might be necessary to maintain the proper pH until the waste reaches the treatment plant.

The processes used are screening, sedimentation, trickling filters and activated sludge. An acceptable degree of sludge digestion has been accomplished in both Imhoff tanks and separate digesters.

The liquid waste from the canning industry is produced by the food cleaning, washing, cooking and blanching operations, and from the necessary washing of equipment and floors. Its characteristics vary widely, depending upon the raw materials being processed. The waste may be either acid or alkaline and the BOD may be as high as 50,000 to 60,000 ppm. In addition, large quantities of solid wastes are produced. These are usually stored as silage. Exceptionally strong liquid waste is produced and will drain from the silos or storage piles.

The satisfactory disposal of these wastes is made more difficult by the seasonal nature of the operation and by the change in character of the waste when operation changes from one fruit or vegetable to another.

In general, it may be said that each plant should assume the responsibility of disposal of its wastes. In any case, preliminary treatment should be provided. The effluents of this treatment may be treated with municipal sewage.

Treatment methods used include screening, lagooning, irrigation, plain sedimentation, chemical coagulation followed by sedimentation. Anaerobic digestion has been recently used and best results are obtained by use of high temperature digesters.

Textile Industries. Because of the many operations involved in textile finishing, the wastes from this industry vary in both strength and composition over very wide ranges. The waste from many of the processes are highly pollutional, and may be highly acid or alkaline. The wastes from dyeing operations are highly colored.

Wool scouring wastes contain high concentrations of putrescible organic matter, grease, alkali and dirt. The grease is usually recovered either by acid treatment or with calcium chloride. There is a relatively new treatment with calcium hypochlorite which causes coagulation of a large part of the colloidal and suspended solids and separation of the grease.

The wastes from textile finishing operations usually are mixed to provide for self-neutralization and interaction between the various types of waste produced by the operations involved.

Chemical precipitation, trickling or rapid sand filters followed by chlorination are used in treatment. Textile wastes may be treated with municipal sewage but equalization or neutralization and regulation of dumping rates usually are necessary.

Laundries. Laundry wastes usually contain soaps, detergents, dirt and grease. These wastes usually are discharged into the municipal sewer. Pretreatment may be necessary when the volume is large as compared to the sewage.

122

Tanneries. The processing of hides in the manufacture of leather involves many separate operations. Each of these produces a waste which is characteristic. If considered separately, certain of these wastes require extensive treatment while others may be discharged with little or no treatment.

The wastes from the various operations are (1) wash water from green hides which are very high in ammonia; (2) wastes from the liming vats and dehairing machines; (3) wash water from fleshing and draining floors; (4) spent tan liquor and rinse water from vats; (5) leakage from the leaching vats, and (6) spent alkali and acids from the bleaching vats.

All wastes should be screened to remove hair, fleshings and hide trimmings. These salvaged materials may be used in the manufacture of glue. Except for the acid bleach and spent tan liquor, the wastes are alkaline.

It is generally agreed that controlled mixing of all the wastes to allow the chemical reactions which aid sedimentation to occur between the various types of waste produced is the best method for primary treatment. After sedimentation, the effluents may be further treated on trickling or high rate filters and followed by humus tanks or sand filters.

The high lime content of the sludge inhibits digestion. It is therefore usually lagooned or dried on sand beds or vacuum filters.

Paper Industries. The paper industry produces large quantities of liquid wastes. The wastes may be divided into two classes: (1) the waste from pulp manufacture, and (2) the waste from the manufacture of paper. Both types may be produced at a given site or either one may be produced alone.

Pulp mills manufacture pulp from various raw materials such as wood, rags, straw jute, hemp or reclaimed paper stock. There are three principal processes used in pulp manufacture, namely, the sulfite, the sulfate and the soda process.

The wastes produced from the sulfite process of wood pulping (cooking) are difficult to treat because of their high concentration. They are highly pollutional and the lignin content is resistent to biological oxidation. Many studies are being made leading toward a change in this process in order to reduce stream pollution. Experimentation is also being carried on in an attempt to find better treatment methods. Chief among these at present is chemical precipitation which produces products which may be used as fuel or binders in the manufacture of coal briquettes. Ponding and evaporation also are used in the treatment of these wastes.

In both the sulfate and the soda process of wood pulping, high recovery of products is possible. The residual wastes from these mills may be treated by lagooning and other simple treatment processes. In some cases they may be satisfactorily disposed of by dilution.

Paper manufacturing processes produce wastes containing fibers, fillers, glue, and dye-stuffs, often in objectionable concentration. These wastes are often referred to as "white-water." They are highly pollutional.

Since these products are important and valuable raw materials, great effort is being made to recover and reuse them.

Treatment methods include sedimentation, filtration and air flotation.

Metal Finishing Industries. The waste from metal finishing industries usually contains acids, metal ions, cyanides, and chromates. These result from steel, iron and copper pickling processes and from electroplating.

Steel pickling liquors have high acid concentrations and usually are high in ferrous iron content. These wastes are extremely difficult to treat and are highly toxic to microorganisms. They should be pretreated before discharge into the sewer system.

Methods of treatment include evaporation, and treatment to recover ferrous sulfate, sulfur and iron oxides.

Copper pickling, washing and processing result in copper in the liquid waste. Very low concentrations of copper are toxic to stream life and will interfere with the biological processes used in sewage treatment.

These wastes should, therefore, be pretreated to recover the copper before disposal into the sewer system. The relatively high value of copper often makes the treatment profitable. This may be done by electrolytic treatment. Other methods are, crystallization of copper sulfate, filtration through scrap iron, chemical coagulation and ion exchange.

The wastes from electroplating are extremely toxic since they often contain cyanides and/or chromates. Pretreatment is, therefore, essential.

Cyanide waste may be treated by chlorination under alkaline conditions. This oxidizes the cyanides to the less toxic cyanates. Additional chlorine will carry the oxidation to ammonia and carbon dioxide.

Chromate waste is usually treated by the process of ion exchange. Sulfur dioxide or a sulfite salt may be used as a reducing agent, and the chromium and other metals precipitated by raising the pH value.

Plating wastes which do not contain cyanides or chromates may be treated by raising the pH value using lime or caustic soda. The metal ions will then precipitate as hydroxides or metal salts.

Oil Industries. The principal wastes from the oil industries are brines and the wastes from petroleum refineries.

The brines are pumped from the wells along with the oil. The solid content is high and they are usually saline to such a degree as to destroy fresh water life if not sufficiently diluted.

There is no satisfactory treatment for these wastes known. Recovery could, however, be made by distillation which is not economically feasible. Evaporation and seepage is used but the method is likely to pollute surface streams. The practice of repumping into the ground often leads to pollution of the ground water. In practice the oil is usually recovered.

Refinery wastes contain acids, alkalies, sulfur compounds, phenols and oil. The oil may be recovered by the use of skimming tanks and separators. These are usually used in the industry and the effluents may be further treated on trickling filters or in oxidation ponds. Unless the acid is recovered these wastes should be neutralized prior to discharge in the sewer system.

Coke and Gas Industries. The wastes from the manufacture of coke and gas are objectionable because of their high BOD and their phenol content. The phenols are extremely toxic and cause serious tastes and odors that are very difficult to remove. These wastes also contain ammonia, cresols, sulfides and cyanides.

Where there is adequate dilution, these wastes may be treated with sewage on trickling filters, or possibly activated sludge. Filtration through beds of fine coal and oxidation by use of ozone is also used.

Pretreatment is used to recover ammonia and evaporation to recover phenol is also practiced.

Mining Industry. The principal wastes from mining operations are the waste water from the washing and processing of coal or ore and the acid waters which drain or are pumped from the mines.

The waste wash water is large in quantity and usually carries high concentrations of fine coal and other refuse. This suspended matter can be removed by either plain sedimentation or by coagulation followed by sedimentation. The coal is recovered from the sludge at many plants.

The waters which drain or are pumped from coal mines are highly acid and carry a high concentration of iron. In coal mining regions the quantity of the drainage is tremendous. Sulfuric acid is produced by the oxidation of sulfur minerals contained in the coal and adjacent rocks. It has been estimated that the daily discharge from both abandoned and operating mines in the anthracite area of Pennsylvania is nearly 500 million gallons and the acid content is equivalent to nearly a thousand tons of sulfuric acid.

Due to the great acid content and the fact that this extremely large quantity of waste would have many different sources, no satisfactory method of treatment is, as yet, known.

Some of the methods used in an attempt to reduce pollution are: the sealing and flooding of abandoned mines; control of seepage into mines and the passage of the mine drainage through limestone beds.

Nuclear Industry. The establishment and unprecedented growth of the nuclear industry has introduced the new factor of radioactivity and has created the latest and perhaps the most baffling problem in industrial waste treatment and disposal.

All production and processing of radioactive materials in the U. S. are under the authority of the Atomic Energy Commission. The Commission and other agencies, including state health departments, regulate experimentation and the manufacturing processes which use radioactive materials. This includes methods used for waste treatment and its final disposal.

Radioactive isotopes have been available to qualified persons for experimentation in institutional, industrial and research laboratories throughout the country since 1946. Before radioactive materials are released by the Commission, careful studies are made of the qualifications of the persons responsible for them and of the methods to be used for the treatment and final disposal of the wastes (solid, liquid and gaseous) which may result from their use. Concentrated solid or liquid wastes may be returned to the Commission for final disposal, usually by burial or by depositing in the ocean. The gaseous wastes are disposed of by dispersion into the atmosphere under rigid regulations.

Liquid wastes having a high level of activity are produced by the chemical plants which process reactor fuels. These wastes usually are further concentrated and either returned to the Commission or disposed of by burial or depositing at sea.

Liquid wastes having a low level of activity result from the use of isotopes in hospitals, industrial and institutional research laboratories, and from the laundries servicing these laboratories. These wastes, after storage for sufficient time to permit decay to a permissible level may be deposited into the sewer system.

The unit of measure of radioactivity is the curie. One curie corresponds to 3.7×10^{10} disintegrations per second. Each isotope decays at a characteristic rate. This rate is expressed in terms of "half-life" which is the time required for one half of the atoms of a particular substance or isotope to disintegrate. The "half-life" of radium 226 is 1620 years. Other radioactive elements vary in "half-life" from a millionth of a second to many thousands of years. This characteristic rate of decay cannot be changed by any known means. The presence of radioactive materials is detected and the intensity of disintegration is estimated by means of Geiger-Muller tubes, ionization chambers and other measuring or counting equipment.

In the process of decay, radioactive materials may emit alpha particles, beta particles and/or gamma rays. Alpha particles are actually the nuclei of helium atoms. Because of their relatively large mass they have a low penetrating power. Beta particles are high speed electrons and have high penetrating power. Gamma rays are a form of radiant energy similar to X-rays and like them have high penetrating power.

Radioactive waste is a hazard to health when man is exposed to radiation. It is also particularly serious when radioactive material is taken into the body by drinking contaminated water, eating contaminated food or breathing contaminated air. The permissible concentrations of the various isotopes in drinking water and sewage and the limit of exposure time to radiation have been established. This detailed information may be obtained in Handbook No. 69 of the National Bureau of Standards. This supersedes Handbook 52 and may be purchased from the Superintendent of Documents, Washington, D. C. for 35 cents.

Radioactive materials may be removed from water and waste water by evaporation, coagulation, ion exchange, sand filtration, electrolytic separation and biological processes.

It is generally accepted that algae and higher plants will concentrate certain isotopes within their cells. This may contaminate food used by man. Furthermore the disposal of long lived isotopes in the oceans may lead to serious food contamination in the future.

It is therefore readily seen that the present known methods of treatment and final disposal of radioactive wastes are far from satisfactory whenever long-lived isotopes are involved.

CHAPTER 11

SAMPLING AND TESTING PROCEDURES

SAMPLING OF SEWAGE

The value of any laboratory result depends on the integrity of the sample. The object of sampling is to collect a portion of sewage small enough in volume to be conveniently handled in the laboratory and still representative of the sewage to be examined. It must be collected in such a manner that nothing is added or lost in the portion taken and no change occurs during the time between collection and laboratory examination. Unless these conditions are met, laboratory results may be misleading and worse than no results.

The location of sampling points and the collection of samples cannot be specified for all sewage plants. Conditions vary in different plants and the sampling procedure must be adapted to each plant. Certain general principles can be listed.

(1) The sample should be taken where the sewage is well mixed. This is most easily accomplished if the sampling point is located where the sewage flow is turbulent, for example, at a tap on the discharge side of a pump, where a free fall from a pipe line occurs, where the discharge from a pipe is against a baffle as at the inlet of a tank, or just as the flow enters a pipe as at the effluent line from a tank.

(2) Large particles should be excluded. Large particles are all those greater than one-quarter inch in diameter. This is reasonable because if one large piece was included in a one-gallon sample, it would mean that sewage would contain one millon large pieces per million gallons of sewage. Raw sewage should be sampled after screening where screens or comminutors are used.

(3) No deposits, growths or floating material that have accumulated at the sampling point should be included. Obviously, such material would not be representative of the sewage. This may be difficult if sampling is at a manhole, but it can be done if care is used.

(4) Samples should be examined as soon as possible. If held for more than one hour, they should be cooled by immersion of the sample bottle in ice water. Bacterial decomposition of sewage continues in the sample bottle. After one hour, the changes due to such decomposition are appreciable. Cooling the sample greatly retards bacterial action.

(5) The collection of proper samples should be made as easy as possible. Sampling points should be readily accessible, proper equipment should be at hand, safety precautions established, and protection of personnel from inclement weather provided, for the easier it is to take proper samples, the more likely it will be done.

There are two types of samples that may be collected, depending on the time available, the tests to be made and the object of the tests. One is called a "catch or grab" sample and consists of a portion of sewage all taken at one time. The other is an integrated sample consisting of portions of sewage taken at regular time intervals, the volume of each portion being proportional to the sewage flow at the time it is collected. All the portions are mixed to produce a final sample representative of the sewage. There are advantages and disadvantages in both types.

Catch samples are not representative of the average sewage since they reflect only the condition at the instant of sampling. However, in many plants the time available for sampling is so limited that catch samples must be used. The samples should be collected at that hour of the day when the treatment plant is operating under maximum load. This usually coincides with the period of maximum flow and occurs at most plants between 9 A.M. and Noon. If good operating efficiency is indicated at this time, it is reasonable to assume that plant efficiency will be satisfactory during other periods. When catch samples are used to determine the efficiency of a treatment process, the effluent sample should be collected after a period of time corresponding to the flowing-through period so that approximately the same sewage is sampled at inlet and outlet.

For some tests, catch samples must be used. Thus, for residual chlorine and pH value if two portions were mixed, reactions would occur and the result would not be an average but the result of interaction and have no relation to the sewage sampled. Sometimes the object is to determine the effect of a substance in sewage on the treatment process. It can happen that the substance is present in high concentration for only a short period of time. If individual portions were integrated, an average concentration would be obtained. Thus to determine the high concentration, catch samples should be examined.

Integrated or composite samples indicate the character of the sewage over a period of time. The effects of intermittent changes in strength and flow are eliminated. The portion used should be collected with sufficient frequency to obtain average results. If the strength and flow do not fluctuate rapidly, hourly portions over a 12 hour period are satisfactory. If the fluctuations are rapid, half-hourly or quarter-hourly samples may be required. The period of sampling may be varied covering four, eight or twelve hours, depending on the personnel available and the use to be made of the results. Generally, integrated samples are used to determine the character of the sewage to be treated and the efficiency of the treatment units.

The rate of sewage flow must be measured when each portion is taken and the volume of the portion adjusted to the flow by use of a factor.

The magnitude of the factor determines the final volume of the integrated sample. Generally a table is prepared as follows:

Time	Flow mgd	Factor	Vol. of portion ml
6 AM	0.3	100	30
7 AM	0.6	"	60
8 AM	0.8	"	80
9 AM	1.0	"	100
10 AM	1.5	"	150
11 AM	1.4	"	140
12 N	1.2	"	120
1 PM	1.0	"	100
2 PM	1.0	"	100
3 PM	0.9	"	90
4 PM	0.8	"	80
5 PM	0.8	"	80
			1130

This would yield an integrated sample of 1130 ml representing the 12 hour interval from 6 AM to 6 PM. If a gallon sample was wanted, the factor would be tripled to 300, making each portion three times as big and yielding 3390 ml of sample.

Equipment. An aluminum dipper six inches in diameter and approximately four inches deep with a long handle is convenient for collecting sewage from tanks and channels. For sampling from manholes a one-quart pail which can be fastened to a wooden pole with a harness snap is used. Graduated cylinders, sample bottles, and some means of refrigeration also needed. Special technic is required for collecting samples for dissolved oxygen and for bacteriological examination.

SAMPLING OF SLUDGE

As in the case of sewage, the value of sludge analyses depends largely upon the accuracy of sampling. Thus it is necessary to observe strict precautions in the selection of sampling points and methods of sampling to insure the collection of representative samples at all times.

To collect samples of sludge from different depths in a tank, a sampling apparatus can be used that is made of cast iron or brass weighted with lead. It can be lowered into the tank by a link chain which carries markings showing the various depths. The apparatus is fitted with valves operated by a cord. A pull on the cord at the desired depth opens the valves and the sludge flows in at the bottom while air escapes at the top. A wide-mouthed stoppered bottle attached to the end of a pole can also be used. The bottle is pushed to the desired depth and the stopper removed by means of an attached cord. Many separate sludge digestion tanks are equipped with sampling taps at various depths. When using these taps enough sludge must be run to waste to free the lines of accumulated sludge so that the sample collected will be representative of the sludge in the tank.

To collect samples of sludge when sludge is being drawn or pumped, take catch samples of equal size in a dipper at the start, during and at the end of the period of drawing. Mix these samples and take about 500 ml for the laboratory sample.

To collect samples of bed dried sludge, take portions of equal size from several scattered points on the bed, taking care not to include sand, mix thoroughly after pulversizing, and use about 500 grams for the laboratory sample. Samples of filter cake sludge may be collected by cutting portions of the cake as discharged from the filter. Doing this with a cookie cutter is a very convenient way to obtain equal size portions at equal time intervals. These portions can then be examined individually or mixed to yield a composite sample.

Examination of the samples should be made as soon as possible after collection.

PUTRESCIBILITY OR METHYLENE BLUE TEST

Sampling. The sample should be collected in the bottle in which the test is to be made. The bottle should be immersed in the liquid to be sampled and completely filled with as little agitation as possible; bubbles of air that cling to the bottle may be removed by tapping the side of the bottle. This test cannot be made on chlorinated effluents.

Equipment. Clear, 8-ounce (250 ml) glass-stoppered bottles, 1 ml pipettes graduated in 0.1 ml, methylene blue solution (0.5 grams per liter), dish pan or wash tub for use as a water bath or a 20°C. incubator.

Procedure.

1. Clean the bottle by washing with washing powder and water; blue discoloration may be removed by washing with a one to one solution of hydrochloric or muriatic acid. Rinse thoroughly before use.

2. Collect the sample as described above.

3. Add 0.7 ml of the methylene blue solution below the surface of the liquid and mix by inversion. Use 0.8 ml with a 300 ml sample bottle.

4. Restopper so that no bubbles of air remain under the stopper.

5. Immerse the bottle in a water bath maintained at room temperature (about 68°F. or 20°C.).

6. Observe daily and record the number of days or fractions of days that elapse before the blue color disappears.

Results are expressed as days elapsed before disappearance of blue color or per cent relative stability.

TABLE 7

RELATIVE STABILITY NUMBERS

Time required for decolorization at 20°C	Relative stability S	Time required for decolorization at 20°C	Relative stability S
Days	Percentage	Days	Percentage
0.5	11	8.0	84
1.0	21	9.0	87
1.5	30	10.0	90
2.0	37	11.0	92
2.5	44	12.0	94
3.0	50	13.0	95
4.0	60	14.0	96
5.0	68	16.0	97
6.0	75	18.0	98
7.0	80	20.0	99

RESIDUAL CHLORINE TEST

Sampling. Only catch samples can be used and they must be taken at a point where the chlorine is well mixed with the sewage. If possible, the sample should be taken at a point where the chlorine has been in contact with the sewage for fifteen minutes. If not, the sample should be held until fifteen minutes have elapsed from the time chlorine was added until the time the test is started.

Equipment. Either a comparator employing standard colored glass discs or 2-ounce French square bottles and permanent chlorine color standards in 2-ounce French square bottles, ortho-tolidine reagent, medicine dropper.

Procedure with comparator kit.

1. Add 1.0 ml of the ortho-tolidine solution to one of the two comparator cells.
2. Fill to the mark each comparator cell with the sample (if the ortho-tolidine is added first, the filling of the cell will cause thorough mixing).
3. If the temperature of the sewage is below 20°C., warm the cell to 20°C. by immersion in a water bath maintained at 25°C.

4. Place the cell containing the indicator in the inner slot, place the cell containing the sewage in the slot back of the disc.

5. Allow the color to develop for exactly five minutes from the time the cell is filled, exposed to a minimum of light.

6. Rotate the disc until the colors as seen through the eyepiece match, and read the residual chlorine content from the exposed number as mg/l of total residual chlorine.

Procedure with 2-ounce French square bottle.

1. Add 5 ml of the ortho-tolidine reagent to a 2-ounce French square bottle.

2. Add 50 ml of the sample to the bottle.

3. If the temperature of the sewage is below 20°C., warm the bottle and sample to 20°C. by immersion in a water bath at 25°C.

4. Add 50 ml of the sample to another 2-ounce bottle.

5. Allow the color to develop for exactly five minutes from the time the bottle is filled. Do not expose to daylight any more than necessary and never to direct sunlight.

6. Compare the color developed in the test sample with that of the standards by superimposing on the standards the bottle to which no reagent was added and superimposing on the test sample a bottle containing distilled water.

7. The standard that matches in color the test sample reads directly ppm chlorine.

Results are expressed as ppm total chlorine.

DETERMINATION OF pH OR HYDROGEN ION CONCENTRATION

Sampling. Only catch samples of sewage should be used, and the test repeated at intervals. Sludge samples should be agitated as little as possible as the pH is largely dependent on the dissolved gas content.

Equipment. A comparator employing standard colored glass discs can be used, or standard color solutions may be purchased from laboratory supply houses. The indicators should be obtained from the same manufacturer that furnished the standards. Dropping bottles for each indicator with graduated dropper. Generally, only the bromthymol blue indicator and standards covering the range 6.0-7.6 are required. One graduated cylinder (250 ml). Distilled water.

Procedure for sewage.

1. Pour about 100 ml of sample in graduated cylinder and allow to stand a few minutes until the coarse suspended matter has settled.

2. Add exactly the required amount of indicator as specified by the manufacturer to one of the two comparator cells.

3. Gently fill to the mark each comparator cell with the supernatant sewage in the cylinder (if the indicator is added first, the filling of the cell will insure thorough mixing).

4. Place the cell containing the indicator in the inner slot; place the cell containing the sewage in the outer slot back of the colored discs.

5. Rotate the disc until the colors seen through the eyepiece match and read the pH value from the exposed number.

Procedure for sludge. If enough clear liquor will separate from the sludge on standing, this may be used and the pH determined as for sewage. If enough clear liquor does not separate,

1. Pour gently about 25 ml of sludge into the graduated cylinder and add distilled water to make a volume of 150 ml.

2. Mix gently but do not agitate violently.

3. Allow to settle and determine the pH of the clear liquor as for sewage.

Results are expressed as pH value.

SETTLEABLE SOLIDS TEST

Sampling. Catch samples at period of maximum flow and if possible allowing for the lag in time equal to the flowing-through period of the various parts of the plant.

Equipment. Two or more Imhoff cones, the number depending on the number of sampling points. These are large glass cones of one-liter capacity, the lower ends of which are graduated in milliliters (ml). They should be cleaned with strong soap and hot water, using a brush. Wetting of the cone with water before use helps to prevent adherence of the solids to the sides. A wooden rack or shelf should be provided to hold the cones.

Procedure.

1. A measured quantity of a well-mixed sample, usually one liter, is gently poured into the cone and allowed to stand for a total period of one hour.

2. After the sample has stood forty-five minutes, gently rotate the cone between the hands so as to loosen the solids that adhere to the sides.

3. Allow to settle fifteen minutes longer.

4. Read from the graduations the volume of solid material deposited in the cone making allowances for any unfilled portions of the cone below the level of the settled solids.

Results are expressed as ml of solids per liter which settled in one hour.

$$\text{ml of solids} \times \frac{1000}{\text{ml of sample}} = \text{ml of settleable solids per liter}$$

If the samples represent the influent and effluent of a tank, the efficiency of the tank may be found.

$$\frac{\frac{\text{ml of solids per}}{\text{liter of influent}} (-) \frac{\text{ml of solids per}}{\text{liter of effluent}}}{\text{ml of solids per liter of influent}} \times 100 = \begin{array}{l}\text{per cent of} \\ \text{settleable} \\ \text{solids} \\ \text{removed}\end{array}$$

SLUDGE SOLIDS TEST

Sampling. Representative samples should be collected as described under sludge sampling.

Equipment, A flat-bottomed nickel or porcelain evaporating dish (100 ml), a trip, torsion, or beam balance sensitive to 0.1 gram, steam bath, drying oven, desiccator, gas burner with tripod and triangles or an electric muffle furnace. Flat piece of metal.

Procedure.

1. Heat a clean evaporating dish over a gas burner or in a muffle furnace for 15 minutes.
2. Cool in a desiccator and weight to nearest 0.1 grams.
3. Add about 50 grams of well-mixed sample and weigh.
4. Evaporate to dryness on a steam bath and place in an oven at 103°C. for one hour.
5. Cool in a desiccator and weigh.
6. Cover the dish with a clean flat piece of metal (to prevent spattering), ignite in a muffle furnace at 600°C., or over a gas burner, until all the carbon or black material has been burned off. Ash adhering to the metal plate is transferred back to dish.
7. Cool in a desiccator and weigh.

Results are expressed as per cent dry solids and per cent moisture. Volatile matter is expressed as per cent of the dry solids.

The difference between the weight of the dish (2) and the weight of the dish plus the wet sample (3) equals the weight of the sample. The difference between the weight of the dish (2) and the weight of the dish plus the dried solids (5) equals the weight of the dry solids.

$$\frac{\text{wt. of dry solids}}{\text{wt. of sample}} \times 100 = \text{per cent solids}$$

$$100 - \text{per cent solids} = \text{per cent moisture}$$

The difference between the weight of the dish plus dry solids (5) and the weight of the dish plus ignited solids (7) equals the weight of volatile matter.

$$\frac{\text{wt. of volatile matter}}{\text{wt. of dry solids}} \times 100 = \text{per cent volatile matter}$$

$$100 - \text{per cent volatile matter} = \text{per cent ash}$$

SUSPENDED SOLIDS TEST

Sampling. The same samples that were collected for the settleable solids test should be used for this test; or *preferably* an integrated sample adequately refrigerated.

Equipment. Gooch crucibles, a filter flask with fittings, aspirator filter pump, drying oven, desiccator, analytical balance with weights, graduated cylinder (100 ml), washed and ignited medium asbestos fibre, and a gas burner with tripod and triangles or an electric muffle furnace.

Procedure.

1. Prepare a suspension of 15 grams of medium asbestos fibre in 1000 ml of distilled water and pour a portion through the Gooch crucible in the filter flask to make a mat about one-eighth inch thick.
2. Carefully remove the mat with a spatula or tweezers. Invert and replace in the Gooch crucible.
3. Wash with 100 ml distilled water.
4. Dry crucible with mat in oven at 103°C.
5. Ignite crucible and mat in muffle furnace or over gas burner.
6. Cool in desiccator and weigh.
7. Again place crucible in filter flask and pour a measured amount of the well-mixed sample into the crucible and filter it through. Filteration is faster if sample is added in small increments. For settled sewage or plant effluents, larger portions should be used.
8. Rinse the graduated cylinder with distilled water and pour through the filter.
9. Dry the crucible in the oven for one hour at 103°C.
10. Cool in desiccator and weigh.
11. Ignite crucible at dull red heat until ash is white or red.
12. Cool in desiccator and weigh.

Results are expressed as parts per million (ppm). The difference between the weight of the crucible before filtering (6) and the weight of the crucible after filtering (10) is the weight in grams of the *total* suspended solids.

$$\text{wt. of suspended solids in grams} \times \frac{1,000.000}{\text{ml of sample}} = \text{ppm total suspended solids}$$

The difference between the weight of the crucible after filtering (10) and the weight of the crucible after ignition (12) is the weight in grams of the loss on ignition.

$$\text{wt. of the loss on ignition} \times \frac{1,000.000}{\text{ml of sample}} = \text{volatile suspended matter}$$

The ppm total suspended solids minus ppm volatile suspended matter equals ppm fixed suspended solids.

TOTAL SOLIDS TEST

Sampling. The same samples should be used as were used for the settleable solids and the suspended solids tests, or *preferably* an integrated sample adequately refrigerated.

Equipment. Porcelain evaporating dishes (100 ml), graduated cylinder (100 ml), drying oven, desiccator, gas burner with tripod and triangle or an electric muffle furnace, analytical balance with weights.

Procedure.

1. Ignite porcelain dish.
2. Cool in desiccator and weigh.
3. Measure 100 ml of well-mixed sample (graduated cylinder) and add to porcelain dish.
4. Evaporate sample to dryness in oven at 103°C. or on a steam bath, followed by the 103° oven.
5. Cool in desiccator and weigh.
6. Ignite porcelain dish at dull red heat until carbonaceous matter has been entirely burned.
7. Cool in desiccator and weigh.

Results are expressed as ppm total solids. The weight of the dish after evaporation of the sample (5) minus the weight of the dish (2) equals the weight of total solids in grams.

$$\text{wt. of total solids in grams} \times \frac{1,000,000}{\text{ml of sample}} = \text{ppm total solids}$$

The weight of the dish after evaporation of the sample (5) minus the weight of the dish after ignition (7) equals the weight of the loss on ignition equals volatile total solids.

$$\text{wt. of the loss on ignition in grams} \times \frac{1,000,000}{\text{ml of sample}} = \text{ppm volatile total solids}$$

The ppm total solids minus ppm volatile total solids equals ppm fixed total solids.

DISSOLVED SOLIDS TEST

Results are expressed as ppm dissolved solids and obtained by subtracting the suspended solids from the total solids.

136

Typical Distribution of Solids in Sewage ppm

Total solids 600
Volatile total solids 300
Fixed total solids 300

Total dissolved solids 400
Volatile dissolved solids 155
Fixed dissolved solids 245

Total suspended solids 200
Volatile suspended solids 145
Fixed suspended solids 55

Settleable solids—ml/liter 120

DISSOLVED OXYGEN TEST

Sampling. Special equipment is require for collecting samples for this test. The samples must be so taken that the bottle will be entirely filled with liquid that has not been in contact with air and no entrained air will collect under the stopper. This requires a volume which will give a threefold displacement of the liquid in the sampling bottle. The temperature of the samples at the time of sampling should be noted.

Equipment. Dissolved oxygen sampler, 300-ml glass-stoppered sample bottles, three 5-ml pipets graduated in 0.1 ml, graduated cylinder, 500-ml Erlenmeyer flask, buret, buret stand, clamp, concentrated sulfuric acid, standard solutions of alkaline-iodide-azide and manganous sulfate, 30-ml dropping bottle, starch indicator solution, N/40 sodium thiosulfate, thermometer.

Procedure for samples in 300-ml bottles.

1. Add 2 ml of manganous sulfate solution and 2 ml of alkaline-iodide-azide solution. Shake by inverting the bottle for twenty seconds.

2. Allow the precipitate to settle below the neck of the bottle; add 2 ml of concentrated sulfuric acid and shake.

3. Measure 200 ml into an Erlenmeyer flask with a minimum loss of iodine.

4. Titrate the liberated iodine with N/40 thiosulfate until the sample is pale yellow, add 1 ml of starch solution, and continue the titration carefully until colorless, disregarding any return of color.

Results are expressed as ppm dissolved oxygen or per cent saturation. If exactly N/40 thiosulfate is used to titrate 200 ml of sample, the number of milliliters of the thiosulate used is equivalent to the ppm dissolved oxygen. The per cent saturation is computed by dividing the dissolved oxygen of the sample in ppm by the dissolved oxygen in ppm of fresh water or sea water of the proper salinity saturated with air at the temperature of the sample and multiplying by 100. See Table 8.

$$\frac{\text{ppm D O found at T}^\circ\text{C.}}{\text{ppm D O of water saturated at T}^\circ\text{C.}} \times 100 = \text{per cent saturation}$$

TABLE 8

Solubility of Oxygen in Fresh Water and in Sea Water of Stated Degrees
of Salinity at Various Temperatures When Exposed to Water-Saturated
Air at a Total Pressure of 760 mm. Hg. Dry Air is Assumed to Contain
20.90% Oxygen. (Calculated by G. C. Whipple and M. C. Whipple from
measurements of C. J. J. Fox.)

C°	Chlorides in Sea Water (parts per million)				
	0	5000	10000	15000	20000
°C	Dissolved oxygen in parts per millions by weight				
0	14.62	13.79	12.97	12.14	11.32
1	14.23	13.41	12.61	11.82	11.03
2	13.84	13.05	12.28	11.52	10.76
3	13.48	12.72	11.98	11.24	10.50
4	13.13	12.41	11.69	10.97	10.25
5	12.80	12.09	11.39	10.70	10.01
6	12.48	11.79	11.12	10.45	9.78
7	12.17	11.51	10.85	10.21	9.57
8	11.87	11.24	10.61	9.98	9.36
9	11.59	10.97	10.36	9.76	9.17
10	11.33	10.73	10.13	9.55	8.98
11	11.08	10.49	9.92	9.35	8.80
12	10.83	10.28	9.72	9.17	8.62
13	10.60	10.05	9.52	8.98	8.46
14	10.37	9.85	9.32	8.80	8.30
15	10.15	9.65	9.14	8.63	8.14
16	9.95	9.46	8.96	8.47	7.99
17	9.74	9.26	8.78	8.30	7.84
18	9.54	9.07	8.62	8.15	7.70
19	9.35	8.89	8.45	8.00	7.56
20	9.17	8.73	8.30	7.86	7.42
21	8.99	8.57	8.14	7.71	7.28
22	8.83	8.42	7.99	7.57	7.14
23	8.68	8.27	7.85	7.43	7.00
24	8.53	8.12	7.71	7.30	6.87
25	8.38	7.96	7.56	7.15	6.74
26	8.22	7.81	7.42	7.02	6.61
27	8.07	7.67	7.28	6.88	6.49
28	7.92	7.53	7.14	6.75	6.37
29	7.77	7.39	7.00	6.62	6.25
30	7.63	7.25	6.86	6.49	6.13

From: American Public Health Association, American Water Works Association,
and Federation of Sewage and Industrial Wastes Associations, Standard Methods
for the Examination of Water, Sewage, and Industrial Wastes, 10th ed., Baltimore,
American Public Health Association, 1955, p. 254.

BIOCHEMICAL OXYGEN DEMAND TEST

Sampling. Samples should be collected as for the dissolved oxygen test when dilution of the samples is not required. Catch samples of raw or treated sewage may be used but integrated samples are more representative of average conditions. This test should not be made on chlorinated effluents.

Equipment. Sampling kit or aluminum dipper, 300-ml clear, glass-stoppered bottles, two 5-ml pipets graduated in 0.1 ml, three 1-ml pipets graduated in 0.1 ml, 250-ml graduated cylinder, 500-ml Erlenmeyer flask, buret, buret stand, clamp, 30-ml dropping bottle, thermometer, five-gallon bottle, aspirator filter pump, transfer pipets (5-, 10-, 20-, 50-, and 100-ml), analytical balance, 20°C. water bath, glass siphon, rubber tubing, pinch cock.

Reagents. For most sewage treatment plant laboratories it is probably advisable to purchase reagents. All are available from commercial supply houses. The preparation of N/40 thiosulfate reagent by dilution of the N/10 solution will have to be done, as will the preparation of dilution water for use in the test.

a. Concentrated sulfuric acid.
b. Manganous sulfate, 480 grams $MnSO_4.4H_2O$ or 400 grams $MnSO_4.2H_2O$ per liter.
c. Alkaline iodide azide, 500 grams of NaOH and 135 grams NaI; dissolve separately and make up to one liter. Just before use dissolve one gram NaN_3 in 100 ml of the alkaline iodide solution. Do not heat. Three hours are required for the sodium azide to dissolve. The alkaline iodide azide solution is stable for only two weeks.
d. N/40 sodium thiosulfate. Dilute one volume of N/10 with three volumes of distilled water to make N/40 sodium thiosulfate which is stable for only about two weeks and must be freshly made or restandardized.
e. Starch indicator, five grams per liter; preserve with 1.25 grams salicylic acid.
f. Ferric chloride, 0.25 grams $FeCl_3.6H_2O$ per liter.
g. Calcium chloride, 27.5 grams $CaCl_2$ per liter.
h. Magnesium sulfate, 22.5 grams $MgSO_4.7H_2O$ per liter.
i. Ammonium phosphate buffer. Dissolve 8.5 grams KH_2PO_4, 21.75 grams K_2HPO_4, 33.4 grams $Na_2HPO_4.7H_2O$, and 1.7 grames NH_4Cl in about 500 ml distilled water and dilute to one liter. The pH of this buffer should be 7.2 without further adjustment.

Procedure.

1. Aerate five gallons of distilled water.
2. Add 18.9 ml of ferric chloride solution, 18.9 ml of calcium chloride solution, 18.9 ml of magnesium sulfate solution, and 18.9 ml of ammonium phosphate buffer solution (pH 7.2) to the dilution water and mix.

3. Siphon the dilution water into 300-ml glass-stoppered bottle until the bottle is about one-half full.

4. To the half-filled bottle add with a pipet the desired quantity of sample. Possible quantities would be:
   Raw sewage 3.0 or 6.0 ml
   Settled sewage 6.0 or 12.0 ml
   Final effluent 50 or 100 ml

5. Fill the bottle into the neck with the dilution water and stopper so that no air bubbles are entrained.

6. Fill another 300-ml bottle with dilution water alone.

7. Place both bottles in a 20°C. water bath or incubator.

8. Determine the dissolved oxygen of the sample if it is an effluent or stream sample. The dissolved oxygen of raw or settled sewage may be considered as zero.

9. After five days determine the dissolved oxygen content of each of the incubated samples by the procedure described earlier.

10. Determine the exact volume of each 300-ml bottle.

Calculation. Results are expressed as ppm biochemical oxygen demand.

	A	B
Number of bottle	A	B
Volume of bottle	305	295
Volume of Sample	0	5
Titration—200 ml after five-day incubation		
(1) Reading of buret after titration	8.2	12.7
(2) Reading of buret before titration	0.0	8.2
(3) Ml of N/40 thiosulfate used (1) minus (2)	8.2	4.5
Dissolved oxygen of sewage sample		0.0
Calculated initial dissolved oxygen	8.2	8.1
Final dissolved oxygen	8.2	4.5
Depletion of dissolved oxygen	0.0	3.6
Five-day biochemical oxygen demand		212 mg/l

Number of bottle. Each bottle must be numbered to permit identification.

Volume of bottle. The volume of each bottle must be determined by filling with water, inserting the stopper, and then measuring the contents in a graduated cylinder, or bottles containing 300 ml may be purchased.

Volume of sample. The volume of sample added to each bottle.

Calculated initial dissolved oxygen. The dissolved oxygen available from the dilution water and the sample.

Volume of diluting water = 295 − 5 = 290 ml

Volume of sample   =   5 ml

Dissolved oxygen of diluting water = 8.2 ppm

Dissolved oxygen of sample   = 0

Initial dissolved oxygen = volume of dilution water × dissolved oxygen of diluting water plus volume of sample × dissolved oxygen of sample divided by volume of sample plus diluting water.

$$\frac{290 \times 8.2 + 5 \times 0.0}{295} = 8.1 \text{ ppm}$$

Final dissolved oxygen is the dissolved oxygen determined by the titration; milliliters of N/40 thiosulfate used equals ppm dissolved oxygen when 200 ml sample is titrated.

Depletion of dissolved oxygen is the difference between the calculated initial dissolved oxygen and the final dissolved oxygen.

Five-day biochemical oxygen demand is the dissolved oxygen required by the undiluted sample expressed as ppm.

$$= \text{depletion of dissolved oxygen} \times \frac{\text{volume of bottle}}{\text{volume of sample}}$$

$$= 3.6 \times \frac{295}{5} = 212 \text{ mg/l}$$

CHLORINE DEMAND TEST

Sampling. Only catch samples should be used and they should be collected during the period of maximum load on the treatment process.

Equipment. A comparator employing standard colored glass discs with four extra cells, or chlorine color standards in 2-ounce French square bottles, one 250-ml graduated cylinder, five 500-ml wide mouth bottles, buret, buret stand, medicine dropper, ortho-tolidine solution, spot plate, 1-ml pipet, stirring rod, chlorine solution, 1000 ppm preferably obtained by dilution and standardization of feed water from a solution feed chlorinator but may be obtained by diluting 10 ml of Zonite solution to 100 ml with water.

Procedure.

1. Add 250 ml of sample to each of five 500-ml wide mouth bottles.
2. To one of these bottles add standard chlorine solution 0.5 ml at a time with mixing, until a spot plate test shows the presence of a trace of residual chlorine.
3. Add this quantity of chlorine water to the first of the 250-ml portions of sample; add this same amount plus an increment of 0.5 ml chlorine water to the second portion; add to the third portion the same amount plus 1 ml; add to the fourth portion the same amount plus 1.5 ml.
4. Mix and allow to stand for fifteen minutes.
5. Determine residual chlorine in each bottle.

Results are expressed as ppm chlorine required to yield an 0.5 ppm residual chlorine value after a fifteen minute period of contact. Each

141

milliliter of the standard chlorine solution added to 250 ml of sample is equivalent to a dosage of

$$4 \times \frac{\text{mg chlorine per liter of standard solution}}{1000} = \text{ppm chlorine}$$

The amount of chlorine in ppm used in treating that sample which shows a residual chlorine content of 0.5 ppm is the chlorine dose. The chlorine dose minus 0.5 ppm is the quantity of chlorine used by the organic matter and is the chlorine demand.

SLUDGE VOLUME INDEX

Sampling. Catch samples of mixed liquor from the effluent of the aeration tank should be taken with as little agitation as possible.

Equipment. One-liter graduated cylinder, Gooch crucibles, a filter flask with fittings, aspirator pump, drying oven, desiccator, analytical balance with weights, 100-ml graduated cylinder, washed and ignited asbestos fibre, gas burner with tripod and triangles or an electric muffle furnace.

Procedure.

1. Gently fill to the mark a 1000-ml graduated cylinder.
2. Allow to settle for thirty minutes.
3. Record the volume occupied by the sludge.
4. Thoroughly mix the sample or use another portion of the original sample and determine the suspended solids.

Results. The sludge volume index is the volume in ml of one gram of activated sludge in the mixed liquor which has settled for thirty minutes and is computed by dividing the volume of settleable sludge by the ppm suspended solids and multiplying by 1000.

$$\frac{\text{Vol. of settleable sludge}}{\text{ppm suspended solids}} \times 1000 = \text{sludge volume index}$$

TEST FOR CONDITIONING SLUDGE FOR VACUUM FILTRATION

Sampling. A grab sample of wet sludge from the conditioning tank may be taken either before or after the conditioning chemicals have been added. If taken before, the test will show the quantity of chemicals to be added. If taken after, the test will show the effectiveness of the chemicals added.

Equipment. 200-ml graduate, 400-ml beakers, trip balance sensitive to 0.1 gm, 10-ml pipets graduated in 0.1 ml, 9-cm Buchner funnel, suction flask, aspirator filter pump with heavy walled rubber tubing, vacuum gauge, stop watch or watch with a second hand, 9-cm filter paper. (No. 1 Whatman).

Procedure for conditioned sludge.

1. Connect the vacuum gauge to the rubber hose between the aspirator and the filter flask, place a filter paper in the Buchner funnel, moisten and draw into position with a slight vacuum.
2. Measure 200 ml of sample with a graduate.
3. Gently pour into the prepared Buchner funnel.
4. Note the time the aspirator is started and the time the vacuum first drops as shown on the vacuum gauge.
5. Results are reported as time in minutes and seconds required for filtration.

Procedure for sludge to be conditioned

Use the same lime and ferric chloride as is used in plant operation. Each gram of hydrated lime used per 200 ml of sample is equal to 42 pounds per 1000 gallons of sludge. Each ml of ferric chloride solution used per 200 ml of sample is equal to five gallons per 1000 gallons of sludge.

1. Measure five 200-ml portions of sample into five 400-ml beakers. Number beakers 1 to 5.
2. Add 1.0, 2.0, 3.0, 4.0, 5.0 ml of ferric chloride to the respective samples. Stir gently about 30 seconds.
3. Determine filtration time as described above.
4. Using that quantity of ferric chloride that requires three or four minutes to filter, repeat the test as follows:
5. Add the ferric chloride dose to each of five 200-ml samples. Stir 30 seconds and then add 1.0, 2.0, 3.0, 4.0, 5.0 grams of hydrated lime to each sample. Stir and determine filtration time as above. Generally any quantity of lime above that required to raise the pH value of the filtrate above 10 is of no value.
6. Determine the optimum combination of ferric chloride and lime that will yield a filtration time of about two to three minutes. Less than one minute is better than necessary and more than four minutes is not satisfactory.

LABORATORY TESTS FOR COLIFORM GROUP BACTERIA

Sampling.

Only catch samples may be used for bacteriologic tests. Since the coliform test is ordinarily applied to samples of chlorinated sewage, sample bottles must contain sodium thiosulfate to destroy residual chlorine at the time of sampling. All samples should be examined as soon as possible after collection.

Equipment.

Balance (0.1 gram accuracy) ; steam pressure sterilizer; oven sterilizer; incubator with automatic temperature control; pipets (bacteriological, 1.1 ml capacity, graduated at 1.0 and 1.1 ml) ; culture tubes (150 mm x 18 mm and 75 mm x 12 mm) ; pH meter or pH color test kit, glass or high temperature resistant polyethylene plastic sample bottles; glass beakers of 1- or 2-quart capacity; graduated cylinders (10, 50, 100, 500 and 1000 ml.)

Reagents and Supplies.

Dehydrated beef extract lactose broth, dehydrated brilliant green bile broth, cotton or polyurethane foam culture tube plugs, potassium dihydrogen phosphate (KH_2PO_4), sodium hydroxide ($NaOH$), sodium thiosulfate ($Na_2S_2O_3.5H_2O$), distilled water.

Preparation of sample bottles and pipets.

To each bottle before sterilization add 0.1 ml of a 10 per cent solution of sodium thiosulfate. If bottle has a ground glass stopper, insert a piece of string between the stopper and its seat to prevent seizure during sterilization. Cover the stopper or cap with heavy paper or metal foil and fasten securely with a string. Sterilize glass bottles and pipets by placing in an oven at 170°C. for one hour. If the bottle is plastic, leave the cap slightly loose to prevent the bottle collapsing during heating. Sterilize in the autoclave for 15 minutes at 15 lbs. pressure (121°C.). Follow the operating instructions of the autoclave manufacturer closely. Allow the sterilizer to cool before opening. Tighten the caps on the plastic bottles.

Preparation of 10 per cent solution of sodium thiosulfate.

Weigh out 10.0 grams of sodium thiosulfate ($Na_2S_2O_3.5H_2O$) and dissolve in 100 ml of distilled water.

Preparation of fermentation tubes containing lactose broth for the presumptive test or brilliant green bile broth for the confirmed test.

Weigh out sufficient dehydrated medium to make 1 liter of broth following the directions on the manufacturer's label. Add the powder to 1 liter of distilled water and stir until the medium is completely dissolved. Prepare each fermentation tube by placing an inverted 75 mm x 12 mm culture tube inside of a 150 mm x 18 mm tube and add 10 ml of the broth. Insert cotton or polyurethane plugs and stack the tubes upright in a basket. Sterilize the tubes by heating in an autoclave for exactly 15 minutes after the pressure has risen to 15 lbs. (121°C.). Permit the autoclave to cool to room temperature before opening. Failure to do this will result in many of the fermentation tubes being made worthless by reason of incomplete filling of the inner tube with medium. The total elapsed time for heating, sterilization and cooling should not exceed 40 minutes. Check the pH of the finished media. It should be 7.2.

Preparation of diluting blanks.

Prepare dilution water by adding 1.25 ml of stock phosphate buffer to 1 liter of distilled water.

Stock phosphate buffer: Dissolve 17.0 grams of potassium dihydrogen phosphate (KH_2PO_4) in 250 ml of distilled water. Adjust the pH to 7.2 by adding slowly and with constant stirring a solution of sodium hydroxide ($NaOH$) containing 40.0 grams of NaOH per liter. Adjustment of the pH can be done most easily with a pH meter but it may also be done colorimetrically by checking the pH at intervals after addition of small increments of the hydroxide solution. Make up to a final volume of 500 ml.

Prepare the buffered dilution water blanks in 150 mm x 18 mm culture tubes by adding sufficient to each tube to yield 9 ml after autoclave sterilization. (This must be determined by trial). Stopper the tubes with cotton or polyurethane foam plugs and sterilize by autoclaving for 15 minutes at 15 lbs pressure (121°C.).

Presumptive test for coliform group.

Add 1 ml of the well shaken sample to a 9-ml buffered water dilution blank using a sterile 1-ml pipet. Mix thoroughly by shaking the tube, taking care not to wet the plug. Label this dilution 1/10, using a glass marking wax pencil for the purpose.

Add 1 ml of sample to each of 3 lactose broth fermentation tubes. It is not necessary to shake the tube for mixing. Label the tubes 1-1, 1-2, and 1-3 respectively.

Using the dilution labeled 1/10 and a fresh sterile pipet make another dilution in the same manner as the first. Label the new dilution 1/100.

Using the 1/10 dilution as a sample, add to each of 3 lactose broth fermentation tubes 1-ml portions labeling them 1/10-1, 1/10-2, and 1/10-3 respectively.

Continue the series, as indicated, preparing first the succeeding dilution and then the fermentation tubes for a given dilution. In principle, the series is continued to the extent that the final dilution yields completely negative results in all three tubes. For samples which are unfamiliar to the technician, it is well to carry the series out to the 1 millionth dilution. Place the inoculated fermentation tubes in an incubator at 35°C. ± 0.5° for 24 hours ± 2 hours. Discard the dilutions of the sample.

At the end of the incubation period note on the record card the observations of each individual fermentation tube. If no gas whatever is noted in the upper portion of the inner tube, record a zero (0) in the space provided. If any gas, even a small bubble, is noted, record the fact by marking a plus sign (+). Carry out the confirmed test on all tubes showing gas making a check mark (✓) to indicate this fact near the plus sign, thus +✓. Place the tubes which do not show gas back in the incubator for an additional 24-hour period. The total incubation period for these tubes is then 48 hours ± 3 hours, and again observe and record the presence or absence of gas.

Interpretation of preumptive test results.

The appearance of gas in any fermentation tube inoculated with a portion of the sample or dilution thereof at any time within 48 hours ± 3 hours is *presumptive* evidence of the presence of coliform bacteria in that tube. Conversely the absence of gas is *definite* evidence of the absence of coliform group bacteria from that tube.

Confirmed test for the coliform group.

Carry out the test on all fermentation tubes which produce gas in the presumptive test. Using a wire loop sterilized by holding it for a moment in a hot flame, transfer a drop of culture from the presumptive test tube to a tube containing brilliant green lactose bile broth. Mark the newly inoculated tube with the same identifying number as the presumptive tube and fasten the two together with a rubber band. Once the transfer has been made, there is no further need for the presumptive test fermentation tube but it is good practice to hold it until final readings are obtained from the confirmed test since errors in identification are often avoided in this manner. Place the tubes in the incubator at 35°C. ± 0.5°. Observe the brilliant green bile broth fermentation tubes after 24 hours ± 2 hours incubation. If gas is present in the inner tube in any amount, record a plus sign (+) in the appropriate space on the record card. If no gas is noted, mark a zero (0) in the appropriate space and incubate the tube in question for an additional 24 hours making a total of 48 hours ± 3 hours. Observe again and record the presence or absence of gas.

Interpretation of confirmed test results.

The appearance of gas within 48 hours ± 3 hours in a brilliant green bile tube inoculated from a presumptive test lactose broth tube is *confirmed* evidence of the presence of coliform bacteria in the presumptive test tube. Conversely the absence of gas in the confirmed test tube is *definite* evidence of the absence of coliform bacteria in the corresponding presumptive test tube. It is not definite evidence of the absence of coliform bacteria from the original sample, however, since it is possible that other confirmed test tubes may yield positive results.

Most probable number index.

By examining different volumes of sample, one-tenth multiples of 1 ml, it is possible to make an approximate estimation of the *number* of coliform bacteria present in the sample through consideration of the relative numbers of tubes in the various dilutions which yield positive and negative results. The estimation is in the form of a "most probable number index" which essentially is a concentration of coliform bacteria in the sample (expressed as the number of bacteria per 100 ml of sample) which would most *probably* yield the same combination of positive and negative tubes as obtained in the examination of the sample. For convenience in calculating, the most probable number index table has been prepared.

When more than 3 dilutions in a decimal series are examined, the results from only 3 of them are significant. The highest dilution giving positive results in all 3 portions tested and the next 2 succeeding higher dilutions are selected. The results of these 3 dilutions are then used in computing the MPN index. The calculated index will equal the tabular index multiplied by a factor equal to the denominator of the highest dilution giving positive results in all 3 tubes. For example, if all tubes in all dilutions are positive until the 1/1000 dilution is reached, we consider only the 1/100, 1/1000 and 1/10,000 dilutions as significant. Suppose the results of analysis indicates that the positive tubes for these 3 dilutions are as follows:

    1/100   3+ 0—
    1/1000   2+ 1—
    1/10,000   1+ 2—

The MPN index then equals $1500 \times 100 = 150,000$ coliform bacteria in 100 ml of the original sample.

Table 9

Most Probable Number (MPN)/100 ml of coliform bacteria in a sample using 3 portions in geometric series.

No positive tubes in dilutions			MPN per 100 ml	No positive tubes in dilutions			MPN per 100 ml
1 ml	1/10 ml	1/100 ml		1 ml	1/10 ml	1/100 ml	
0	0	0	<30	2	0	0	91
0	0	1	30	2	0	1	140
0	0	2	60	2	0	2	200
0	0	3	90	2	0	3	260
0	1	0	30	2	1	0	150
0	1	1	61	2	1	1	200
0	1	2	92	2	1	2	270
0	1	3	120	2	1	3	340
0	2	0	62	2	2	0	210
0	2	1	93	2	2	1	280
0	2	2	120	2	2	2	350
0	2	3	160	2	2	3	420
0	3	0	94	2	3	0	290
0	3	1	130	2	3	1	360
0	3	2	160	2	3	2	440
0	3	3	190	2	3	3	530
1	0	0	36	3	0	0	230
1	0	1	73	3	0	1	390
1	0	2	110	3	0	2	640
1	0	3	150	3	0	3	950
1	1	0	73	3	1	0	430
1	1	1	110	3	1	1	750
1	1	2	150	3	1	2	1200
1	1	3	190	3	1	3	1600
1	2	0	110	3	2	0	930
1	2	1	150	3	2	1	1500
1	2	2	200	3	2	2	2100
1	2	3	240	3	2	3	2900
1	3	0	160	3	3	0	2400
1	3	1	200	3	3	1	4600
1	3	2	240	3	3	2	11000
1	3	3	290	3	3	3	24000 or >

CHAPTER 12

RECORDS AND REPORTS

IMPORTANCE OF RECORDS

The keeping of adequate records of performance is an integral part of good sewage treatment plant operation. It is only by making a clear and concise memorandum of what has happened and what has been accomplished that the experiences will be of assistance in meeting future operation situations. Pertinent and complete records are a necessary aid to control procedures. Most important of all, records should be used as a basis for plant operation and for interpreting the results of sewage treatment.

Records also provide an excellent check on things done or to be done, especially as regards maintenance problems. Equipment in sewage treatment plants requires periodic service; some daily, some weekly, and others monthly or yearly. Adequate records note when service was last performed, and when the time for service approaches, thus a schedule can be maintained, and nothing is overlooked or forgotten.

The significant details of day-to-day experience also have an important historical value in that they form a running account of the operation of the plant. When accurately kept, records provide an essential basis for the design of future changes or expansions of the treatment plant and also can be used to aid in the design of sewage treatment facilities for other locations where similar problems may be encountered. In the event of legal questions in connection with sewage treatment or plant operations, accurate and complete records would be urgently required as evidence of what actually occurred at any given time or over any particular period of time. Thus, records and their proper maintenance are essential in any type of sewage treatment. However, only those records should be kept which are known to be useful; the temptation to accumulate minutiae of no significant value must be guarded against.

INFORMATION TO BE INCLUDED IN RECORDS

The extent to which record keeping should be practiced depends entirely upon their potential use. The type of treatment, the volume of sewage treated, and the kind and importance of installations auxiliary to the treatment plant will control the amount of necessary record keeping. If only preliminary treatment methods are employed, daily notes of sewage flow, some descriptive information as to its appearance, and weights or volumes of screenings and grit removed may be sufficient for practical purposes. Should prechlorination for odor control or to reduce septicity be in use, data on the amount of chlorine used per day and the residual chlorine determined at given locations should be noted for future reference. With any type of treatment, meteorological data such as temperature, rainfall, wind direction, and velocity are pertinent.

Primary treatment processes require rather detailed records to note all pertinent data regarding operation and, obviously, the more complex procedures of secondary treatment necessitate even more extensive records.

For example, trickling filter operation would require the recording of volume of sewage treated, nozzles cleaned each day, and similar facts. With Imhoff tanks, the amount of sludge drawn, depth of scum, if any, and any necessary repair or cleaning work undertaken should be recorded. Since all treatment procedures must be controlled by significant laboratory tests made on representative samples, the results of such tests must be carefully and fully set down.

When laboratory determinations are made, it is essential that not only the final results of each tests be recorded, but also that all of the test data, frequently called the working data, such as buret readings and the necessary computations, be noted for future reference. Although such details may seem superfluous, should any question arise as to the accuracy of final data obtained in the laboratory, the notes on technical procedures, if available, will prove the accuracy or inaccuracy of the final result reported. Thus, for his own potential protection in maintaining the integrity of his work, the analyst in the laboratory should keep complete records in most cases. This actually means that full records of tests must be maintained in the laboratory, although the separate plant operation records will contain only the final result of such laboratory determinations.

Frequently, state and municipal regulations govern the operation of many sewage treatment installations. These regulations require that certain operating records be maintained and reported to the supervising agency at specified intervals. These records must be kept, but should be in addition to adequate plant operating data and should not be considered a substitute for plant records.

HOW RECORDS SHOULD BE KEPT

Record systems can be developed that are either simple or complex. However, they should be realistic and apply to the operating problems involved at each particular treatment facility.

The most efficient way to keep records is to plan what data are essential and useful and then to prepare forms on which the information may be quickly entered in the proper spaces. Forms not only indicate the data to be obtained but provide for entering them with a minimum possibility of error or omission. Prepared forms can be used both for plant operations and for laboratory determinations. To keep records without the use of well-designed forms increases the labor and time involved and promotes inaccuracies. It must be remembered that inaccurate or incomplete records are worse than no records at all. Business firms specializing in the printing of forms usually have staff trained to give advice in setting up records systems and choosing the type of form best suited to the need.

Forms in use at treatment plants of a similar type are useful in preparing forms, and can be secured on request.

Records should be permanent, and consequently entries on the forms should be made with ink or with indelible pencil. Ordinary lead pencil notations smudge easily and can be too readily erased or altered; a lead pencil should never be used.

Once made, records of any type should be carefully preserved and filed where they can be located rapidly. This requires the establishment of a filing system that will be used and understood by everyone concerned with making and using records. The corollary is that filing of completed record forms must be attended to promptly and with care. A record misfiled is a record lost, and a lost record is of no value.

A pertinent question which always arises is how long records should be kept. Obviously, they should be kept as long as they may be useful, with due consideration given to the historical value of some types of data. Some information will have little utility after a short time, while other information may be found of great value even after the passage of many years.

Any data that might be used in future as a basis of design for plant expansion or for new construction should be kept indefinitely. Results of laboratory analyses of the condition of the receiving stream or water course will always be pertinent and likewise should be kept indefinitely. Detailed operating data related to a given treatment device may have little permanent significance and can be kept for a year or some other indicated period and then discarded. For some types of records, official approval is required before they can be discarded or destroyed. The fact that old records are not consulted every day in no way lessens their potential value. It is the best modern practice to set up a disposal schedule for each type of record maintained in order to avoid the accumulation of useless files. A decision can be made at the time a record is set up limiting the period for which it must be available.

Records must be stored in a manner to insure their permanence and safety, as well as their accessibility.

Records should be made at the time the data are obtained by the person directly concerned with making the particular measurements. Responsibility for proper filing, care, and use of records will rest with the supervisor or the person in charge of the treatment plant, or someone delegated by him.

The problem of records of sewage treatment plant operation has been considered by various groups for many years past. In 1931 a committee of the New England Sewage Works Association published a report detailing the items which should be recorded for various types of treatment units. Even after so many years, a review of this report will indicate the possible form and extent of record keeping for many individual treatment plants. The report stresses that not only should operational data be recorded, but structural features, sizes, design, construction, etc. should be an integral part of plant records for eventual use. Because of the date of this report (1931) some types of treatment are included which are not mentioned in this manual while other types not included are discussed in this manual.

Two appendices from this report are reproduced at the end of this chapter to illustrate the kind of data of value for various types of sewage treatment plants. Not all plants would need or find it desirable to record all the data suggested, and some of the analytical determinations such as chlorides and nitrogen would probably not be made except for special purposes. However, every plant operator should find some of the information valuable.

REPORTS

With the accumulation of all of the essential data including authentic records in the manner outlined above, the basis or groundwork for the report is established. Just as the maintenance of complete and accurate records can be of definite value in the evaluation of sewage treatment performance, the development of the report is of inestimable value for many reasons that will be alluded to later.

In the preparation of the report, the period which shall be covered shall be predetermined such as monthly, quarterly, annually or any other set period. For all practical purposes, in the consideration of sewage treatment plant operation and performance, a report on an annual basis not only appears to be the most widely accepted but also has proven to be most effective as a means of advising and informing the governing body such as the Village Board, City Council or the Board of Sewer Commissioners as to the status of the sewerage system and sewage treatment plant. The report should not only include data to show the effectiveness of sewage treatment but should also include cost data of labor, chemicals, power and for any other items that may have a bearing on the operation of the sewage treatment plant in question.

Furthermore, deficiencies such as physicial limitations of plant capacity should be included. For example, it may be that while the sewage treatment plant was properly designed and in satisfactory operation from a hydraulic loading, an increase in the organic loading may develop due to the installation of household garbage disposal units resulting in inadequate sludge digestion capacity. These facts should be brought out in the report and recommendations made for the correction of the apparent deficiencies. In this manner, the governing body and anyone to whom the report is directed becomes aware that a problem in operation exists due to factors other than operation. It then becomes the responsibility of the governing body to recommend budgetary provisions to increase the deficient units in the plant to correct the problem.

Another very important reason for a report of the operation of a sewage treatment plant on an annual basis is the education of the public. Operators should obtain the cooperation of their respective governing bodies in making available to the local press a copy of the report each year. Experience has shown that local newspaper editors are most cooperative and in many instances do give wide coverage on the reporting of sewage treatment operation when such information is made available to them. The annual report can be and in many instances has been the basis for an annual news story. One newspaper has taken an annual report of the operation of a sewerage system and sewage department plant and has developed a series of six articles appearing daily for a week. In this series, a certain phase of operation was dealt with each day with the final article a discussion of the effect of the effluent on the receiving water course. These articles written for the average news reader were developed in such a way that there was no doubt in any readers mind that there was a sewage treatment plant but that such a plant had a beneficial effect on the receiving stream, protected bathing and fish life as well as downstream water supplies and, therefore, was a definite asset to the community and the surrounding area. In other words there was no doubt in the average readers mind that the community and general area could not develop and prosper without a sewage treatment plant.

Now, what affect has this series of articles or publicity had on the superintendent of sewage treatment or operator who took the time and the effort to prepare the report.

There was no question that the public, if they did not already know, soon learned who was responsible for plant operation and in like manner responsible for maintaining the water course free from objectionable pollution. Therefore, the stature of the operator in the community was elevated immeasurably. The sum and substance of a good and amicable relationship between the operator and the public through the medium of the press has been a foundation for a sound public relations program which has among other advantages enhanced the stature of the operator in his community. This was reflected by the granting of a substantial increase in salary for his efforts in reporting and establishing workable relationship between himself and his governing body and most important of all, the public or taxpayers who pay for the necessary improvements.

With a sound public relations program in effect, this becomes an effective channel of communication between the operator through the governing body and to the public. In other words, it is a two way street.

While it is realized that the preparation of reports requires a development of technique or ability which is not found in all operators. First and foremost is that the data and facts presented shall be accurate and complete and should be prepared in such a manner so as to leave no doubt in the mind of the person or persons intended to receive and read the report what the report is supposed to portray.

Following are some points that should be considered in the preparation of a report:

1. Introduction—This should be merely a few short paragraphs or sentences to proved a proper background to the reader.

2. Body of Report—This should include a description of the various components in the treatment process, statements relative to the quantities of labor, chemicals, power, etc. used, the flow, amounts of solids removed, gas produced, etc. Included in the body of the report should be charts or tables to demonstrate what has been related in the narrative portion. It is desirable to include appropriate snapshots or other pictures of plant components to make the narrative portion more understandable.

3. Conclusion—This is a summary of the items in the body of the report pointing out the effect of the plant operation on the receiving body of water or stream any deficiencies in plant structures and

equipment which might have had a degrading effect of the effectiveness of the sewage treatment plant. Appropriate statements should be made in the form of recommendations to correct the deficiencies pointed out and demonstrated in the report.

AWARDS FOR OPERATION REPORTS

In many places reports of operation of sewage treatment plants are required at regular intervals. Even when not required officially, these should be prepared by an alert operator on an annual basis at least. Many of the local associations of sewage treatment plant operators have established service awards for outstanding reports of operation. The Water Pollution Control Federation has established awards for the preparation of annual reports. This system of awards is known as the William D. Hatfield Award established by the Federation in 1955.

The purpose of the William D. Hatfield Award is to recognize operators of sewage and waste treatment plants who are doing an outstanding job in performance of their duties as well as to operators demonstrating distinguished professionalism. The aspects of plant operation upon which the award is based serve these purposes:

1. Encourage better public relations between the plant operator and the public.
2. Recognize businesslike accounting of expenditure of funds and care of the treatment plant and accessories entrusted to the operator.
3. Recognize the outstanding reports which serve the requirements of the operator's superior officials and provide a basis for recommendations by the operator for improvements to his plant for better efficiency of treatment and economy of operation.
4. Advancement of the art and knowledge of sewage and waste treatment by dissemination to other engineers and operators the basic information and data concerning a particular plant and process through papers, articles, meetings and reports.

The schedule entitles each Member Association to name one of its operator members to receive the Federation's Hatfield Award, provided the operator has not previously been the recipient of such an award. Operators of industrial wastes treatment plants as well as operators of municipal and privately-owned sewage treatment plants are eligible. Each nominee must be an Active Member of the Member Association.

Basis of Nomination.

The New York Water Pollution Control Association has adopted the following procedure and criteria for selecting its winner of this award each year:

1. Reports must be printed, mimeographed or typewritten. The length is optional. However, discretion must be used in the presentation of sufficient background material so that the operating data will have significant meaning. Operating data should include 12 consecutive months of operation not earlier than the previous July 1 and not later than March 31 of the year of the report. It is logical

to assume that definite conclusions can be drawn from an analysis of the data. From these conclusions, recommendations are made for a future plan of action.

2. Three copies of the report shall be sent to the Executive Secretary of the New York Water Pollution Control Association.

3. Three awards are made by the NYWPCA annually, one in each of the following population groups:
   (a) Less than 10,000 or population equivalent.
   (b) From 10,000 to 100,000 or population equivalent.
   (c) Greater than 100,000 or population equivalent.

4. As a guide, the rating awards committee has adopted the following schedule in the grading of the reports:

Item	Maximum Percentage Points
a. Efficiency of treatment, considering available facilities and effects of plant effluents on receiving waters	25
b. Good Housekeeping	10
c. Public Relations	10
d. In-service training and certification of subordinate operators	5
e. Emergency operation	5
f. Compilation of and dissemination of routine operation data to regulatory agencies and to the profession	15
g. Preparation and dissemination of annual report	15
h. Preventative maintenance and safety	10
i. General administration	5
	100

CHAPTER 13

MAINTENANCE OF PLANT AND EQUIPMENT

The term maintenance in an engineering sense may be defined as the art of keeping plant equipment, structures and other related facilities in a suitable condition to perform the services for which they were intended.

Maintenance should be carried out in a manner which prevents emergencies or unscheduled shut-downs. There are three factors which must be considered in the field of maintenance, namely: design, construction and operation. If the basic design is good and the facility is constructed with the best of material in a workmanlike manner, operation should be accomplished with a minimum of maintenance. Plans or blueprint designs of the plant showing the dimensions of each unit and all pipes, valves, gates, etc. should be available for ready reference.

The provision and regular use of water under pressure for cleaning and washing tanks, lines, channels, etc. is essential for the proper maintenance and operation of modern sewage treatment plants.

All maintenance requires considerable skill, which can only be acquired by experience, study and practice. Basically, any maintenance program should start with good housekeeping and should observe the following simple rules:

1. Keep a clean, neat and orderly plant.
2. Establish a systematic (both inside and outside) plan for execution of daily operation.
3. Establish a routine schedule for inspection and lubrication.
4. Keep data and records of each piece of equipment with emphasis on unusual incidents and faulty operating conditions.
5. Observe safety measures.

Too much emphasis cannot be placed on record keeping. An operator from a review of such records can determine the weaknesses of various pieces of equipment and will be able to determine which repair parts should be kept in stock.

Such records may be kept on cards, one card for each piece of equipment. On these cards should be kept a record of regular periodic lubrication, inspections, cleaning and replacement of worn parts and other data which is felt of importance to record. The date when the next regular servicing of the equipment is scheduled should appear on the card where it can be easily seen. In some plants, in addition to the cards a lubrication record should be kept. On this record, the equipment is listed as well as instructions for lubricating, including the type of oil suggested and the frequency of lubrication. From this record the operator should be able to see when equipment should be lubricated again. A very helpful scheme for planning preventive maintenance is to review the maintenance cards and set up ahead of time lists of operations to be done on certain dates. If the plants and list are small the items can be entered in advance on a memo calendar pad. For larger plants the lists can be filed by date or code and simply noted ahead of time on a calendar.

EQUIPMENT INSPECTION AND SERVICE RECORD

Worthington Raw Sewage Pump No. 3   Main Pump Room

Name Plate Data

(Enter here all data from Pump Name Plate)

Date	Work Done	Init.	Remarks
9-5-54	Installed 5 rings of new packing	JB	
9-18-54	Checked grease in upper & lower bearing	DB	
10-5-54	Lubricated magnetic drive	DB	
12-15-54	Removed impeller for inspection	JB	Pump not pumping at rating-Impeller badly worn
12-28-54	Installed new impeller	RT	
12-29-54	Adjusted packing to correct leaking	RT	
3-5-55	Checked grease in upper & lower bgs.	DB	
4-3-55	Lubricated motor	DB	
5-15-55	Replaced wearing rings	DM	
6-15-55	Installed 5 rings of new packing	JB	
6-28-55	Lubricated and checked magnetic drive	RT	

	SERVICE RECORD		
Date	Work Done	Init.	Remarks
7-2-55	Upper bearing noisy; reported to Supt.	JB	
8-3-55	Upper bearing flushed and added grease	RT	
8-15-55	Bearing still noisy. Replaced bearing	RT	
10-4-55	Lubricated motor	DB	

FIGURE 19

Typical Equipment Inspection & Service Record Card

For any program to be successful, it must be accepted by the plant personnel. Sometimes this will make or break the entire program. Unless the personnel can be sold on the value and importance of such a program the entire plan will fail. The cards should be simple and instructions regarding the routine work to be done concise and clear. A very clear account of a good preventive maintenance program is given in references at the end of this chapter.

A typical equipment inspection and service record card is shown in Figure 19.

All manufacturers of equipment provide certain basic information which normally is derived from years of experience and should be studied carefully by the operator of a sewage plant. The information should include the following:

1. Recommended installation instructions.
2. Lubrication instructions.
3. Operation instructions.
4. Procedures for dismantling and re-assembling.
5. Parts list and repair order instructions.

Any maintenance program for a particular piece of equipment should be in accordance with the manufacturers' recommendations.

In order for any maintenance program to work effectively four basic elements must be followed:

1. Thorough knowledge of the equipment.
2. Use of proper tools.
3. Adequate repair parts.
4. Planned program.

ELECTRICAL EQUIPMENT

Practically all plants depend on electricity for operation. No plant can operate continually without a maintenance program to keep all electrical units functioning efficiently. It is well known that 90 per cent of motor failures are due to four causes; dirt, moisture, friction and vibration. A routine cleaning program eliminates dirt. Anti-moisture precautions are effective in combating moisture, proper oil and grease tend to eliminate friction and regular daily inspections check for vibration. Electrical control equipment should be checked regularly for tightness and to see that moving parts are free, contact pressures firm and shunts unfrayed. Controls should also be checked to see that they are operating at rated voltage. Most important of all is to see that all electrical controls are kept clean and dry.

Every six months each starter should be checked to be sure that the tripping element is free to offer protection to the motor. If the contact points are pitted or corroded, the tips can be replaced or filed smooth. When a starter trips out, the cause should be found before it is started again. Dirty contacts should be cleaned, and the cabinet cleaned with a blower or vacuum type cleaner when necessary.

Most motors are protected by a fused main line switch and an across-the-line or step-type starter. Fuses and thermal units usually are rated at 125 per cent of the nameplate amperage. Each new motor should be checked to see that adequate protection is provided. Over-size heaters or a "jumper" does not furnish protection and may permit destruction of a motor.

LUBRICATION

Lubrication is probably the most important function of a maintenance program and if possible should be the responsibility of one man. Economy dictates that the best quality of oils and grease obtainable should be used. Again it cannot be overstressed that the manufacturers' recommendation should be studied carefully and followed as they know the lubricating requirements of the machines they design and sell.

It is important to warn against over lubrication of motor bearings. This has been the cause of an untold number of motor failure. The present trend is toward the use of more sealed bearings which require no additional grease for their lifetime.

PUMPS

Sewage pumps are perhaps the most important piece of equipment in any sewage plant. Normally, a breakdown of pumping equipment means that sewage must be by-passed. A complete understanding of the pump construction and operation is essential to provide proper maintenance. Daily inspection should be made giving special attention to the following:

1. Bearings—heat and noise.
2. Motors—operating speed.
3. Control Equipment—cleanliness and condition.
4. Pump Operation—vibration and noise.
5. Packing Glands—excessive leakage.

Sewage is more difficult to pump than water. The presence of grit and sand in sewage has an abrasive effect on pumps. Rags, sticks and almost any object one might name are apt to be present. Each presents a problem in sewage pumping. If the pump that has been installed has not been carefully designed to pump sewage, the operator will be in difficulty.

Centrifugal pumps are widely used for pumping sewage. In order to better understand the performance and operating characteristics, the operator should become familiar with the pump curve which is supplied by the manufacturer for each pump. A typical pump curve is shown on Figure 20. Pump curves usually show three curves on one sheet. The head-capacity curve shows the discharge in gallons per minute (gpm) which the pump will deliver against various heads when operating at the proper speed. A little study of this curve shows that as the head increases the discharge decreases, until there is no further discharge. The head at which this happens is called the shut-off head.

The second curve shows the efficiency at which the pump operates at various points on the head-capacity curve.

The third curve shows the horsepower input required to pump at various points on the curve. This is called the brake horsepower curve. By computing the total head at which the pump is operating, the gallons

TYPICAL PUMP CURVE

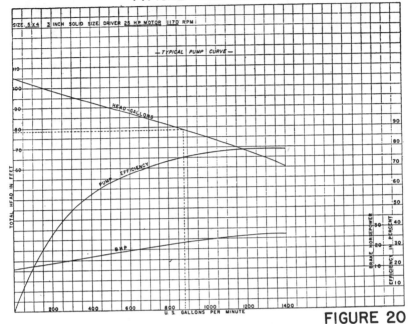

FIGURE 20

pumped can be found from the curve. Likewise, the power required by the pump as well as the pump efficiency can be computed or read from the curve for any set of conditions. Large centrifugal pumps usually operate at slow speeds to minimize wear and maintenance costs.

Figures 21, 22 and 23 together with the formulae in Chapter 15 shows methods of computing total pumping head and required horsepower.

On the pump curves, Figure 20, dotted lines indicate how values can be read from these curves. The pump for which these curves were prepared, running at a speed of 1170 revolutions per minute (rpm), will deliver 880 gpm at a total head of 79 feet. The brake horsepower (bhp) of the pump is 23 and the pump efficiency 75 per cent. For a motor 92 per cent efficient, the hp should be 25. The shutoff head or head at which this pump would deliver no water is 105 feet.

The only moving part of a centrifugal pump is the impeller rotating in a casing. The impeller is carried on a shaft and is supported by thrust bearings and one or more guide bearings, depending on the length of the shaft. In submerged type pumps the guide bearing or intermediate bearings cannot be ball bearings since there is no way of keeping the sewage which would cause rust and corrosion out of the bearing. These bearings are built with sleeve type guide bearings of bronze. The thrust bearing is usually a ball bearing located above the level of the sewage near the motor. The greasing of these bearings should be carefully considered and the manufacturers' instructions carefully followed. Over greasing should be avoided as too much grease will cause damage as fast as lack

161

of lubrication. Where bearings do not require lubrication daily or where damage can result from over lubrication, it is not wise to leave a pressure type fitting in place. It is better to use a plug which can be replaced with a fitting when the bearing requires lubrication. The plug at the underside of the bearing which serves as a relief vent should be opened while the bearing is being lubricated, and the bearing operated for a few minutes with the plug out so that excess grease can work its way out of the bearing.

The manufacturers' recommendations should be followed in choosing a packing. A soft asbestos packing impregnated with graphite is commonly used especially if grease or water seals are not provided. The packing should be well lubricated since it increases the efficiency of the pump by reducing air leakage and prolongs the life of the packing and shaft by reducing friction. Spring loaded grease cups can be used, but an external supply of water is the most effective lubricant and seal. *Seal water should never be obtained by direct connection with a potable supply because of the danger of cross connections.* A separate system should be used, and a pressure greater than the operating head of the pump maintained.

Never tighten a packing follower too tightly. A trickle of water should be allowed to keep the gland cool. A wrench is not desirable since tightening the nuts finger tight is all that is required. If the packing box leaks excessively, remove the packing and repack with fresh packing. If the shaft is scored, the shaft should be replaced or the life of the packing will be shortened. Never repack with part new and old packing, and when repacking be sure that the water seal ring is in proper position in the stuffing box to receive the seal water. A water seal serves a dual purpose in that, as well as lubricating, it keeps gritty material from entering the packing box and thus increases the life of the packing and shaft.

SLUDGE PUMPS

The most common type of sludge pump, the plunger pump, is a positive displacement type which will pump mixtures of sludge, gas and air as well as liquids. The packing should be tight enough to prevent leakage and prevent air from being sucked into the cylinder. Too tight a packing will result in scored pistons, broken shear pins and even cracked cylinders. A liberal use of oil around the packing will prolong the life of the packing and make it possible to keep it tight enough to prevent leakage. Ball valves must operate freely and should be replaced when worn. Never tighten the eccentric flange and eccentric body so tight that pins cannot shear.

TOOLS

Good maintenace depends on the availability of proper tools to do the job. An important consideration in caring for a good stock of tools is to have regular places of storage for them. A plant operating around the clock, seven days a week presents a real problem in maintaining order in tool assembly. If free access is allowed to the tool racks they are readily used but often not put back. A good solution seems to lie in the plan of locking up the tools and assigning responsibility to one man on the day shift. A duplicate key should be on file. The night shift can be allowed access to a minimum number of necessary tools such as an adjustable end wrench, pliers, screw driver, several pipe wrenches and a hammer.

PLANT STRUCTURES

Mechanical equipment should be kept in perfect working order. Moving parts should be regularly lubricated. Pipes and air lines should be kept open and free from obstructions and accumulations of any sort. Where there are two units or where it is possible to cut a unit without seriously interfering with subsequent treatment, a complete cleaning of the units should be made at regularly scheduled intervals.

Sewage plant structures such as channels, tanks and wet wells should be dewatered at least once a year for inspection and protective coatings applied as necessary. Lead base paints should not be used in a sewage plant where it is possible to have hydrogen sulfide present. There are many good special paints on the market which are satisfactory for use in sewage plants.

For metal and concrete in contact with sewage, sludge or sludge gas, the bituminous or asphaltic base paints applied over bituminous or asphaltic primers on clean surfaces usually give satisfactory service. However, these materials are black and not attractive. In locations where moisture and fume conditions are less severe and appearance is important, the colored alkyd resin, chlorinated rubber base, and vinyl paints and enamels can be used on woodwork, concrete, brick and plaster and metal surfaces in the order given, according to the severity of the service to be encountered.

Screening devices and collector mechanisms in tanks should be maintained in such a manner that safety devices used to protect the equipment will function when the units become overloaded. Practically all motors are protected by a thermal relay which will trip out the motor before the motor has been damaged. It is important that the overload device be in accordance with the manufacturers' recommendations. If shear pin or other devices are used, never use a shear pin of greater strength than that recommended. Such practice can result in serious damage and costly repairs.

Chains on straight line collectors should be kept tight enough to prevent flights from chattering and causing uneven wear. Wearing shoes on flights should be kept tight and replaced when worn to prevent flights from dragging on the bottom of tanks.

Digesters and gas collection systems are normally protected by pressure relief and vacuum breakers, flame traps, and pressure regulating devices. It is important that such devices be kept in good operating condition to prevent serious damage to structures and to minimize the possibility of fire or explosion.

Comminutor, barminutor and other submerged screening and chopping device should be inspected periodically by draining the channels. Any collection of materials left in the drained channel should be removed. The cutting mechanism should be examined and any damaged cutting teeth be replaced. Shear bars which show considerable wear should be replaced. The manufacturers' instruction book should give the allowable wear on the shear bars. Since these types of units are cutting devices, it is important to maintain good cutting edges for efficient operation.

Chlorinators should be maintained in a manner to prevent all chlorine leakage. Chlorine in the atmosphere is very corrosive and eventually destructive to chlorinator parts, and electrical and mechanical equipment located in the proximity of the chlorinator installation. The presence of a chlorine leak can be detected easily by the nose and can be located by an ammonia swab held near but not on a leaking part. Ammonia in the presence of chlorine produces a white vapor. Some metal plating is damaged by contact with the liquid, however. Even a small leak should be stopped as soon as detected.

Sludge drying beds should be resanded when half the original sand depth is lost. All dirty sand should be carefully removed and a new sand of the proper uniformity and coarseness should be used. Use of too coarse a sand will permit solids to pass down into the old sand where they would not be accessible for removal, causing subsurface clogging. Sand which is too fine or dirty will retard drainage. A good practice is to use washed sand having a uniformity coefficient of 4.0 or less and an effective size between 0.3 and 0.5 mm. A good concrete sand usually has satisfactory characteristics.

PIPE LINES

The following color scheme for purposes of standardization has been recommended for the piping systems in a sewage treatment plant.

Sludge line	Brown
Gas line	Red
Potable water line	Blue
Chlorine line	Yellow
Sewage line	Gray
Compressed air line	Green
Heating water lines for digesters or bldgs.	Blue with 6 in. red bands spaced 30 in. apart

BUILDINGS

Maintenance of mechanical parts of the plant should not be the only item of interest. Included in the list of items to be looked after on buildings are roofs, gutters, skylights, windows and door frames, screens, metal work such as motor and pump housings, metal railings, grating and miscellaneous metal coverings.

Roof inspection should be made yearly. The commonly used gravel and tarred felt roof needs an occasional recoating. Often it is best to obtain the services of a competent local roofing man rather than to attempt the job with plant personnel. Gutters, where they have been provided, should be cleaned and painted. The protection of metal or concrete surfaces is important both to protect the surfaces from corrosion and to lend an attractive appearance to the structure. In painting any structure the surface should be thoroughly cleaned, old and loose paint removed and even taken down to bare metal, if possible. If this is not done, the labor spent on painting will not be fully realized, as the paint will not hold to the surface for any length of time.

Consideration should be given to the purchase of quality paints even though they may be more costly. Experience has shown them to be more economical in the long run. Operators can experiment with different types of paint to determine which type best suits their needs. Test areas should be chosen which are subject to the conditions to be encountered and different types of paint applied to these areas. The surface should be inspected every three months and a record kept of the condition of the paint over a long period of time so that the suitability of the paint can be evaluated. Lead paints should not be used where hydrogen sulfide may be present because dark colored lead sulfide will be formed. Zinc-titanium pigment paints will not discolor and are usually satisfactory for general work on plant buildings.

Painting serves the twofold purpose of preventing deterioration of the structure as well as providing a pleasing appearance. The operator should be sure that the exterior as well as the interior painting of all the buildings is well maintained.

PLANT GROUNDS

General Appearance of Plant. One of the aims of a sewage plant operator should be to interest the taxpayers in their plant and to help them learn something about their investment. He can be helped in securing his goal by keeping the plant in a neat and tidy condition and by doing what he can to beautify the plant and its surroundings to make it more attractive. The operator will find that this will pay dividends if done wisely and not extravagantly and will help to secure needed funds for operating purposes and for enlarging and improving sewage treatment plants.

Not infrequently when a plant is completed, the grounds are left in an untidy condition. As well as grading, roads and lawns must be built. In grading, it is well to remember that steep grades should be avoided where possible. It is sometimes better to cover a steep slope with vines instead of grass. At established plants the lawn should be kept well trimmed and use should be made of sewage sludge, as a soil conditioner where it is available. Good results from the use of sludge may well help find a market for the surplus sludge. The planting of deciduous or evergreen trees in appropriate locations does a lot to blend the treatment plant into the surroundings. In general, a sewage plant should be made to look attractive. It may take time but it is never too early to take the initial steps to make the plant area look like a park, of which the whole community can be justly proud. Civic groups as well as schools should be encouraged to take the opportunity of inspecting a well laid out, well cared for and well operated plant. When groups do come the operator should see that they are cordially received and guided through the plant with explanations and descriptions suited to the group.

SEWER MAINTENANCE

Because many sewage plant operators are responsible for the operation of the sewer system tributary to the plant, sewer maintenance has a logical place in this manual.

A sewer maintenance program is a procedure of continuous inspection of the sewer system including appurtenances, and should cover each section with reasonable frequency to accomplish the early detection and prevention of stoppages, deterioration or faulty operation. Sewer maintenance is probably the most important function of the operation of a sewer system but it is usually considered the least pleasant and most tedious.

The prime requisite for efficient sewer maintenance is an up-to-date plan of the system with sufficient survey measurements to permit a cleaning crew to locate manholes promptly when needed. Areas where there have been recurrence of trouble should be clearly marked. Field notes should be kept to refresh the crew as to the nature of past trouble. The practice as to the frequency of routine inspection varies according to size and age of systems, the extent of past troubles and quite often, by the personnel available for the job. Most sewer maintenance programs give first attention to sewers which by records show poor performance, usually as a result of flat grades or tree roots. If personnel is available, it would be desirable to have routine inspections as follows:

Large trunk sewers	Annually
Smaller sub-trunk sewers	Semi-annually
Inverted siphons	Weekly
Storm water overflows and regulators	During and after storms
Lateral sewers	Every three months

The program should be set up to carry out the following objectives:

1. Inspection of sewers and appurtenances, including testing of manholes and structures for hazardous gases, particularly toxic types.
2. Cleaning.
3. Repairs.
4. Checking for sources of infiltration and surface waters entering a sanitary sewer system.
5. Checking for sources of unusual amounts of industrial wastes.

The most common obstructions in sewers, in the order of greatest frequency are: (1) roots, (2) accumulations of grease, (3) grit, (4) miscellaneous debris.

SEWAGE PUMPING STATIONS

Regular inspections and cleaning of the bottom and sides of wet wells including the removal of grit are desirable. Flow tubes in wells used to control pump operation require frequent inspection to assure proper operation. Bar screens installed ahead of wells should be cleaned daily at which time inspection should be made of all pumps and mechanical equipment such as comminutors or barminutors.

CLEANING OF SEWERS

The most common method of removing roots from sewers is by use of flexible type rods with cutters. Roots may also be removed with the use of winches and cables using cutting drags. Attempts have been made in many areas to control the growth of roots by use of copper sulfate. Some cities have attempted to repair sewer joints where there is a recurrence of root trouble but the cost of this method is generally prohibitive. The only positive cure is to remove trees causing the trouble. In some instances control of planting of poplar and willow trees which are the worst offenders has been attempted.

Accumulation of greases is normally removed by flushing, by use of rods and cutters, or by means of winches using cable with buckets.

Grit in small quantities may be removed by flushing. Larger quantities must be removed with use of winches with cable and buckets. Grit may also be removed by means of "go-devils" or turbine type agitators. In both cases water is used as the vehicle to carry the sand or grit. The grit problem in some sewers may be aggravated because of the increased use of garbage grinders. Miscellaneous debris is usually removed by a combination use of rods and cutters or augers followed by cable and buckets.

In many sewer cleaning operations, it is a general policy to finish by pulling through the sewer a stiff wire brush which fits tightly and scours the entire periphery of the sewer. There are several specialized methods of cleaning sewers such as by the use of a sewer hoe, beach ball, or one of several power or water operated revolving devices. If the equipment used gets caught in a sewer, it may be necessary to excavate and cut into the sewer to remove the equipment. Such a practice is very costly and should be a reminder to use equipment which has been designed to be as near fool proof as possible. Experience will establish the best means and methods of sewer cleaning.

Sewers are constructed for the purpose of protecting health, welfare, and convenience of the public and every effort should be made to maintain sewers in a manner to minimize inconvenience.

Probably no other public utility is misused to so great a degree as is a public sewerage system, and every municipality should have regulations with which to provide some degree of control. Such regulations should provide for the control of connections to the system, materials which may be discharged into sewers, quantities which may be discharged and penalties for violations of the regulations as well as for malicious damage by vandals.

SPECIAL REFERENCES FOR CHAPTER 13

Sanders, Sewage & Industrial Wastes—Pp. 329, Vol. 26, March '54
Ref. & Data Sect. Water & Sewage Works—June '55

CHAPTER 14

TREATMENT PLANT SAFETY

Although this manual is intended primarily for the sewage treatment plant operator, it is known that the operators of many small plants have responsibilities in connection with sewer maintenance and, since the safety measures that apply to a sewage treatment plant apply equally well to sewers, both will be discussed here.

"Accidents do not just happen—they are caused!," are the opening words of an excellent series of articles written by LeRoy W. Van Kleeck, the Chairman of the Committee on the Occupational Hazards in the Operation of Sewage Works of the Federation of Sewage and Industrial Wastes Association.

Accident prevention is the result of thoughtfulness, and the application of a few basic principles and knowledge of the hazards involved. It has been said that the "A, B, C" of accident prevention is

"ALWAYS BE CAREFUL."

However, one must learn how to be careful and what to avoid. With this knowledge one can then always think and practice safety. One good way of bringing out hazards is by conference and suggestion. This has been the responsibility of a committee in some plants.

It may seem that accidents at any one sewage treatment plant are infrequent, but on a country-wide basis, the frequency is far greater than usually realized. The Federation of Sewage and Industrial Wastes Association Manual of Practice on Safety gives insurance data on the trend of such accidents. Sewage works deaths reported are considerably higher on a man-hour basis than those occurring in machine shops. Deaths in sewer manholes have been as many as twelve in a two-year period and, in one case, two men died and two others were overcome, all in the same manhole. In Westchester County, New York, 1956, two men lost their lives by entering a manhole on a large diameter sewer to rescue a third man who had collapsed. The rescuers apparently were overcome and were swept away through the large sewer. Their bodies were recovered five hours later, a half mile down stream. Manholes have been classified by one writer as "Death Traps."

THE HAZARDS

The overall dangers of accident are much the same whether in manholes, pumping stations or treatment plants. These hazards may be:

    A. Physical Injuries.

    B. Body Infections.

    C. Dangers from Noxious Gases or Vapors and Oxygen Deficiency.

    D. Radiological Hazards.

These hazards may, in some cases, be inherent in design that, once recognized, can be readily corrected or can, at least, be guarded against by warnings and by proper safety procedures. Safety design features are well covered in the Federation of Sewage and Industrial Wastes Association's, Manual of Practice No. 1.

PREVENTION OF PHYSICAL INJURIES

The prevention of physical injuries begins with good housekeeping. Tools, parts and other things should not be left lying around. Warning signs, railings and covers in place can protect against low piping, open tanks and open manholes or hatches. The simple knowledge that bending the knees and lifting with muscles of the legs can save many strained or injured backs or ruptures.

Manholes. For work in manholes in streets, safety requires full protective measures from traffic hazards. Warning signs and red flags should be set up at a suitable distance on each side of the manhole. On extremely busy streets, it may be desirable to station men to flag down and detour fast moving vehicles. On wide streets, the service truck can be stationed on the side of the manhole toward the on-coming traffic. It is important that sufficient workers be provided for the job at hand. There should be at least two men at the top when one goes below. A cage or guard device around a manhole adds protection and aids entering and leaving the manhole. Manhole covers should be lifted with a hook made to fit a ventilation hole or lifting notch. Sometimes a piece of flat car spring about eighteen inches long is helpful as a pry or wedge. A pick-axe may slip and cause injury or, if struck hard, may give off an igniting spark. Unless a cover is very heavy, it is safer for one man to handle it alone.

Two men working as a team must carefully coordinate their efforts to avoid injuries to hands or feet. A cover should not be partially removed except to obtain an air sample, after which it should be replaced immediately. Before descending into a manhole, note should be taken of the width, spacing, and arrangement of manhole rungs and, if staggered, particular care must be taken to get started with the proper foot and to avoid falling. Each rung should be tested during descent and weight distributed between feet and arms. Steel rungs may lose their galvanizing and corrode to a dangerous extent. Rubbers on the feet help to prevent slips and prevent infection.

Safety Belts. On small sewers, no one should enter a manhole deeper than the height of his chin without wearing an approved safety belt with rope attached. For entering manholes on sewers greater than twenty-four inches in diameter the safety line should always be worn, regardless of manhole depth, to guard against the possibility of slipping into the sewer. In an emergency, when a safety belt may not be at hand, a stout rope tied snugly under the arms with a square or other non-slip knot may be the means of saving a life. In either case, at least two men should be at the top of a manhole at all times when a third man is inside in order to handle the life line and help him out if necessary. The safety belt should also be worn when entering any enclosed spaces around the treatment plant, such as pump suction wells, empty digestion tanks, sludge storage wells or any other space where access is difficult and assistance may be needed to climb out.

Lighting. Wherever sunlight can be reflected by the use of mirrors into a manhole, tank or other closed space, it gives excellent and safe lighting. Otherwise, even in the absence of flammable gases, safe practice dictates the use of an explosion-proof lamp—several types of which are on the market. Around the treatment plant only grounded, explosion-proof extension lamps or explosion-proof portable lamps should be used in hazardous locations.

Electrical Hazards. Electrical shock hazards are present in many of the older pumping stations and sewage treatment plants. New types, enclosed switch gear is quite safe, but the older open types of switch boards need to be approached with care. A rubber mat on the floor is an added safety factor for either type. Grounding of all equipment is essential. Portable power tools should be equipped with ground wire and special outlet and plug. Accidents can be, and have been, caused by such equipment not being grounded. When work is to be done on equipment controlled by a switch located at some distance from the equipment, the switch should be tagged out with a red card to prevent others from closing the circuit.

Ladders. Vertical ladders over ten feet in height should be equipped with a hoop cage, surrounding the ladder in such a manner that a man climbs within the cage and is protected.

Fire Extinguishers. It is recommended that fire extinguishers suitable for electrical fires be provided in readily available places at pumping stations and treatment plants. Extinguishers of the carbon dioxide or carbon tetrachloride type do not injure equipment. However, in closed spaces, there is a danger of asphyxiation from noxious fumes which may result from the use of the carbon dioxide or carbon tetrachloride types.

PREVENTION OF BODY INFECTIONS

Workers who come into contact with sewage are exposed to all the hazards of water-borne diseases, including typhoid fever, para-typhoid fever, amoebic dysentery, infectious jaundice and other intestinal infections. Tetanus and skin infections must also be guarded against.

First Aid. Except for minor injuries, wounds should be treated by a doctor and reported for possible workmen's compensation. Service trucks and treatment plants should have first aid kits, and as many of the personnel as possible should have had Red Cross first aid instruction. No cut or scratch is too minor to receive attention. A two per cent tincture of iodine or tincture of methiolate should be immediately applied to all wounds or cuts.

Wearing Apparel. Rubberized cotton gloves are inexpensive and afford good protection to the hands. In wet places, boots or rubber overshoes protect the feet from dampness and infection. Work clothes or cover-alls should be worn in dirty places such as manholes, and should be laundered frequently. Some sewage treatment plants have been provided with washing machines or laundry service. For extremely dirty jobs, such as cleaning out a pump suction well, there are available rubberized fabric suits with hoods which can be washed off with a hose.

Personal Habits. Smoking should *not* be done in sewers nor in other hazardous locations. It is practically impossible to avoid contamination by sewage of the ends of pipes, cigars or cigarettes. Smoking is a potential source of ignition for any flammable vapors present.

"Keeping the hands below one's collar," while at work in sewers, pump suction wells or while handling sewage or sludge is an excellent rule. A majority of infections reach the body by way of the mouth, nose, eyes or ears. Hands of sewage workers should be washed before smoking or eating. Soap preparations requiring no water rinse are available for field use. Of course, the common drinking cup should be banned and paper cups used. Typhoid inoculations are recommended and many sewer departments provide this service for their workers. For protection against tetanus, a series of two injections of tetanus toxoid (one month apart) should be given and repeated every five years.

NOXIOUS GASES OR VAPORS, AND OXYGEN DEFICIENCY

A few definitions are in order here. *Gas* is a state of matter in which the movement of molecules is practically unrestricted.

Vapor is the gaseous phase of a substance which substance can exist also in the form of a liquid at common temperatures and pressures. Water vapor and gasoline vapor are examples. A *Noxious gas or vapor* is one that is directly or indirectly injurious or destructive to the health or life of humans. They may cause burns, explosions, asphyxiation or poisoning. Non-poisonous gases may asphyxiate simply by mechanically excluding oxygen.

Sewer Gas is a misnomer since it is not a single but a mixture of gases from the decomposition of organic matter. It is actually sewage sludge gas with a high content of carbon dioxide and varying amounts of methane, hydrogen, hydrogen sulfide and a small amount of oxygen. The hazard is usually from an explosive mixture of methane and oxygen or, more often, from an oxygen deficiency. This definition does not include the extraneous gases or vapors which may be present in sewers from gas main leaks or from gasoline or other volatile solvents which frequently find their way into sewers.

Oxygen Deficiency. Air normally contains by volume about 21 per cent oxygen and 79 per cent nitrogen and traces of other gases. Air containing less than 13 per cent oxygen by volume is decidedly dangerous to humans. Oxygen deficiency appears to be the leading cause of death in sewers. It has even been the apparent cause of death in one manhole on a new system where there was no ventilation and for some obscure reason oxygen had been depleted to a point too low for human existence. It is likely that some deaths attributed to hydrogen sulfide may actually have been caused by an oxygen deficiency.

Explosive Range. Flammable or burnable gases, when mixed with air (oxygen) in certain proportions, will explode violently upon ignition. No explosion will occur when the mixture is outside this range. The minimum concentration of a gas-air or vapor-air mixture which will explode if ignited is known as the lower explosive limit, while the maximum concentration for explosion is called the upper explosive limit. These are respectively the leanest and richest mixtures needed for an explosion. The accompanying table gives the explosive range of the gases and vapors most apt to be encountered in sewage work.

Hazardous Locations. The places which are most likely to be dangerous from a noxious gas or vapor situation or oxygen deficiency, and which should be carefully investigated before entering are:

1. All large trunk sewers, particularly in industrial areas.
2. Sewers located in the vicinity of gas mains or gasoline storage tanks.
3. Sewers on flat grades where solids may settle and decompose.
4. Sewers with manholes over three hundred feet apart, particularly if solid manhole covers are used and the houses connected to the sewers have main sewer traps which prevent ventilation through house stacks.
5. All sewers and manholes more than ten feet deep.
6. Any tightly covered pit, tank or valve chamber, regardless of depth.
7. Deep tanks, sludge digestion tanks and pump suction wells.

Characteristics. The characteristics of noxious gas and vapors and their most likely source, as well as the conditions leading to oxygen deficiency, are given in the accompanying table.

Detection. Detection of an existing gas or vapor hazard and then taking steps to remove or to protect against it are the sure ways to prevent accidents and loss of life. Fortunately, a fairly simple method of detection of the common hazards is available at reasonable cost. Tests should be made in the order given below. Samples may be taken through a ventilation hole in a manhole cover, under a cover removed partially, or with the cover entirely removed. Care must be taken in all cases to avoid the creation of sparks. It is common practice to test at a depth about six feet above the manhole or tank floor, assuming that lighter-than-air gases will be vented from the top. If flammable gas is detected, it is wise to continue testing for the entire depth of the structure.

Test for Flammable or Explosive Gases. These gases may be any of those which are explosive as shown in the table. They may be detected by relatively inexpensive combustible gas indicators. These instruments are battery operated units which oxidize or burn a sample of the atmosphere under test over a heated catalytic filament which is part of a balanced electrical circuit. Any combustible gas or vapor in the tested sample will unbalance the circuit, cause a deflection of an indicating needle to show on a scale the concentration of combustible gases or vapors in the sample. This scale is graduated in per cent of the lower explosive limit. For example, if methane alone were present in the sample and the scale pointer read "50 per cent," then $2\frac{1}{2}$ per cent of methane by volume is present in the atmosphere tested since the lower explosive limit of methane is 5 per cent. This would be a hazardous condition and the manhole should be ventilated and retested. In general, readings in excess of 20 per cent of the lower explosive limit should be considered hazardous. The sample is obtained by a tube or probe lowered to the desired depth in the structure and a bulb is used to aspirate the sample through the

TABLE 10

COMMON DANGEROUS GASES ENCOUNTERED IN SEWERS AND AT SEWAGE TREATMENT PLANTS*

Name of Gas	Chemical Formulae	Specific Gravity of Vapor Density** (Air = 1)	Explosive Range (% by volume in air) Lower Limit	Explosive Range (% by volume in air) Upper Limit	Common Properties (Percentages below are per cent in air by volume)	Physiological Effects (Percentages below are per cent in air by volume)	Most Common Sources in Sewers	Simplest and Cheapest Safe Method of Testing†
Oxygen (In air)	O_2	1.11	Not flammable		Colorless, odorless, tasteless, non-poisonous gas. Supports combustion.	Normal air contains 20.93% of O_2. Man tolerates down to 12%. Below 5 to 7% likely to be fatal.	Oxygen depletion from poor ventilation and absorption or chemical consumption of available O_2.	Oxygen deficiency indicator.
Gasoline Vapor	C_5H_{12} to C_9H_{20}	3.0 to 4.0	1.3	7.0	Colorless, odor noticeable in 0.03%. Flammable. Explosive.	Anesthetic effects when inhaled. 2.43% rapidly fatal. 1.1% to 2.2% dangerous for even short exposure.	Leaking storage tanks, discharges from garages, and commercial or home dry-cleaning operations.	1. Combustible gas indicator. 2. Oxygen deficiency indicator for concentrations over 0.3%.
Carbon Monoxide	CO	0.97	12.5	74.2	Colorless, odorless, tasteless, Flammable. Explosive.	Hemoglobin of blood has strong affinity for gas causing oxygen starvation. 0.2 to 0.25% causes unconsciousness in 30 minutes.	Manufactured fuel gas.	CO ampoules.
Hydrogen	H_2	0.07	4.0	74.2	Colorless, odorless, tasteless, non-poisonous, flammable. Explosive. Propagates flame rapidly; very dangerous.	Acts mechanically to deprive tissues of oxygen. Does not support life. A simple asphyxiant.	Manufactured fuel gas.	Combustible gas indicator.
Methane	CH_4	0.55	5.0	15.0	Colorless, tasteless, odorless, non-poisonous. Flame	See hydrogen.	Natural gas, marsh gas, mfg. fuel gas.	1. Combustible gas indicator.

174

Name	Formula	Sp. Gr.			Properties	Physiological Effect	Source	Testing Method
Hydrogen Sulfide	H₂S	1.19	4.3	46.0	Rotten egg odor in small concentrations but sense of smell rapidly impaired. Odor not evident at high concentrations. Colorless. Flammable. Explosive. Poisonous.	Death in few minutes at 0.2%. Paralyzes respiratory center.	Petroleum fumes, from blasting, sewer gas.	1. H₂S ampoules. 2. 5% by wt. lead acetate solution.
Carbon Dioxide	CO₂	1.53	Not flammable		Colorless, odorless, non-flammable. Not generally present in dangerous amounts unless there is already a deficiency of oxygen.	10% cannot be endured for more than a few minutes. Acts on nerves of respiration.	Issues from carbonaceous strata. Sewer gas.	Oxygen deficiency indicator.
Nitrogen	N₂	0.97	Not flammable		Colorless, tasteless. Non-flammable. Non-poisonous. Principal constituent of air (about 79%).	See hydrogen.	Issues from some rock strata. Sewer gas.	Oxygen deficiency indicator.
Ethane	C₂H₆	1.05	3.1	15.0	Colorless, tasteless, odorless, non-poisonous. Flammable. Explosive.	See hydrogen.	Natural gas.	Combustible gas indicator.
Chlorine	Cl₂	2.5	Not flammable Not explosive		Greenish yellow gas, or amber color liquid under pressure. Highly irritating and penetrating odor. Highly corrosive in presence of moisture.	Respiratory irritant, irritating to eyes and mucous membranes. 30 ppm causes coughing. 40-60 ppm dangerous in 30 minutes. 1000 ppm apt to be fatal in few breaths.	Leaking pipe connections. Overdosage.	Odor, strong ammonia on swab gives off white fumes.

*From Water and Sewage Works—Van Kleeck—August 1953.

**Gases with a specific gravity less than 1.0 are lighter than air; those more than 1.0 heavier than air.

†The first method given is the preferable testing procedure.

unit. The instruments are usually calibrated for petroleum vapors and do not give exact accuracy for other vapors. They are sufficiently close, however, so as to give a degree of accuracy which is adequate for complete safety of personnel.

Test for Hydrogen Sulfide. Lead acetate in a cotton mesh covered ampoule which may be crushed between the fingers and exposed in the atmosphere under test for one minute, turns from a yellow to brown color in the presence of hydrogen sulfide. The color is compared to a chart which indicates concentrations from 5 to 25 ppm. Precautions to be taken are given on the chart. A concentration of 20 ppm is indicated as the maximum allowable for eight hour exposure.

Test for Carbon Monoxide. Ampoules similar to those described above contain palladium chloride which, when exposed to the gas, turns from yellow to dark gray. A color chart is used to determine gas concentration up to 0.1 per cent by volume. The chart points out the precautions which should be taken. The exposure time for these ampoules is ten minutes for normal temperatures, and twenty minutes for temperatures below freezing. A maximum allowable concentration for eight hour exposure is indicated to be 100 ppm.

Test for Oxygen Deficiency. This test is made by aspirating a sample of the atmosphere through a sampling tube and over a flame in an oxygen deficiency indicator. This is an adaptation of the miner's flare safety lamp, but since it is not the same, it should never be lowered into an atmosphere where hydrogen might be present, such as in a sewer. The instrument should be equipped with a hydrogen flame flash-back arrester. Oxygen deficiency is indicated by the extinguishing or by a decrease in height of the flame. If an explosive amount of flammable gas is present, the flame will flare up and then be extinguished. The flame will usually be extinguished by an atmosphere containing less than 16 per cent of oxygen and always by one containing less than 13 per cent of oxygen. The extinguishing of the flame is a good indication, therefore, of oxygen deficiency but at elevations over 5,000 feet above sea level, the flame may continue to burn in atmosphere dangerous to life.

Unreliable Testing. The use of canaries, relying on the detection of odor alone, and even ventilation of sewers without testing may be hazardous procedures. Birds require much less oxygen than humans and can build up a tolerance to carbon monoxide. Some of the hazardous gases are odorless and continued ventilation, when a gas leak is serious, may not correct a hazardous situation. The safest method is the sure method of testing.

SUMMARY OF SAFE PRACTICES IN SEWERS, PUMP SUCTION WELLS AND OTHER ENCLOSED PLACES

Condition 1. Tests show no hazardous situation as to gases, vapors or lack of oxygen. Workmen entering sewers or enclosed places over ten feet deep should wear safety belts with at least *two* men available at the top. Even though tests show no hazards, the situation may change or the workmen may be injured. No one should smoke within the manhole and sparks from tools should be prevented by the use of non-sparking,

176

beryllium-copper alloy tools. Rubbers should be worn on the feet, and only approved safety lighting should be used. Tests should be repeated at intervals if the work is prolonged.

Condition II. Tests show noxious gases or vapors or oxygen deficiency. The structure should be thoroughly ventilated with extreme care taken to avoid ignition of flammable gas, and retested. Ventilation may be done in one of several ways:

1. By placing a canvas or metal deflector to direct natural air currents into the manhole with adjacent manhole covers removed. Moderate to strong winds are necessary.
2. A fire hose stream directed into the manhole with adjacent covers open may create sufficient draft.
3. Introduce compressed air from a hose to a point near bottom of manhole.
4. Use a portable blower with discharge hose well down in manhole, and with engine or motor-driven unit well away from manhole to prevent ignition and to keep exhaust fumes away. After thorough ventilation, and tests indicate a safe situation, proceed as in Condition I.

Condition III. Tests show a hazardous situation, but an emergency exists because of flooding or a workman may have been overcome. Workmen, in addition to the provisions of Condition I, must be equipped with the proper type of respiratory apparatus. If tools are needed, only non-sparking, beryllium-copper alloy tools should be used. Great care must be exercised to avoid all sources of ignition. *Work in flammable gas atmospheres is extremely hazardous and must never be attempted except by those fully aware of the dangers.*

GAS MASKS

Respiratory Apparatus. This type of apparatus should be relied upon only when the situation does not permit the creation of a safe atmosphere by ventilation. Most respiratory apparatus consists of a face piece with adjustable head straps so that it may be fitted snugly; a flexible hose from the mask leads to a source of safe air or oxygen supply, and a discharge valve or tube to take away the respired atmosphere. It is essential to have the face piece fit tightly so that gas cannot enter under it. The usual test for this is to pinch closed the flexible supply tube and take a quick, deep breath. The face piece, if tight, will collapse against the face.

Canister Type Masks. Canister type masks of the filter type should never be worn in manholes, pump suction wells or other places where there may be a deficiency of oxygen. They serve only to filter out or neutralize a low concentration of a particular gas for which a special canister must be supplied. With the proper canister, these masks are suitable for attending to small chlorine gas leaks where there is no oxygen deficiency and less than two per cent noxious gas. *They do not supply oxygen.*

The Hose Mask. The hose mask is suitable for all situations where a supply of fresh air can be obtained by using up to 25 feet of hose without a blower and up to 150 feet for one or two men with a blower. This is the safest and most dependable device.

Self-contained Breathing Apparatus. One type of oxygen supplying equipment consists of a canister containing a chemical, potassium tetroxide, a vigorous oxidizing agent, which supplies oxygen. *This device is not recommended for use in sewer manholes, pump suction wells or other locations* where oil, grease or gasoline might come into contact with the neck of the canister and cause its deterioration and combustion with dire results.

Another self-contained device supplies oxygen from a cylinder, has a rubber breathing bag, a regenerator and mouthpiece, or face piece, with the necessary regulating valves. This device is also *hazardous in atmospheres containing petroleum vapors* which might cause its deterioration and should be used only in their known absence.

Other Self-contained or Demand-type Apparatus. Demand-type apparatus, as supplied by several manufacturers, furnishes oxygen from a cylinder or compressed air as required to a face piece. The safe time limit for strenuous work with this device using oxygen is one-half hour The same hazard exists with this type oxygen-supplied apparatus in the presence of petroleum vapor, oil or grease, and thus, the safest practice dictates that it should not be used in sewer manholes and pump suction wells. With a compressed air cylinder, the above hazard is removed and the device can be supplied from a back-packed cylinder lasting 30 minutes or from a large separate cylinder through reinforced feed hose for six to eight hours.

Proper maintenance and repair of gas masks and the renewal of canisters are vital.

RESUSCITATION

When a person has been overcome by gases, vapor or oxygen deficiency, rescue must be followed immediately by resuscitation. The heart will stop beating in six to ten minutes after the lungs stop functioning. This shows the extreme importance of workers wearing a safety belt in hazardous locations.

RESCUE BREATHING

Rescue breathing is the use of a person's breath to revive someone who is unable to breathe for himself. It is the oldest and most effective method of resuscitation.

Absence of breathing movements or blue color of lips, tongue, and fingernails are danger signs indicating a lack of oxygen in the blood and the need for help with breathing. When in doubt, begin rescue breathing. No harm can come from its use, but grave consequences follow if it is not used promptly.

Whether or not the unconscious person is trying to breathe, chances are that his breathing is fully or partially block by his tongue. Tilting the head backward, or displacing the jaw forward moves the tongue out of the throat and allows air to reach the lungs. Sometimes the victim who is not breathing will start breathing by himself if the tongue obstruction is relieved.

178

The air you breathe is not "spent." It contains enough oxygen to save a person's life. If you breathe twice as deep as usual, your exhaled breath contains more than enough oxygen for any adult victim. When each inflation expands the victim's chest, you can be sure rescue breathing is working. Inflate the adult's chest at least ten times each minute. Infants require smaller and more frequent inflations, at least 20 times each minute.

CLEARING VICTIM'S THROAT

Place the victim on his back and begin rescue breathing. Any delay may be fatal.

DON'T WASTE TIME BY: Feeling victim's pulse . . . finding special equipment . . . moving the victim . . . going for help . . . getting to shore. Only a short time without oxygen can cause serious damage to the brain.

If the first inflation effort fails, make sure the tongue or some foreign object is not blocking air flow to the lungs. Sweep your fingers through his throat to clear any obstructions.

If obstructing foreign material is obviously present, such as food particles, secretions, false teeth, blood or blood clots, or chewing gum, it must be removed immediately with the fingers or by any other means possible. The first blowing effort will determine whether or not obstruction exists, and in the absence of obstruction, will provide the urgently needed oxygen. Clear throat.

If aspiration of a foreign body is suspected in an adult after failure of mouth-to-mouth ventilation to move air into the lungs, the victim should be placed on his side and a sharp blow administered between the shoulders to jar the obstructing material free. Again, the rescuer's fingers should sweep through the victim's mouth to remove such material.

An asphyxiated small child suspected of having a foreign body in the airway should be suspended momentarily by the ankles, or inverted over one arm, and given two or three sharp pats between the shoulder blades in the hope of dislodging obstructing material.

RESCUE BREATHING FOR ADULT VICTIMS

Lift the neck and tilt the head backward (B). Hold the head tilted *as far back as possible*. One hand pushes the head, the other pulls the chin. The extreme tilt prevents obstruction. Halfway tilt is not enough, full extreme tilt is necessary.

Take a deep breath. Open your mouth as wide as you can. Seal your lips on the victim's cheeks around nose (D). *If the lips press the victim's nostrils, your mouth is not open wide enough.*

Blow air into the victim's mouth until you see the chest rise. To do this, push his mouth open as you blow, or pull his lower lip down (E). Seal your lips around his opened mouth and press your cheek against his nostrils to stop air leaks.

Then remove your mouth to let him breathe out. Take your next breath as you listen to the sound of his exhalation. Reinflate his lungs again as soon as he has exhaled. *Continue inflations at least 10 times a minute.*

SAFETY WITH CHLORINE

Chapter 7 on Chlorination of Sewage contains a paragraph on chlorine hazards. Some additional pointers on the safe handling of chlorine will be given here and more can be obtained from published literature.

Anhydrous liquid chlorine is available as follows:

In 100, 105, and 150 lb cylinders

Ton containers

Tank cars of 16, 30, and 55 tons capacity

Each container is a steel cylinder equipped with special connections and safety reliefs. The small cylinders have a fusible plug built into the valve. All the ton containers each have three fusible plugs in each end. The standard Chlorine Institute valve on cylinders and ton containers is similar in design but the latter has a larger internal opening and does not have the fusible plug. In both types of cylinders the fusible plugs are designed to melt between 158° and 165° F. Chlorine cylinders and ton containers, empty or full, should never be dropped or permitted to strike each other with any force. Tank care have a spring loaded safety valve located at the center of the dome. This relief is set to be gas tight at or below 180 psi gauge and pops at 225.

Cylinders and ton containers should be stored in a cool, dry place away from direct sources of heat and away from combustible flammable materials. It is recommended that cylinders be stored on end and ton containers on their side, both with valve protectors in place. It is further recommended that containers longest in storage be used first. Cylinders should be moved about carefully, preferably on a hand truck with a strap to secure the cylinder to the truck. Ton containers should be moved about only by an approved lifting bar with hooks over chines at end and never by any type of sling.

Connections to cylinders and containers are made by clamp adaptors or by union connections. See that connecting surfaces and threads are clean and *always use a new gasket of standard material.* Connections are always a possible source of leakage and so is the packing of valves. *Do not use a wrench over six inches* long on a cylinder or ton container valve.

On making a new connection, open valve slightly and test for chlorine leakage with a swab wet with ammonia, held close to valve and connection. White fumes of ammonium chloride locate a leak. If connection and valve are tight one full turn of valve gives full capacity. Avoid getting ammonia on valves and connections for it removes some types of plating. Leaks around valve stems can usually be stopped by tightening slightly the packing nut. All connections in chlorine lines should be tested frequently. The slightest leak of chlorine should be corrected, because chlorine is very corrosive in the presence of moisture and small leaks increase rapidly in size. Every user of chlorine should obtain from the suppler, and post conspicuously, the telephone number of the nearest emergency service for severe chlorine leaks. The manufacturers of chlorine have developed measures for dealing with leaks from serous situations such as broken valves, holes in containers and other conditions.

The handling of chlorine in tank cars must be done in compliance with requirements of the Interstate Commerce Commission and the Association of American Railroads. Suppliers have prepared helpful suggestions in their bulletins. Private sidings must be provided, and reliable persons must be properly instructed and made responsible for compliance with regulations.

SAFETY WITH SEWAGE SLUDGE GAS

The hazards in connection with the collection and utilization of sewage sludge gas were covered to some extent in Chapter 8. The hazards are mainly those of fire, explosion and asphyxiation. Fire may occur wherever gas may leak, and explosions whenever an explosive mixture receives the ignition necessary to set it off. Such ignition may come from a broken light bulb in an ordinary extension cord and fixture, a sparking switch, sparks from shoe nails or tools, smoking or striking of matches, and use of ordinary flash lights. In the dismantling of sludge gas piping within digesters under repair, the rapid oxidation of iron sulfide deposits within such piping may create heat or flame.

When gas piping and appurtenances are dispersed throughout a plant, positive ventilation should be maintained to prevent the accumulation of gas-air mixtures should a gas line leak occur. Gas piping should be maintained tight and frequent tests for leakage should be made with a combustible gas indicator.

The interlocking safety controls provided in gas boilers should be checked periodically to see that they operate as intended when there is a failure of gas pressure or when a pilot is extinguished for any reason.

GASOLINE AND VOLATILE SOLVENT HAZARDS

Mention has been made in several places of the possible presence of flammable vapors of gasoline and other volatile solvents. In wet wells, pump suction wells and enclosed grit chambers, such vapors may come in from the sewer and accumulate at low points. Gasoline vapor is heavier than air, and presents all the hazards of asphyxiation and explosion. In one plant a violent explosion occurred in a grit chamber where a coal burning heater had been installed to reduce condensation. Fortunately, there were no injuries but the force of the explosion completely removed a concrete roof, cracked masonry walls and blew off buried sewer manhole covers located at considerable distance from the building. The grit chamber and sewer had some natural ventilation. There was some odor of gasoline or other volatile solvent after the explosion. It is believed that such vapors were ignited by the coal burning heater.

Such places should be provided with forced ventilation. All electrical switches, lights, motors and fixtures should be explosion proof, and smoking absolutely prohibited. Tests should be made frequently for the noxious vapors and, when found, investigations should be made to determine the source.

RADIOLOGICAL HAZARDS

The increased use of radioactive isotopes in medicine, industry and research may well lead to accidental discharge or loss of such materials to the sewers leading to sewage treatment plants. Studies by the United States Public Health Service indicate that dilution in the average sewer system together with the usual safeguards in handling such material are normally adequate to prevent the creation of any health hazard. In war time a radioactive hazard might occur in sewers and treatment plants following an underwater or ground burst of an atomic bomb.

An excellent article on this subject appeared in the *Sewage and Industrial Wastes*, for October, 1951. The article gives basic information on terms and measurements of radiation. Portable Geiger meters are available which would be suitable for determining background or normal activity counts, and their periodic use would determine any increase beyond minimums set up tentatively by the National Bureau of Standards.

At the end of this chapter on Safety, it may be well to recall and repeat the statement at the beginning that the "A, B, C" of safety is "ALWAYS BE CAREFUL," and add to it the safety slogan which headed a code adopted several years ago by the New England and the New York State Sewage Works Associations—

"ALERT TODAY—ALIVE TOMORROW."

SPECIAL REFERENCES FOR CHAPTER 14

Peter Safar, M.D. and Martin C. McMahon, "Resuscitation of the Unconscious Victim," Charles C. Thomas, Publisher, 1959
New York State Department of Health and New York State Civil Defense Commission, "Rescue Breathing"

CHAPTER 15

HYDRAULICS AND ELECTRICITY

To a certain point, there are similarities between the elemental considerations of fluids and electricity which help to understand the fundamentals of both. For example, we have the following units of measurement:

	Fluid	*Electricity*
Pressure	Pounds per square inch (psi or feet of water)	Electromotive Force (emf, E or Volts)
Flow	Gallons per minute (gpm) or cubic feet per second (cfs)	Ampere (Amp)
Resistance to flow	Head loss Feet of Fluid or psi	Resistance (**Ohms**)
Quantity	Gallons or cubic feet (gal) or (cf)	Kilowatt hours (KWH)

HYDRAULICS

This is the name given to that branch of science which deals with fluids at rest and in motion. The former is sometimes spoken of as hydrostatics and the latter has hydrodynamics. We are concerned here mainly with water at rest and in motion, although many of the same principles apply to air and gases.

Our consideration will be of water or sewage usually moving or flowing through pipes, channels and pumps, and ways of measuring the quantity flowing in a given time. In this consideration we must be careful of units, the basic ones being:

Length in feet	ft
Area in square feet	sq ft or ft²
Rate: Gallons per minute	gpm
Million gallons per day	mgd
Cu ft per second	cfs or sec ft
Weight: 1 gallon of water weighs	8.34 lb
1 cu ft water weighs	62.4 lb
Speed or velocity of flow:	
Feet per second	ft/sec

Pumping. Pumps are used to move liquids from one level to a higher level and sometimes simply to increase the rate of flow. Figure 21 and Figure 22 show two typical pumping conditions. To understand these

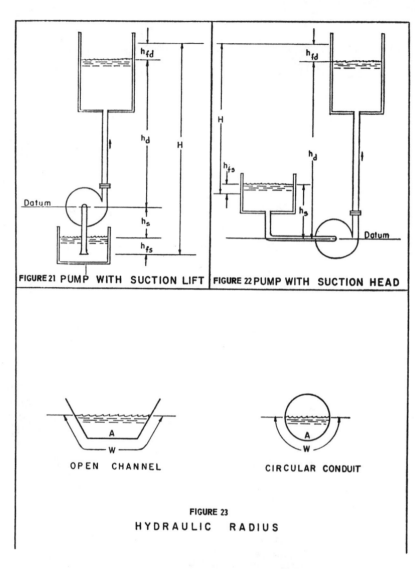

FIGURE 21 PUMP WITH SUCTION LIFT

FIGURE 22 PUMP WITH SUCTION HEAD

OPEN CHANNEL

CIRCULAR CONDUIT

FIGURE 23

HYDRAULIC RADIUS

figures it is necessary to know that in a liquid at rest the pressure at any point is equal to the weight of the liquid above the point, plus the weight of the atmosphere above the surface of the liquid, both expressed in the same units. These units are usually pounds per square inch (psi) or feet of water. Since most pumping problems involve difference in pressure, the atmospheric pressure may be neglected and gage pressures (psig) or feet used alone. Pressure in feet can be considered as the height of a column of water which because of its weight would produce the pressure at the point in question. Pressure in feet is usually referred to as "head." For water and sewage:

184

psi $\times$ 2.31 = head in feet.

For Figure 21—Pump operating with a suction lift:

$$H = h_d + h_s + h_{fd} + h_{fs} + \frac{V_d^2}{2g} \quad \frac{V_s^2}{2g}$$

For Figure 22—Pump operating with suction head:

$$H = h_d - h_s + h_{fd} + h_{fs} + \frac{V_d^2}{2g} \quad \frac{V_s^2}{2g}$$

Where—

H = Total head in feet (formerly called total dynamic head or TDH) at which the pump operates.

h_d = Static discharge head in feet, or the vertical distance between the pump datum and liquid surface in the receiving tank. The pump datum is at the center line for horizontal pumps and at the entrance eye of the impeller for vertical pumps.

h_s = Static suction head or lift in feet or vertical distance between pump datum and liquid surface in the suction well.

h_{fd} = Friction head in discharge in feet or the head necessary to overcome friction in valves, fittings, etc. in the discharge piping.

h_{fs} = Friction head in suction in feet.

$\dfrac{V_d^2}{2g}$ and $\dfrac{V_s^2}{2g}$ are the Velocity heads in feet, respectively, at the discharge nozzle and suction nozzle of the pump. When the nozzles are of the same diameter these values are equal and cancel out. Velocity head represents energy which the pump must deliver to the liquid but which is not measured by a pressure gage. It is the head required to give to the liquid the velocity "V" in feet per second.

Pipe Friction. The h_{fd} and h_{fs} in the preceding paragraph are those portions of the total head necessary to overcome friction between the fluid and the walls of the suction and discharge piping. The values of these terms depend upon the length of the pipe line, its diameter, the velocity of the flowing liquid and on the condition of the internal walls of the pipe, usually called the roughness factor. These influences are expressed in the formula:

$$h_f = \text{Friction head} = f\frac{L}{d}\frac{V^2}{2g}$$

Where f = roughness factor

L = length of pipe

d = diameter

$\dfrac{V}{2g}$ = velocity head

Tables are available for the value of f which varies with both V and d in this formula. The value of f is fractional, varying from .04 for small V and d to .01 for large values of V and d. Another formula derived from this basic one expresses the roughness factor as a whole number known as the C value in the Hazen & Williams formula. Tables and a special slide rule have been developed for solving pipe problems by this formula. The value of C varies from 140 for very smooth large pipe to a low of 40 or less for badly corroded or dirty pipe.

Other losses are derived from fittings and bends in pipe which are allowed for by a term called "equivalent length" of straight pipe. Minor losses due to entrance and discharge arrangements are allowed for as a proportion of a velocity head. Values for various conditions can be found in handbooks on hydraulics.

Power Requirements for Pumping. Work must be done to move liquid against the total heads (H) indicated in Figures 21 and 22. The unit of work is the foot pound which is the amount of work or energy required to lift one pound a vertical distance of one foot. The common unit of power or rate of doing work is horsepower (hp) equal to 33,000 ft. lbs. per minute. In electrical units one horsepower is equivalent to 746 watts.

The power required to drive a pump can be computed as follows:

Work done by the pump or water horsepower

$$\text{Whp} = \frac{\text{lbs. of water raised per minute} \times H}{33,000}$$

$$= \frac{\text{gpm} \times 8.33 \times H}{33,000} = \frac{\text{gpm} \times H}{3,960}$$

Since all the power delivered by the driving unit cannot be converted to useful work the ratio between output and input is called pump efficiency.

Power required to drive the pump or brake horsepower

$$\text{bhp} = \frac{\text{whp}}{\text{pump eff.}} = \frac{\text{gpm} \times H}{3960 \times \text{pump eff.}}$$

and again since motors are not 100% efficient

$$\text{Motor hp} = \frac{\text{whp}}{\text{pump eff.} \times \text{motor eff.}}$$

$$= \frac{\text{gpm} \times H}{3960 \times \text{pump eff.} \times \text{motor eff.}}$$

Flow in Long Pipe Lines. In the previous paragraphs, we have considered power required to move water by pumping. From these considerations it can be seen that water flowing through a long pipe line must have a difference in elevation between inlet and outlet sufficient to overcome the friction, velocity and miscellaneous losses which make the Total Head.

Flow in Open Channels. Flow in open conduits and in partially filled pipes such as sewers is affected by the same factors as those for pipes flowing full. It is these combined factors that determine the slope at which a sewer or open channel must be constructed to maintain a certain flow at a minimum velocity. This slope which determines the velocity is actually the slope of the water surface but it is usually also the slope of the invert of the pipe so that the water flows at a constant depth. The slope of the water surface is called the hydraulic gradient. The extent of the frictional effect between water and the conduit walls again depends upon the roughness and texture of the surface, but the formula for it is different in that the liquid now has a free surface and the length of contact depends upon the shape of the conduit and the depth of flow. These factors are combined in the *hydraulic* radius which is found by dividing the cross-sectional area of the flowing water by the length along the sides of that area which are in contact with the walls of the conduit. This is called the wetted perimeter. Thus

$$\text{Hyd Rad } r = \frac{A}{W} \text{ feet (Figure 23)}$$

From these considerations, there has been developed the Chezy formula:

$v = C \sqrt{r\,s}$ feet per sec

where C = coefficient based on roughness, slope and value of r.

s = slope of the hydraulic gradient or water surface in open channels usually expressed as ft. per foot or ft. per thousand. Thus, a slope of .004 indicates a drop of four feet in a thousand foot length.

The two principal formulas for determining C called the Kutter and Manning formulas depend largely upon values of "n," the coefficient of friction which have become quite well known for various types of surfaces and materials. Thus $n = .013$ is commonly used for design of vitrified tile sewers and commonly used for large diameter pre-cast concrete pipe sewers.

Tables and diagrams have been published from which velocities, rates of flow and slopes can be determined for various diameters of sewers and values of "n."

Weirs. There are numerous ways of measuring flowing water, but three devices most commonly used at sewage treatment plants are weirs, Venturi meters and Parshall flumes.

The weir consists of a rectangular or V notch opening having sharp edges and set vertically so that the flow passes over it and falls away freely, Figure 24. It is only necessary to measure the height of water above the crest of the weir at a point sufficiently upstream to avoid the curve of the water surface over the weir. With this one measurement the flow is determined from the formula:

187

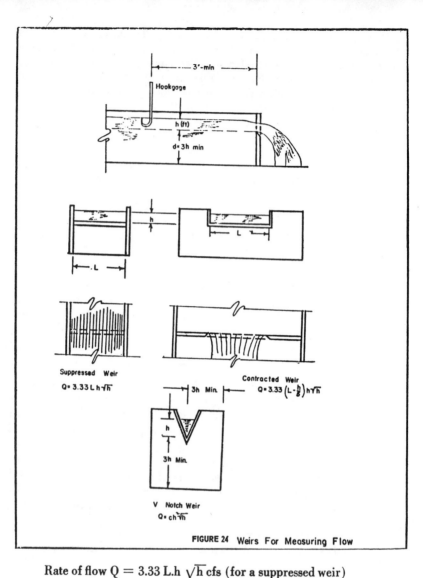

FIGURE 24 Weirs For Measuring Flow

Rate of flow $Q = 3.33\ L.h\ \sqrt{h}$ cfs (for a suppressed weir)

and

$$Q = 3.33 \left(L - \frac{h}{5} \right) h.\ \sqrt{h} \text{ cfs (for a contracted weir)}$$

where h = the height of horizontal water surface above crest of weir, L = horizontal length of weir.

The V notch weir is more accurate than the rectangular weir for small flows. For a 90 degree notch, the formula is:

$$Q = Ch^2\ \sqrt{h} \text{ cfs where}$$

188

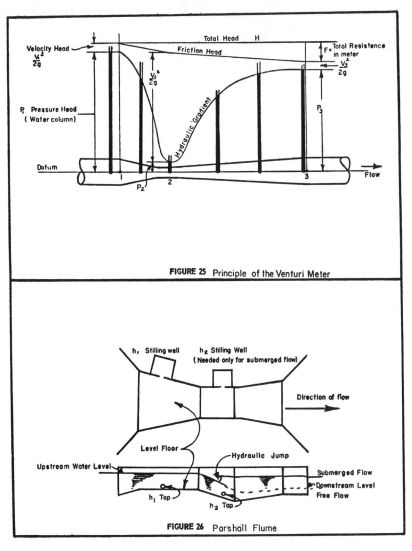

FIGURE 25 Principle of the Venturi Meter

FIGURE 26 Parshall Flume

C is a coefficient depending upon the material of the weir and the range of head. Values of C are given in handbooks for various materials and heads. The V notch weir is suitable for measuring flows from 10 to 3,500 gpm.

Venturi Meter. This type of flow measuring device is installed in a pipe line and consists of a throat carefully machined to a given diameter, a converging section which tapers from the pipe line diameter to the throat and a diverging section from the throat to the pipe line diameter. Taps are provided for measuring pressure head at a point just before convergence and at the throat. In measuring sewage, means are provided by plungers and a small in-flow of water to keep these taps from being clogged. The only measurements necessary to compute the flow from formulas or to convert it into records by mechanical devices is the difference in pressure head between the two tap points. The theory is well explained in text and handbooks and, therefore, is considered beyond the scope of this manual. Figure 25 shows graphically how the pressure and velocity heads change in the Venturi Meter.

Parshall Flume. This type of flow measuring device was developed for measuring irrigation water in open channels where there can be much debris and silt and where little loss of head can be afforded.

In principle, the flume is similar to the Venturi meter in that it has an inlet section with slides converging slowly to a throat of carefully fixed dimensions and an outlet section diverging more rapidly to the original channel width. For non-submerged condition, which is usually the case, only one measurement, the depth of water at a fixed distance upstream from the throat, is necessary for determination of the flow by formula or from charts. The flume may be constructed of almost any building material, but for greatest accuracy the throat is often made to accurate dimensions of corrosion resistant metal. Figure 26 illustrates the Parshall Flume.

Magnetic Flow Meter. Each of the previously described flow measuring devices involve an appreciable loss of head but a new development consists of a non-magnetic tube of the same internal diameter as the pipe line in which it is installed and across which a magnetic field is established. Sewage flowing through the magnetic field produces a voltage proportional to the velocity and which is converted by electrical and mechanical means to indicate and record the rate of flow.

An important operating and maintenance requirement of any flow measuring device is that pressure connections, stilling wells, floats and float tubes be kept clean and free from obstructions in order that the equipment may function properly.

ELECTRICITY

Electrical Units. The volt, as indicated in the introduction to this chapter, expresses electrical pressure just as feet, or head, or psi expresses water pressure or the force which is ready to do work. It is represented by the symbol "E" or sometimes emf, the abbreviation for electro-motive force.

For years, standard voltages have been 110, 220, 440, 2200, 4400, and 13,200. In sewage plants the voltage seldom exceeds 440, the higher ones being used for transmission lines. In some places the 110 and 220 standards have been replaced by 120 and 208. Just as for higher water pressures, the higher voltages require proper equipment to prevent leaks (short circuits) and deserve respect from the safety angle. However, pressures as low as 110 volts have been known to deliver fatal currents and no chances should be taken with the low voltages. Proper equipment should be used for the furnished voltage. If the average voltage is 120 on lighting currents, then 120 and not 110 volt lamps should be used since they will last about three times as long.

For large motors over 50 HP, designers find an economy in cost of motor and elimination of transformer losses by using the higher voltages in excess of 440 volts. For 5 to 50 HP motors, economy dictates the use of 220 or 440 volts.

The *ampere* (amp) in electricity expresses the rate of flow just as gpm expresses water flows. In equations, the ampere is represented by I. Just as large pipes are required for large flows of water, large wire sizes are required for heavy amperages to keep down the transmission losses in resistance which cause voltage drop.

Each appliance, motor or other current-using device, has a current rating depending upon its design and resistance to flow. In motors the current varies with the load. Some appliances such as wires, fuses and switches are rated as to the current which they may safely carry. These ratings are fixed by a National Electric Code and should not be exceeded. Thus, an appliance rated for 25 amps should be protected by a fuse of that capacity to act as a safety valve. In an attempt to carry more than their rated capacity, wires and appliances become overheated and may themselves burn out or cause a fire.

The *Ohm* is the unit of electrical resistance. It is represented by R. Just as the resistance of a valve stops flow of water, the resistance of a non-conductor such as an insulator, or an air break such as an open switch, prevents the flow of electrical current. Similarly, resistors are employed to control the rate of current flow.

In electrical circuits the loss of voltage, voltage drop or loss in pressure is proportional to the resistance and the rate of current flow, thus we have the simple relation or Ohm's Law $E = R\,I$. Values of resistance R for unit lengths or conductors of various sizes and materials are not to be found in handbooks.

Direct and Alternating Currents. The expression $E = R\,I$ holds true only for currents flowing in one direction, known as direct current or DC. If the current flows first in one and then the other direction, it is known as alternating current (AC) and the number of times that it flows in each direction in a second is known as the number of cycles. Thus, a current that flows in each or in any one direction 60 times per second is called 60 cycle current. This is the standard for alternating current in this country.

Transformers are used to increase or decrease voltage and current and consist of two stationary coils of wire insulated from each other but wound around a common iron core. Current flowing through the primary coil induces a current in the secondary of emf directly proportional to the number of turns of wire on the primary and secondary and of amperage inversely proportional to the number of turns.

The *Watt* (W) is the unit of electrical power (P) and is most commonly used as a thousand watts or the kilowatt (KW). The mechanical unit of power or horsepower (HP) is equivalent to 746 watts, or for rough computation it can be remembered that a horsepower is approximately equivalent to three-quarters of a KW. Since the efficiency of many small motors is about 75%, the kilowatt in-put is roughly equivalent to the mechanical HP out-put.

For direct current:

P = E I and by substitution for E

P = R I² or by substitution for I

$$P = \frac{E^2}{R}$$

From these expressions it can be seen that power varies directly with both current and voltage if resistance is not considered, but as the square of either one when resistance is considered.

Kilowatt Hour. Kilowatt hour is the pay unit for electricity. As the term indicates, it is the average power requirement in KW multiplied by the time over which it is supplied in hours.

Circuits. The *single phase,* two-wire system shown in Figure 27a is the simplest circuit. Figure 27b shows a single phase, three-wire system that can furnish two voltages. One wire in the two-wire system, and the neutral in the three-wire system, must be of the same size as the others, it must have white covering, it must be grounded, it must always be attached to the white terminal in all receptacles and must never be fused nor connected to any switch.

The *three phase* (three-wire) is the standard system for motor loads except for fractional horsepower. There are two different arrangements of leads from generators or transformers known as delta, Figure 28a and Y shown in Figure 28b. Lighting circuits can be taken off as shown. However, unless motor loads are light and infrequently started, it is better to separate power and lighting circuits to avoid dimming of the lights when motors start.

Circuit protection is provided by fuses which consist of a special alloy wire or tape designed to melt at the maximum current enclosed in some type of flame-proof case. They are not always suitable however, and more complicated thermal relays, air circuit breakers or oil breakers, which can allow a heavy flow of current for a specified time before acting to open a circuit, are required. Such devices are most necessary with heavy motor loads. A special oil is needed in circuit breakers and no other should be used. When a circuit breaker operates frequently, investigation of the cause should be made and corrective steps taken. Protective devices should never be "jumped."

Grounding is extremely important and grounds should be maintained and never left disconnected. They protect human life and property and without them our electrical systems would not work.

Motors. Most alternating current motors are either of the induction or synchronous type. *Synchronous* motor speed is determined by the formula

$$N = \frac{120 \text{ f}}{P} \text{ when N = revolutions of motor per minute = rpm.}$$

for 60 cycles

$$N = \frac{7200}{P}$$ f = frequency

P = number of poles

Electric Circuits

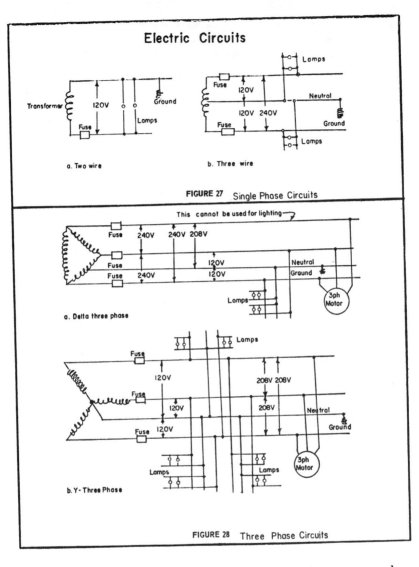

a. Two wire

b. Three wire

FIGURE 27 Single Phase Circuits

a. Delta three phase

b. Y-Three Phase

FIGURE 28 Three Phase Circuits

Since the least number of poles is two and there must be an even number of poles, the greatest synchronous speed for 60 cycles, is 3,600, and other speeds are 1,800, 1,200, 900, 450, etc., rpm. The synchronous motor operates accurately at the given speed and this is valuable for clocks and timing devices. However, the synchronous motor has definite poles which must be excited or magnetized by some source of direct current. Synchronous motors have low starting torque or twist which make them unsatisfactory for many loads. For this reason it is fortunate that centrifugal pumps can usually be started with little load. Synchronous motors are sometimes used because of their favorable power factor.

193

Induction Motors have no salient poles which need excitation, and can run at variable speeds. They are sometimes called squirrel cage because of the fact that the rotor is made up of bars parallel to the axis. Without load this motor will run at a speed close to the synchronous speed, but as load increases, the speed is reduced until at full load the speed has slipped off from 2 to 4% of the synchronous speed. If the load is sufficiently increased the motor will stop or "pull out."

Induction motors require relatively small starting current. Maintenance calls for keeping air ducts and windings of the motor clean. Oil in bearings should be flushed and changed at least once per year. The smaller motors require no special starting devices and thus may be started "across the line" directly. Larger motors usually require reduced voltage for starting.

Variable speed is obtained in an induction motor by having a wound rotor, into the circuit of which external resistance may be added to control the speed or the slip. Thus a manufacturer can build a motor with external controls to give the speed and power required to operate a pump or other piece of equipment as desired.

Motor Ratings as well as that for other electrical equipment are based upon the temperature rise which will occur when operating continuously at normal full load and proper voltage. This rise is usually limited to 40 or 45 degrees Centigrade. Thus, a motor may run hot to the touch, yet be within its safe rating. A thermometer should be used to check the temperature on small motors. Large motors usually have temperature measuring devices built into them.

SPECIAL REFERENCES FOR CHAPTER 15

Angus, Robert W. "Hydraulics for the Practical Operator" Water and Sewage Works, Reference and Data, 1948, R-13

Van Kleeck, Roy W. "Measurement of Liquid and Sludge Quantities" Wastes Engineering, April 1955, Pp. 171

Smith, Marsden C. "Practical Electricity in the Plant" Water and Sewage Works, Reference and Data, 1947, R-59

APPENDIX I

GLOSSARY

(A)

Activated Sludge Process.—See *Process, Activated Sludge.*

Acre-Foot.—A unit of volume used to express the amount of material in a trickling filter. A depth of one foot on an area of one acre is an acre-foot. Regardless of shape, 43,560 cubic feet is equivalent to one acre foot.

Adsorption.—The adherence of dissolved, colloidal, or finely divided solids on the surfaces of solid bodies with which they are brought into contact.

Aeration.—The bringing about of intimate contact between air and a liquid by one of the following methods: Spraying the liquid in the air; or by agitation of the liquid to promote surface absorption of air.

Diffused Air.—Aeration produced in a liquid by air passed through a diffuser.

Mechanical.—(1) The mixing, by mechanical means, of sewage and activated sludge, in the aeration tank of the activated sludge process, to bring fresh surfaces of liquid into contact with the atmosphere. (2) The introduction of atmospheric oxygen into a liquid by the mechanical action of paddle or spray mechanisms.

Modified.—A modification of the activated sludge process in which a shortened period of aeration is employed with a reduced quantity of suspended solids in the mixed liquor.

Paddle-Wheel.—The mechanical agitation of sewage in the aeration tanks of the activated sludge process by means of paddle wheels.

Spiral Flow.—A method of diffusing air in an aeration tank of the activated sludge process, where, by means of properly designed baffles, and the proper location of diffusers, a spiral or helical movement is given to the air and the tank liquor.

Stage.—Division of activated sludge treatment into stages with intermediate settling tanks and return of sludge in each stage.

Step.—A procedure for adding increments of sewage along the line of flow in the aeration tanks of an activated sludge plant. (C. F. Gould, U. S. Patent 2,337,384.)

Tapered.—The method of supplying varying amounts of air into the different parts of an aeration tank in the activated sludge process, more at the inlet, less near the outlet, and approximately proportional to the oxygen demand of the mixed liquor under aeration.

Algae.—Primitive plants, one or many-celled, usually aquatic and capable of elaborating their foodstuffs by photosynthesis.

Algicide.—Any substance which kills algae.

195

Alkaline.—Water or soils containing sufficient amounts of alkaline substances to raise the pH above 7.0, or to harm the growth of crops.

Alkalinity.—A term used to represent the content of carbonates, bicarbonates, hydroxides, and occasionally borates, silicates, and phosphates in water. It is expressed in parts per million of calcium carbonate.

Alum.—A common name for aluminum sulfate.

Arrester, Flame.—A safety device on a gas line which allows gas, but not a flame, to pass through.

(B)

Bacteria.—Primitive plants, generally free of pigment, which reproduce by dividing in one, two, or three planes. They occur as single cells, groups, chains, or filaments, and do not require light for their life processes. They may be grown by special culturing out of their native habitat.

    Aerobic.—Bacteria which require free (elementary) oxygen for their growth.

    Anaerobic.—Bacteria which grow in the absence of free oxygen and derive oxygen from breaking down complex substances.

    Coli-Aerogenes.—See Bacteria, Coliform Group.

    Coliform Group.—A group of bacteria, predominantly inhabitants of the intestine of man but also found on vegetation, including all aerobic and facultative anaerobic gram-negative, non-spore-forming bacilli that ferment lactose with gas formation. This group includes five tribes of which the very great majority are Eschericheae. The Eschericheae tribe comprises three genera and ten species, of which *Escherichia Coli* and *Aerobacter Aerogenes* are dominant. The *Escherichia Coli* are normal inhabitants of the intestine of man and all vertebrates whereas *Aerobacter Aerogenes* normally are found on grain and plants, and only to a varying degree in the intestine of man and animals. Formerly referred to as *B.Coli*, B.Coli group, *Coli-Aerogenes Group.*

    Facultative Anaerobic.—Bacteria which can adapt themselves to growth in the presence, as well as in the absence, of uncombined oxygen.

    Parasitic.—Bacteria which thrive on other living organisms.

    Pathogenic.—Bacteria which can cause disease.

    Saprophytic.—Bacteria which thrive upon dead organic matter.

Bacterial Count.—A measure of the concentration of bacteria.

    Most Probable Number.—See Page 00.

    Plate.—Number of colonies of bacteria grown on selected solid media at a given temperature and incubation period, usually expressed as the number of bacteria per milliliter of sample.

Bed, Sludge.—An area comprising natural or artificial layers of porous material upon which digested sewage sludge is dried by drainage and evaporation. A sludge bed may be opened to the atmosphere or covered usually with a greenhouse-type superstructure. Also called *Sludge Drying Bed.*

Biochemical.—Resulting from biologic growth or activity, and measured by or expressed in terms of the ensuing chemical change.

Biochemical Action.—Chemical changes resulting from the metabolism of living organisms.

Biochemical Oxygen Demand (BOD).—The quantity of oxygen utilized in the biochemical oxidation of organic matter in a specified time and at a specified temperature. It is not related to the oxygen requirements in chemical combustion, being determined entirely by the availability of the material as a biological food and by the amount of oxygen utilized by the microorganisms during oxidation.

Biochemical Oxygen Demand, Standard.—Biochemical oxygen demand as determined under standard laboratory procedure for five days at 20°C, usually expressed in parts per million.

Buffer.—The action of certain solutions in opposing a change of composition, especially of hydrogen-ion concentration.

Burner, Waste Gas.—A device in a sewage treatment plant for burning the waste gas from a sludge-digestion tank.

(C)

Centrifuge.—A mechanical device utilizing centrifugal force to separate solids from liquids or for separating liquid emulsions.

Chamber.—A general term applied to a space enclosed by walls or to a compartment, often prefixed by a descriptive word, such as "grit chamber," "screen chamber," "discharge chamber," or "flushing chamber," indicating its function.

Chloramines.—Compounds of organic amines or inorganic ammonia with chlorine.

Chloride of Lime.—Obsolete term; see *Chlorinated Lime.*

Chlorinated Lime.—A combination of slaked lime and chlorine gas (also termed Bleaching Powder, Chloride of Lime, Hypochlorite of Lime, etc.). When dissolved in water, it serves as a source of chlorine.

Chlorination.—The application of chlorine.

    Break-Point.—The application of chlorine to water, sewage or industrial wastes containing free ammonia to provide free residual chlorination.

    Post.—The application of chlorine to water, sewage, or industrial wastes subsequent to any treatment. The term refers only to a point of application.

    Pre.—The application of chlorine to water, sewage, or industrial wastes prior to any treatment. This term refers only to a point of application.

Chlorine.—An element, when uncombined, exists as a greenish yellow gas about 2.5 times as heavy as air. Under atmospheric pressure and at a temperature of —30.1°F the gas becomes an amber liquid about 1.5 times as heavy as water. The chemical symbol of chlorine is Cl, its atomic weight is 35.457, and its molecular weight is 70.914.

    Available.—A term used in rating chlorinated lime and hypochlorites as to their total oxidizing power.

197

Combined Available Residual.—That portion of the total residual chlorine remaining in water, sewage, or industrial wastes at the end of a specified contact period, which will react chemically and biologically as chloramines, or organic chloramines.

Demand.—The difference between the amount of chlorine added to water, sewage, or industrial wastes and the amount of residual chlorine remaining at the end of a specified contact period. The demand for any given water varies with the amount of chlorine applied, time of contact, and temperature.

Dose.—The amount of chlorine applied to a liquid, usually expressed in parts per million, or pounds per million gallons.

Free Available Residual.—That portion of the total residual chlorine remaining in water, sewage, or industrial wastes at the end of a specified contact period, which will react chemically and biologically as hypochlorous acid, hypochlorite ion, or molecular chlorine.

Liquid.—An article of commerce. Chlorine gas is generally manufactured by the electrolysis of a solution of common salt. The gas is dried and purified and is then liquefied by a combination of compression and refrigeration. Liquid chlorine is shipped under pressure in steel containers.

Residual.—The total amount of chlorine (combined and free available chlorine) remaining in water, sewage, or industrial wastes at the end of a specified contact period following chlorination.

Test, Iodometric.—The determination of residual chlorine in water, sewage, or industrial wastes by adding potassium iodide and titrating the liberated iodine with a standard solution of sodium thiosulfate, using starch solution as a colorimetric indicator.

Test, Ortho-Tolidine.—The determination of residual chlorine in water, sewage, or industrial wastes, using ortho-tolidine reagent and colorimetric standards.

Clarifier.—See *Tank, Sedimentation.*

Coagulation.—(1) The agglomeration of colloidal or finely divided suspended matter by the addition to the liquid of an appropriate chemical coagulant, by biological processes, or by other means. (2) The process of adding a coagulant and the necessary reacting chemicals.

Coils, Digester.—A system of pipes for hot water or steam installed in a sludge-digestion tank for the purpose of heating the sludge.

Coli-Aerogenes, or *Coliform Group.*—See *Bacteria, Coliform Group.*

Collector, Grit.—A device placed in a grit chamber to convey deposited grit to one end of the chamber for removal.

Scum.—A mechanical device for skimming and removing scum from the surface of settling tanks.

Sludge.—A mechanical device for scraping the sludge on the bottom of a settling tank to a sump, from which it can be drawn by hydrostatic or mechanical action.

Colloids.—Finely divided solids which will not settle but may be removed by coagulation or biochemical action.

Comminution.—The process of screening sewage and cutting the screenings into particles sufficiently fine to pass through the screen openings.

Concentration, Hydrogen-Ion.—See *pH*.

Copperas.—A common name for ferrous sulfate.

Copperas, Chlorinated.—A solution of ferrous sulfate and ferric chloride produced by chlorinating a solution of ferrous sulfate.

Cross Connection.—In plumbing, a physical connection through which a supply of potable water could be contaminated, polluted, or infected. A physical connection between water supplies from different systems.

Cubic Foot per Second.—A unit of discharge for measurement of flowing liquid, equal to a flow of one cubic foot per second past a given section. Also called *Second-Foot.*

(D)

Decomposition of Sewage.—The breakdown of the organic matter in sewage through aerobic and anaerobic processes.

Denitrification.—The reduction of nitrates in solution by biochemical action.

Deoxygenation.—The depletion of the dissolved oxygen in a liquid. Under natural conditions associated with the biochemical oxidation of organic matter present.

Detritus.—The sand, grit, and other coarse material removed by differential sedimentation in a relatively short period of detention.

Diffuser.—A porous plate or tube through which air is forced and divided into minute bubbles for diffusion in liquids. Commonly made of carborundum, alundum, or silica sand.

Digester.—A tank in which the solids resulting from the sedimentation of sewage are stored for the purpose of permitting anaerobic decomposition to the point of rendering the product nonputrescible and inoffensive. Erroneously termed digestor.

Digestion.—The processes occurring in a digester.

> *Mesophilic.*—Digestion by biological action at or below 113°F.

> *Separate Sludge.*—The digestion of sludge in separate tanks in which it is placed after it has been allowed to settle in other tanks.

> *Single-Stage Sludge.*—Sludge digestion limited to a single tank for the entire digestion period.

> *Stage.*—The digestion of sludge progressively in several tanks arranged in series.

> *Thermophilic.*—Digestion carried on at a temperature generally between 113°F and 145°F.

Dilution.—(1) A method of disposing of sewage, industrial waste, or sewage treatment plant effluent by discharging it into a stream or body of water. (2) The ratio of volume of flow of a stream to the total volume of sewage or sewage treatment plant effluent discharged into it.

Disinfection.—The killing of the larger portion (but not necessarily all) of the harmful and objectional microorganisms in, or on, a medium by means of chemicals, heat, ultraviolet light, etc.

Distributor.—A device used to apply liquid to the surface of a filter or contact bed, of two general types, fixed or movable. The fixed type may consist of perforated pipes or notched troughs, sloping boards, or sprinkler nozzles. The movable type may consist of rotating disks or rotating, reciprocating, or traveling perforated pipes or troughs applying a spray, or a thin sheet of liquid.

Dosing Tank.—A tank into which raw or partly treated sewage is introduced and held until the desired quantity has been accumulated, after which it is discharged at such a rate as may be necessary for the subsequent treatment.

Dryer.—A device utilizing heat to remove water.

Flash.—A device for vaporizing water from partly dewatered and finely divided sludge through contact with a current of hot gas or superheated vapor. Included is a squirrel cage mill for separating the sludge cake into fine particles.

Rotary.—A long steel cylinder, slowly revolving, with its long axis slightly inclined, through which passes the material to be dried in hot air. The material passes through from inlet to outlet, tumbling about.

(E)

E. Coli.—(Escherichia Coli).—A species of genus Escherichia bacteria, normal inhabitant of the intestine of man and all vertebrates. This species is classified among the *Coliform Group*. See *Bacteria, Coliform Group*.

Efficiency.—The ratio of the actual performance of a device to the theoretically perfect performance usually expressed as a percentage.

Average.—The efficiency of a machine or mechanical device over the range of load through which the machine operates.

Filter.—The operating results from a filter as measured by various criteria such as percentage reduction in suspended matter, total solids, biochemical oxygen demand, bacteria, color, etc.

Pump.—The ratio of energy converted into useful work to the energy applied to the pump shaft, or the energy difference in the water at the discharge and suction nozzles divided by the energy input at the pump shaft.

Wire-to-Water.—The ratio of the mechanical output of a pump, to the electrical input at the meter.

Effluent.—(1) A liquid which flows out of a containing space. (2) Sewage, water, or other liquid, partially or completely treated, or in its natural state, as the case may be, flowing out of a reservoir, basin, or treatment plant, or part thereof.

Final.—The effluent from the final unit of a sewage treatment plant.

Stable.—A treated sewage which contains enough oxygen to satisfy its oxygen demand.

Ejector, Pneumatic.—A device for raising sewage, sludge, or other liquid by alternately admitting such through an inward swinging check valve into the bottom of an airtight pot and then discharging it through an outward swinging check valve by admitting compressed air to the pot above the liquid.

Elutriation.—A process of sludge conditioning in which certain constituents are removed by successive decantations with fresh water or plant effluent, thereby reducing the demand for conditioning chemicals.

(F)

Factor.—Frequently a ratio used to express operating conditions.

Load.—The ratio of the average load carried by any operation to the maximum load carried, during a given period of time, expressed as a percentage. The load may consist of almost anything, such as electrical power, number of persons served, amount of water carried by a conduit, etc.

Power.—An electrical term describing the ratio of the true power passing through an electric circuit to the product of the volts times the amperes in the circuit. It is a measure of the lag or lead of the current in respect to the voltage. While the power of a current is the product of the voltage times the amperes in the circuit, in alternating current the voltage and amperes are not always in phase, hence the true power may be less than that determined by the product of volts times amperes.

Filter.—A term meaning (1) an oxidizing bed (2) a device for removing solids from a liquid by some type of strainer.

Biological.—A bed of sand, gravel, broken stone, or other media through which sewage flows or trickles, which depends on biological action for its effectiveness.

High-Rate.—A trickling filter operated at a high average daily dosing rate usually between 10-30 mgd per acre, sometimes including recirculation of effluent.

Low-Rate.—A trickling filter designed to receive a small load of BOD per unit volume of filtering material and to have a low dosage rate per unit of surface area (usually 1 to 4 mgd per acre). Also called Standard Rate Filter.

Roughing.—A sewage filter of relatively coarse material operated at a high rate as a preliminary treatment.

Sand.—A filter in which sand is used as a filtering medium.

Sand Sludge.—A bed of sand used to dewater sludge by drainage and evaporation.

Sludge.—The solid matter in sewage that is removed by settling in primary and secondary settling tanks.

Trickling.—A treatment unit consisting of a material such as broken stone, clinkers, slate, slats, or brush, over which sewage is distributed and applied in drops, films, or spray, from troughs, drippers, moving distributors, or fixed nozzles, and through which it trickles to the underdrains, giving opportunity for the formation of zoological slimes which clarify and oxidize the sewage.

Vacuum.—A filter consisting of a cylindrical drum mounted on a horizontal axis, covered with filtering material made of wool, felt, cotton, saran, nylon, dacron, polyethylene or similar substance, by stainless steel coil springs or metal screen, revolving with a partial submergence in the liquid. A vacuum is maintained under the cloth for the larger part of a revolution to extract moisture. The cake is scraped off continuously.

Filtrate.—The effluent of a Filter.

Floc.—Small gelatinous masses, formed in a liquid by the addition of coagulants thereto or through biochemical processes or by agglomeration.

Flocculator.—An apparatus for the formation of floc in water or sewage.

Flotation.—A method of raising suspended matter to the surface of the liquid in a tank as scum—by aeration, by the evolution of gas, chemicals, electrolysis, heat, or bacterial decomposition—and the subsequent removal of the scum by skimming.

Freeboard.—The vertical distance between the normal maximum level of the surface of the liquid in a conduit, reservoir, tank, canal, etc., and the top of the sides of an open conduit, the top of a dam or levee, etc., which is provided so that waves and other movements of the liquid will not overtop the confining structure.

Fungi.—Small nonchlorophyll-bearing plants which lack roots, stems, or leaves and which occur (among other places) in water, sewage, or sewage effluents, growing best in the absence of light. Their decomposition after death may cause disagreeable tastes and odors in water; in some sewage treatment processes they are helpful and in others they are detrimental.

(G)

Gage.—A device for measuring any physical magnitude.

Float.—A device for measuring the elevation of the surface of a liquid, the actuation element being a buoyant float which rests upon the surface of the liquid.

Indicator.—A gage that shows by means of an index, pointer, dial, etc., the instantaneous value of such characteristics as depth, pressure, velocity, stage, discharge, or the movements or positions of water-controlling devices.

Mercury.—A gage wherein pressure of a fluid is measured by the height of a column of mercury which the fluid pressure will sustain. The mercury is usually contained in a tube, attached to the vessel or pipe containing the fluid.

Pressure.—A device for registering the pressure of solids, liquids, or gases. It may be graduated to the register pressure in any units desired.

Garbage, Ground.—*Garbage* shredded or ground by apparatus installed in sinks and discharged to the sewerage system; or *garbage* collected and hauled to a central grinding station, shredded preliminary to disposal, usually, by digestion with sewage sludge.

Gas.—One of the three states of matter.

Sewage.—(1) The gas produced by the septicization of sewage. (2) The gas produced during the digestion of sewage sludge, usually collected and utilized.

Sewer.—Gas evolved in sewers from the decomposition of the organic matter in the sewage. Also any gas present in the sewerage system, even though it is from gas mains, gasoline, cleaning fluid, etc.

Gasification.—The transformation of sewage solids into gas in the decomposition of sewage.

Go Devil.—A scraper with self-adjusting spring blades, inserted in a pipe line, and carried forward by the fluid pressure for clearing away accumulations, tuberculations, etc.

Grade.—(1) The inclination or slope of a stream channel, conduit, or natural ground surface, usually expressed in terms of the ratio or percentage of number of units of vertical rise or fall per unit of horizontal distance. (2) The elevation of the invert of the bottom of a pipe line, canal, culvert, sewer, etc. (3) The finished surface of a canal bed, road bed, top of an embankment, or bottom of an excavation. (4) In plumbing, the fall in inches per foot of length of pipe.

Grease.—In sewage, grease including fats, waxes, free fatty acids, calcium and magnesium soaps, mineral oils, and other non-fatty materials. The type of solvent used for its extraction should be stated.

Grinder, Screenings.—A device for grinding, shredding, or comminuting material removed from sewage by screens.

Grit.—The heavy mineral matter in water or sewage, such as gravel, cinders, etc.

(H)

Head.—Energy per unit weight of liquid at a specified point. It is expressed in feet.

   Dynamic.—The head against which a pump works.

   Friction.—The head lost by water flowing in a stream or conduit as the result of the disturbances set up by the contact between the moving water and its containing conduit, and by intermolecular friction. In laminar flow the head lost is approximately proportional to the first power of the velocity; in turbulent flow to a higher power, approximately the square of the velocity. While strictly speaking, head losses due to bends, expansions, obstructions, impact, etc., are not included in this term, the usual practice is to include all such head losses under this term.

   Loss of.—The decrease in head between two points.

   Static.—The vertical distance between the free level of the source of supply, and the point of free discharge, or the level of the free surface.

   Total Dynamic.—The difference between the elevation corresponding to the pressure at the discharge flange of a pump and the elevation corresponding to the vacuum or pressure at the suction flange of the pump, corrected to the same datum plane, plus the velocity head at the discharge flange of the pump, minus the velocity head at the suction flange of the pump. It includes the friction head.

   Velocity.—The theoretical vertical height through which a liquid body may be raised due to its kinetic energy. It is equal to the square of the velocity divided by twice the acceleration due to gravity.

Humus.—The dark or black carboniferous residue in the soil resulting from the decomposition of vegetable tissues of plants originally growing therein. Residues similar in appearance and behavior are found in well-digested sludges and in activated sludge.

Hypochlorite.—Compounds of chlorine in which the radical (OCl) is present. They are usually inorganic.

    High Test.—A solid triple salt containing $Ca(OCl)_2$ to the extent that the fresh solid has approximately 70 percent available chlorine. It is not the same as chlorinated lime.

    Sodium.—A solution containing NaOCl, prepared by passing chlorine into solutions of soda ash, or reacting soda ash solutions with high-test hypochlorites and decanting from the precipitated sludge.

(I)

Imhoff Cone.—A conically shaped graduated glass vessel used to measure approximately the volume of settleable solids in various liquids of sewage origin.

Imhoff Tank.—See *Tank, Imhoff.*

Impeller.—The rotating part of a centrifugal pump, containing the curved vanes.

    Closed.—An impeller having the side walls extended from the outer circumference of the suction opening to the vane tips.

    Nonclogging.—An impeller of the open, closed, or semi-closed type designed with large passages for passing large solids.

    Open.—An impeller without attached side walls.

    Screw.—The helical impeller of a screw pump.

Index, Sludge Volume.—The volume is milliliters occupied by one gram of dry solids after the aerated mixed liquor settles 30 minutes, commonly referred to as the Mohlman index.

Influent.—Sewage, water, or other liquid, raw or partly treated, flowing into a reservoir, basin, or treatment plant, or part thereof.

(L)

Lagoon, Sludge.—A relatively shallow basin, or natural depression, used for the storage or digestion of sludge, and sometimes for its ultimate detention or dewatering.

Lift, Air.—A device for raising liquid by injecting air in and near the bottom of a riser pipe submerged in the liquid to be raised.

Liquefaction.—The changing of the organic matter in sewage from an insoluble to a soluble state, and effecting a reduction in its solid contents.

Liquor.—Any liquid.

    Mixed.—A mixture of activated sludge and sewage in the aeration tank undergoing activated sludge treatment.

    Supernatant.—(1) The liquor overlying deposited solids. (2) The liquid in a sludge-digestion tank which lies between the sludge at the bottom and the floating scum at the top.

Loading.—The time rate at which material is applied to a treatment device involving length, area, or volume or other design factor.

BOD, Filter.—The pounds of oxygen demand in the applied liquid per unit of filter bed area, or volume of stone per day.

Weir.—Gallons overflow per day per foot of weir length.

(M)

Main, Force.—A pipe line on the discharge side of a water or sewage pumping station, usually under pressure.

Manometer.—An instrument for measuring pressure; usually it consists of a U-shaped tube containing a liquid, the surface of which in one end of the tube moves proportionally with changes in pressure upon the liquid in the other end. The term is also applied to a tube type of differential pressure gage.

Matter.—Solids, liquids, and gases.

Inorganic.—Chemical substances of mineral origin. They are not usually volatile with heat.

Organic.—Chemical substances of animal, vegetable and industrial origin. They include most carbon compounds, combustible and volatile with heat.

Suspended.—(1) Solids in suspension in sewage or effluent. (2) Commonly used for solids in suspension in sewage or effluent which can readily be removed by filtering in a laboratory.

Microorganism.—Minute organisms either plant or animal, invisible or barely visible to the naked eye.

Moisture, Percentage.—The water content of sludge expressed as the ratio of the loss in weight after drying at 103°C, to the original weight of the sample, multiplied by one hundred.

Mold.—See *Fungi.*

Most Probable Number, (MPN).—In the testing of bacterial density by the dilution method, that number of organisms per unit volume which, in accordance with statistical theory, would be more likely than any other possible number to yield the observed test result or which would yield the observed test result with the greatest frequency. Expressed as density of organisms per 100 ml.

(N)

Nitrification.—The oxidation of ammonia nitrogen into nitrates through biochemical action.

(O)

Overflow Rate.—One of the criteria for the design of settling tanks in treatment plants; expressed in gallons per day per square foot of surface area in the settling tank. See *Surface Settling Rate.*

Oxidation.—The addition of oxygen, removal of hydrogen, or the increase in the valence of an element.

Biochemical.—See *Oxidation, Sewage.*

Biological.—See *Oxidation, Sewage.*

Direct.—Oxidation of substances in sewage without the benefit of living organisms, by the direct application of air or oxidizing agents such as chlorine.

Sewage.—The process whereby, through the agency of living organisms in the presence of oxygen, the organic matter contained in sewage is converted into a more stable form.

Oxygen.—A chemical element.

Available.—The quantity of uncombined or free oxygen dissolved in the water of a stream.

Balance.—The relation between the biochemical oxygen demand of a sewage or treatment plant effluent and the oxygen available in the diluting water.

Consumed.—The quantity of oxygen taken from potassium permanganate in solution by a liquid containing organic matter. Commonly regarded as an index of the carbonaceous matter present. Time and temperature must be specified. The chemical oxygen demand (COD) uses potassium dichromate.

Deficiency.—The additional quantity of oxygen required to satisfy the biochemical oxygen demand in a given liquid. Usually expressed in parts per million.

Dissolved.—Usually designated as DO. The oxygen dissolved in sewage, water or other liquid usually expressed in parts per million or percent of saturation.

Residual.—The dissolved oxygen content of a stream after deoxygenation has begun.

Sag.—A curve that represents the profile of dissolved oxygen content along the course of a stream, resulting from deoxygenation associated with biochemical oxidation of organic matter, and reoxygenation through the absorption of atmospheric oxygen and through biological photosynthesis.

(P)

Parts Per Million.—Milligrams per liter expressing the concentration of a specified component in a dilute sewage. A ratio of pounds per million pounds, grams per million grams, etc.

Percolation.—The flow or trickling of a liquid downward through a contact or filtering medium. The liquid may or may not fill the pores of the medium.

Period.—A time interval.

Aeration.—(1) The theoretical time, usually expressed in hours that the mixed liquor is subjected to aeration in an aeration tank undergoing activated sludge treatment; is equal to (a) the volume of the tank divided by (b) the volumetric rate of flow of the sewage and return sludge. (2) The theoretical time that water is subjected to aeration.

Detention.—The theoretical time required to displace the contents of a tank or unit at a given rate of discharge (volume divided by rate of discharge).

Flowing-Through.—The average time required for a small unit volume of liquid to pass through a basin from inlet to outlet. In a tank where there is no short-circuiting, and no spaces, the detention period and the flowing-through period are the same.

pH.—The logarithm of the reciprocal of the hydrogen-ion concentration. It is not the same as the alkalinity and cannot be calculated therefrom.

Plankton.—Drifting organisms, usually microscopic.

Pollution.—The addition of sewage, industrial wastes, or other harmful or objectionable material to water.

Ponding, Filter.—See *Pooling, Filter.*

Pooling, Filter.—The formation of pools of sewage on the surface of filters caused by clogging.

Population Equivalent.—(1) The calculated population which would normally contribute the same amount of biochemical oxygen demand (BOD) per day. A common base is 0.167 lb. of 5-day BOD per capita per day. (2) For an industrial waste, the estimated number of people contributing sewage equal in strength to a unit volume of the waste or to some other unit involved in producing or manufacturing a particular commodity.

Pre-Aeration.—A preparatory treatment of sewage comprising aeration to remove gases, add oxygen, or promote flotation of grease, and aid coagulation.

Precipitation, Chemical.—Precipitation induced by addition of chemicals.

Pressure.—Pounds per square inch or square foot.

    Atmospheric.—The pressure exerted by the atmosphere at any point. Such pressure decreases the elevation of the point above sea level increases. One atmosphere is equal to 14.7 lb. per sq. in., 29.92 in. or 760 mm of mercury column or 33.90 ft. of water column at average sea level under standard conditions.

    Hydrostatic.—The pressure, expressed as a total force per unit of area, exerted by a body of water at rest.

    Negative.—A pressure less than the local atmospheric pressure at a given point.

Process.—A sequence of operations.

    Activated Sludge.—A biological sewage treatment process in which a mixture of sewage and activated sludge is agitated and aerated. The activated sludge is subsequently separated from the treated sewage (mixed liquor) by sedimentation, and wasted or returned to the process as needed. The treated sewage overflows the weir of the settling tank in which separation from the sludge takes place.

    Biological.—The process by which the life activities of bacteria, and other microorganisms in the search for food, break down complex organic materials into simple, more stable substances. Self-purification of sewage-polluted streams, sludge digestion, and all so-called secondary sewage treatments result from this process. Also called Biochemical Process.

Pump.—A device used to increase the head on a liquid.

Booster.—A pump installed on a pipe line to raise the pressure of the water on the discharge side of the pump.

Centrifugal, Fluid.—A pump consisting of an impeller fixed on a rotating shaft and enclosed in a casing, having an inlet and a discharge connection. The rotating impeller creates pressure in the liquid by the velocity derived from centrifugal force.

Centrifugal, Screw.—A centrifugal pump having a screw-type impeller; may be axial-flow, or combined axial and radial-flow, type.

Centrifugal, Closed.—A centrifugal pump where the impeller is built with the vanes enclosed within circular disks.

Diaphragm.—A pump in which a flexible diaphragm, generally of rubber, is the operating part; it is fastened at the outer rim; when the diaphragm is moved in one direction, suction is exerted and when it is moved in the opposite direction, the liquid is forced through a discharge valve.

Double-Suction.—A centrifugal pump with suction pipes connected to the casing from both sides.

Duplex.—A reciprocating pump consisting of two cylinders placed side by side and connected to the same suction and discharge pipe, the pistons moving so that one exerts suction while the other exerts pressure, with the result that the discharge from the pump is continuous.

Horizontal Screw.—A pump with a horizontal cylindrical casing, in which operates a runner with radial blades, like those of a ship's propeller. The pump has a high efficiency at low heads and high discharges, and is used extensively in drainage work.

Mixed Flow.—A centrifugal pump in which the head is developed partly by centrifugal force and partly by the lift of the vanes on the liquid.

Open Centrifugal.—A centrifugal pump where the impeller is built with a set of independent vanes.

Propeller.—A centrifugal pump which develops most of its head by the propelling or lifting action of the vanes on the liquids.

Purification.—The removal, by natural or artificial methods, or objectionable matter from water.

Putrefaction.—Biological decomposition of organic matter with the production of ill-smelling products associated with anaerobic conditions.

Putrescibility.—(1) The relative tendency of organic matter to undergo decomposition in the absence of oxygen. (2) The susceptibility of waste waters, sewage, effluent, or sludge to putrefaction. (3) Term used in water or sewage analysis to define stability of a polluted water or raw or partially treated sewage.

(Q)

Quicklime.—A calcined material, the major part of which is calcium oxide or calcium oxide in natural association with a lesser amount of magnesium oxide, capable of slaking with water.

(R)

Rack.—An arrangement of parallel bars.

Bar.—A screen composed of parallel bars, either vertical or inclined, placed in a waterway to catch floating debris, and from which the screenings may be raked. Also called rack.

Coarse.—A rack with ¾ inch to 6 inch spaces between bars.

Fine.—Generally used for a screen or rack which has openings of 3/32 to 3/16 inches. Some screens have less than 3/32 inch openings.

Radius, Hydraulic.—The cross-sectional area of a stream of water divided by the length of that part of its periphery in contact with its containing conduit; the ratio of area to wetted perimeter.

Rate.—The result of dividing one concrete number by another.

Filtration.—The rate of application of water or sewage to a filter, usually expressed in million gallons per acre per day, or gallons per minute per square foot.

Infiltration.—The rate, usually expressed in cubic feet per second, or million gallons per day per mile of waterway, at which ground water enters an infiltration ditch or gallery, drain, sewer, or other underground conduit.

Surface Settling.—Gallons per day per square foot of free horizontal water surface. Used in design of sedimentation tanks.

Reaeration.—The absorption of oxygen by a liquid, the dissolved oxygen content of which has been depleted.

Reaeration, Sludge.—The continuous aeration of sludge after its initial aeration in the activated sludge process.

Recirculation.—(1) The refiltration of all or a portion of the effluent in a high-rate trickling filter for the purpose of maintaining a uniform high rate through the filter. (2) The return of effluent to the incoming flow to reduce its strength.

Reduction.—The decrease in a specific variable.

Over-All.—The percentage reduction in the final effluent as compared to the raw sewage.

Percentage.—The ratio of material removed from water or sewage by treatment, to the material originally present (expressed as a percentage).

Sludge.—The reduction in the quantity and change in character of sewage sludge as the result of digestion.

Regulator.—A device or apparatus for controlling the quantity of sewage admitted to an intercepting sewer or a unit of a sewage treatment plant.

Reoxygenation.—The replenishment of oxygen in a stream from (1) dilution water entering stream, (2) biological reoxygenation through the activities of certain oxygen-producing plants, and (3) atmospheric reaction.

Residual, Chlorine.—See *Chlorine, residual.*

Rotor.—The member of an electric generator or water wheel which rotates.

Screen.—A device with openings, generally of uniform size, used to retain or remove suspended or floating solids in flowing water or sewage, and to prevent them from entering an intake or passing a given point in a conduit. The screening element may consist of parallel bars, rods, wires, grating, wire mesh, or perforated plate, and the openings may be of any shape, although they are generally circular or rectangular. The device may also be used to segregate granular material, such as sand, crushed rock, and soil, into various sizes.

Scum.—A mass of sewage matter which floats on the surface of sewage.

Second-Foot.—An abbreviated expression for cubic foot per second.

Sedimentation.—The process of subsidence and deposition of suspended matter carried by water, sewage, or other liquids, by gravity. It is usually accomplished by reducing the velocity of the liquid below the point where it can transport the suspended material. Also called Settling. See *Precipitation, Chemical.*
    Final.—Settling of partly settled, flocculated or oxidized sewage in a final tank.
    Plain.—The sedimentation of suspended matter in a liquid unaided by chemicals or other special means, and without provision for the decomposition of deposited solids in contact with the sewage.

Seeding, Sludge.—The inoculation of undigested sewage solids with sludge that has undergone decomposition, for the purpose of introducing favorable organisms, thereby accelerating the initial stages of digestion.

Self-Purification.—The natural processes of purification in a moving or still body of water whereby the bacterial content is reduced, the BOD is largely satisfied, the organic content is stabilized, and the dissolved oxygen returned to normal.

Sewage.—Largely the water supply of a community after it has been fouled by various uses. From the standpoint of source it may be a combination of the liquid or water-carried wastes from residences, business buildings, and institutions, together with those from industrial establishments, and with such ground water, surface water, and storm water as may be present.
    Domestic.—Sewage derived principally from dwellings, business buildings, institutions, and the like. (It may or may not contain ground water, surface water, or storm water.)
    Fresh.—Sewage of recent origin containing dissolved oxygen at the point of examination.
    Industrial.—Sewage in which industrial wastes predominate.
    Stable.—Sewage in which the organic matter has been stabilized.
    Raw.—Sewage prior to receiving any treatment.
    Sanitary.—(1) Domestic sewage with storm and surface water excluded. (2) Sewage discharging from the sanitary conveniences of dwellings (including apartment houses and hotels), office buildings, factories, or institutions. (3) The water supply of a community after it has been used and discharged into a sewer.

Septic.—Sewage undergoing putrefaction under anaerobic conditions.

Settled.—Sewage from which most of the settleable solids have been removed by sedimentation.

Stale.—A sewage containing little or no oxygen, but as yet free from putrefaction.

Sewer.—A pipe or conduit, generally closed, but normally not flowing full, for carrying sewage and other waste liquids.

Branch.—A sewer which receives sewage from a relatively small area, and discharges into a main sewer.

Combined.—A sewer receiving both surface runoff and sewage.

House.—A pipe conveying sewage from a single building to a common sewer or point of immediate disposal.

Intercepting.—A sewer which receives dry-weather flow from a number of transverse sewers or outlets and frequently additional predetermined quantities of storm water (if from a combined system), and conducts such waters to a point for treatment or disposal.

Lateral.—A sewer which discharges into a branch or other sewer and has no other common sewer tributary to it.

Main.—(1) A sewer to which one or more branch sewers are tributary. Also called *Trunk Sewer*. (2) In plumbing, the public sewer in a street, alley, or other premises under the jurisdiction of a municipality.

Sanitary.—A sewer which carries sewage and to which storm, surface, and ground waters are not intentionally admitted.

Separate.—See Sewer, Sanitary.

Storm.—A sewer which carries storm water and surface water, street wash and other wash waters, or drainage, but excludes sewage and industrial wastes. Also called Storm Drain.

Trunk.—A sewer which receives many tributary branches and serves a large territory. See *Sewer, Main.*

Outfall.—A sewer which receives the sewage from a collecting system and carries it to a point of final discharge.

Outlet.—The point of final discharge of sewage or treatment plant effluent.

Sewerage.—A comprehensive term which includes facilities for collecting, pumping, treating, and disposing of sewage; the sewerage system and the sewage treatment works.

Shredder.—A device for size reduction.

Screenings.—A device which disintegrates screenings.

Sludge.—An apparatus to break down lumps in air-dried digested sludge.

Siphon.—A closed conduit, a portion of which lies above the hydraulic grade line. This results in a pressure less than atmospheric in that portion, and hence requires that a vacuum be created to start flow.

Skimmer, Grease.—A device for removing floating grease or scum from the surface of sewage in a tank.

Skimming.—The process of removing floating grease or scum from the surface of sewage in a tank.

Sleek.—The thin oily film usually present which gives characteristic appearance to the surface of water into which sewage or oily waste has discharged. Also termed slick.

Sloughing.—The phenomenon associated with trickling filters and contact aerators, whereby slime and solids accumulated in the media are discharged with the effluent.

Sludge.—The accumulated settled solids deposited from sewage or industrial wastes, raw or treated, in tanks or basins, and containing more or less water to form a semiliquid mass.

  Activated.—Sludge floc produced in raw or settled sewage by the growth of zoogleal bacteria and other organisms in the presence of dissolved oxygen, and accumulated in sufficient concentration by returning floc previously formed.

  Bulking.—A phenomenon that occurs in activated sludge plants whereby the sludge occupies excessive volumes and will not concentrate readily.

  Conditioning.—Treatment of liquid sludge preliminary to dewatering and drainability, usually by the addition of chemicals.

  Dewatering.—The process of removing a part of the water in sludge by any method, such as draining, evaporation, pressing, centrifuging, exhausting, passing between rollers, or acid flotation, with or without heat. It involves reducing from a liquid to a spadable condition rather than merely changing the density of the liquid (concentration) on the one hand or drying (as in a kiln) on the other.

  Digestion.—The process by which organic or volatile matter in sludge is gasified, liquefied, mineralized, or converted into more stable organic matter, through the activities of living organisms.

  Humus.—See *Humus*.

Solids.—Material in the solid state.

  Dissolved.—Solids which are present in solution.

  Nonsettleable.—Finely divided suspended solids which will not subside in quiescent water, sewage, or other liquid in a reasonable period. Such period is commonly, though arbitrarily, taken as two hours.

  Settleable.—Suspended solids which will subside in quiescent water, sewage, or other liquid in a reasonable period. Such period is commonly, though arbitrarily, taken as one hour. Also called Settling Solids.

  Suspended.—The quantity of material deposited when a quantity of water, sewage, or other liquid is filtered through an asbestos mat in a Gooch crucible.

  Total.—The solids in water, sewage, or other liquids; it includes the suspended solids (largely removable by filter paper) and the filterable solids (those which pass through filter paper).

  Volatile.—The quantity of solids in water, sewage, or other liquid, lost on ignition of the total solids.

Squeegee.—(1) A device, generally with a soft rubber edge, used for dislodging and removing deposited sewage solids from the walls and bottoms of sedimentation tanks. (2) The metal blades attached to the lower arms of a clarifier mechanism to move the sludge along the tank **bottom.**

212

Stability.—The ability of any substance, such as sewage, effluent, or digested sludge, to resist putrefaction. It is the antonym of putrescibility.

Standard Methods.—Methods of analysis of water, sewage, and sludge approved by a Joint Committee of the American Public Health Association, American Water Works Association, and Federation of Sewage Works Associations.

Stator.—The stationary member of an electric generator or motor.

Sterilization.—The destruction of all living organisms, ordinarily through the agency of heat or of some chemical.

(T)

Tank.—A circular or rectangular vessel.

Detritus.—A detention chamber larger than a grit chamber, usually with provision for removing the sediment without interrupting the flow of sewage. A settling tank of short detention period designed, primarily, to remove heavy settleable solids.

Final Settling.—A tank through which the effluent from a trickling filter, or aeration or contact aeration tank flows for the purpose of removing the settleable solids.

Flocculating.—A tank used for the formation of floc by the agitation of liquids.

Imhoff.—A deep two-storied sewage tank originally patented by Karl Imhoff, consisting of an upper or continuous flow sedimentation chamber and a lower or sludge-digestion chamber. The floor of the upper chamber slopes steeply to trapped slots, through which solids may slide into the lower chamber. The lower chamber receives no fresh sewage directly, but is provided with gas vents and with means for drawing digested sludge from near the bottom.

Primary Settling.—The first settling tank through which sewage is passed in a treatment works.

Secondary.—A tank following a trickling filter or activated sludge aeration chamber.

Sedimentation.—A tank or basin, in which water, sewage, or other liquid containing settleable solids, is retained for a sufficient time, and in which the velocity of flow is sufficiently low, to remove by gravity a part of the suspended matter. Usually, in sewage treatment, the detention period is short enough to avoid anaerobic decomposition. Also termed Settling or Subsidence Tank.

Septic.—A single-story settling tank in which the settled sludge is in immediate contact with the sewage flowing through the tank, while the organic solids are decomposed by anaerobic bacterial action.

Sludge-Digestion—See *Digester.*

Thickener, Sludge.—A type of sedimentation tank in which the sludge is permitted to settle, usually equipped with scrapers traveling along the bottom of the tank which push the settled sludge to a sump, from which it is removed by gravity or by pumping.

Treatment.—Any definite process for modifying the state of matter.

Preliminary.—The conditioning of an industrial waste at its source prior to discharge, to remove or to neutralize substances injurious to sewers and treatment processes or to effect a partial reduction in load on the treatment process. In the treatment process, unit operations which prepare the liquor for subsequent major operations.

Primary.—The first major (sometimes the only) treatment in a sewage treatment works, usually sedimentation. The removal of a high percentage of suspended matter but little or no colloidal and dissolved matter.

Secondary.—The treatment of sewage by biological methods after primary treatment by sedimentation.

Sewage.—Any artificial process to which sewage is subjected in order to remove or alter its objectional constituents and thus to render it less offensive or dangerous.

Trap, Flame.—A device containing a fine metal gauze placed in a gas pipe, which prevents a flame from traveling back in the pipe and causing an explosion. See *Arrester, Flame.*

(V)

Venturi Meter.—A meter for measuring flow of water or other fluid through closed conduits or pipes, consisting of a Venturi tube and one of several proprietary forms of flow registering devices. The device was developed as a measuring device and patented by Clemens Herschel.

(W)

Waste Stabilization Pond.—Any pond, natural or artificial, receiving raw or partially treated sewage or waste, in which stabilization occurs due to sunlight, air, and microoganisms.

Water, Potable.—Water which does not contain objectionable pollution, contamination, minerals, or infection, and is considered satisfactory for domestic consumption.

Weir.—A dam with an edge or notch, sometimes arranged for measuring liquid flow.

Effluent.—A weir at the outflow end of a sedimentation basin or other hydraulic structure.

Influent.—A weir at the inflow end of a sedimentation basin.

Rectangular.—A weir whose notch is rectangular in shape.

Triangular.—A weir whose notch is triangular in shape, usually used to measure very small flows. Also called a V-notch.

Peripheral.—The outlet weir in a circular settling tank, extending around the inside of its circumference and over which the effluent discharges.

Rate.—See *Loading*, Weir.

(Z)

Zooglea.—A jelly-like matrix developed by bacteria, associated with growths in oxidizing beds.

APPENDIX II

ARITHMETIC OF SEWAGE TREATMENT

The English system of measurements is used for computations at sewage treatment works, except in the case of a few determinations. The metric system will be mentioned where the metric units are used.

Basic Units

Linear	1 inch (in.)	= 2.540 centimeters (cm)
	1 foot (ft.)	= 12 inches (in.)
	1 yard (yd.)	= 3 feet (ft.)
	1 mile	= 5,280 feet
	1 meter (m)	= 39.37 in. = 3.281 ft.
		= 1.094 yd.
	1 meter	= 100 centimeters
Area	1 square foot (sq. ft.)	= 144 square inches (sq. in.)
	1 square yard (sq. yd.)	= 9 sq. ft.
	1 acre	= 43,560 sq. ft.
	1 square mile	= 640 acres
Volume	1 cubic foot	= 1728 cubic inches (cu. in.)
	1 cubic yard	= 27 cu. ft.
	1 cubic foot	= 7.48 gallons
	1 gallon (gal.)	= 231 cu. in.
	1 gallon	= 4 quarts (qt)
	1 gallon	= 3.785 liters (l)
	1 liter	= 1000 milliliters (ml)
Weight	1 pound (lb.)	= 16 ounces = 7000 grains
		= 453.6 grams
	1 ounce	= 28.35 grams (g)
	1 kilogram	= 1000 grams
	1 gram	= 1000 milligrams (mg)
	1 cu. ft. water	= 62.4 pounds
	1 gallon water	= 8.33 pounds
	1 liter water	= 1 kilogram
	1 milliliter water	= 1 gram

Definition of Terms

A *ratio* is the indicated division of two pure numbers. As such is indicates the relative magnitude of two quantities. The ratio of 2 to 3 is written 2/3.

A *pure* number is used without reference to any particular thing.

A *concrete* number applies to a particular thing and is the product of a pure number and a physical unit. 5 ft. means 5 times 1 ft. or 5 $\times$ (1 ft.).

Rate units are formed when one physical unit is divided by another.

$$\frac{60 \text{ ft.}}{2 \text{ sec.}} = 30 \frac{(\text{ft.})}{(\text{sec.})}$$

Physical units can be formed by multiplying two or more other physical units.

1 ft. $\times$ 1 ft. = 1 ft. $\times$ ft. = 1 ft.² (square foot)

Physical units may cancel each other.

$$\frac{6 \text{ ft.} \times 7.48 \text{ gallons}}{1 \text{ ft.}} = 6 \times 7.48 \text{ gallons}$$

Per cent means per 100 and is the numerator of a fraction whose denominator is always 100. It may be expressed by the symbol "%." The word *per* refers to a fraction whose numerator precedes *per* and whose denominator follows. Hence "per" means "divided by." It is often indicated by a sloping line as "/."

Problem: What is 15 per cent of 60?

$$60 \times \frac{15}{100} = \frac{900}{100} = 9$$

Problem: One pound of lime is stirred into one gallon of water.

What is the per cent of lime in the slurry?

$$\frac{1}{1 + 8.33} \times 100 = \frac{100}{1 + 8.33} = 10.7 \text{ per cent}$$

Formulas

Circumference of a circle $= \Pi$ D $= 2\,\Pi$ R

Area of a circle $\qquad = \Pi$ R² $= \dfrac{\Pi\, \text{D}^2}{4}$

$\Pi = 3.1416$

Area of triangle $= \frac{1}{2}$ base $\times$ altitude

Area of rectangle $=$ base $\times$ altitude

Cylindrical area $=$ circumference of base $\times$ length

Volume of cylinder $=$ area of base $\times$ length

Volume of rectangular tank $=$ area of bottom $\times$ depth

Volume of cone $= 1/3 \times$ area of base $\times$ height

Velocity $=$ distance divided by time. Inches, feet, or miles divided by hours, minutes, or seconds.

Discharge $=$ volume of flow divided by time.
    Gallons or cubic feet divided by days, hours, minutes, or seconds.
    1 cu. ft. per sec. $= 647,000$ gallons per day.
    1 mgd $= 1.54$ cfs $= 92.4$ cfm

Detention Time. The theoretical time equals the volume of tank divided by the flow per unit time. The flow volume and tank volume must be in the same units.

$$\frac{20,000 \text{ gal.}}{200 \;\frac{\text{gal.}}{\text{min.}}} = 100 \text{ minutes}$$

Problem: A tank is $60 \times 20 \times 30$ ft. The flow is 5 mgd.

What is the detention time in hours?

1 mgd = 92.4 cfm

$$\frac{60 \text{ ft.} \times 20 \text{ ft.} \times 30 \text{ ft.}}{92.4 \times 5 \;\frac{\text{ft.}^3}{\text{min.}}} = 78 \text{ min. or 1 hr. and 18 min. or 1.3 hours}$$

Surface Settling Rate:

This means gallons per square foot of tank surface per day.

Problem: If the daily flow is 0.5 mgd and the tank is 50 ft. long and 12 ft. wide, calculate the surface settling rate.

$$\frac{500,000 \text{ gal./day}}{50 \text{ ft.} \times 12 \text{ ft.}} = \frac{833 \text{ gal.}}{\text{ft.}^2 \times \text{day}}$$

Weir Overflow Rate:

This means gallons per day per foot length of weir.

Problem: A circular settling tank is 90 ft. in diameter. The flow is 3.0 mgd. Calculate the weir overflow rate.

$$\frac{3,000,000 \text{ gal./day}}{\Pi \times 90 \text{ ft.}} = \frac{10,600 \text{ gal.}}{\text{ft.} \times \text{day}}$$

Rate of Filtration: The mgd is divided by the acres of stone to give

$$\frac{\text{mg}}{\text{acre} \times \text{day}} = \text{mgad}$$

$$\frac{\text{mg}}{\text{acre} \times \text{ft.} \times \text{day}} = \text{mgaftd}$$

An acre-ft. is an acre in area and 1 ft. deep.
A fixed-nozzle filter is 140×125 feet. Stone is six feet deep. Flow is 9 mgd. Calculate the rate of dosing or hydraulic loading in mg per acre-foot per day.

$$\frac{140 \times 125}{43560} = \text{acres} = 0.402$$

$$0.402 \times 6 = 2.412 \text{ acre-feet}$$

$$\frac{9}{2.412} = \frac{\text{mg}}{\text{acre} \times \text{ft.} \times \text{day}} = 3.73$$

The BOD of a settling tank effluent is 200 ppm. If 15 lb. of BOD per 1000 ft.³ of stone is to be the organic loading, how many cubic feet of stone are necessary with a hydraulic loading of 3 mgd.

$$\frac{200 \times 8.33 \times 3 \times 1000}{15} = 333,333 \text{ ft.}^3$$

$$\frac{333,333}{6} = 55,500 \text{ ft.}^2 \text{ for filter area if stone is 6 ft. deep.}$$

Parts per million:

This is a weight ratio. Any unit may be used; pounds per million pounds or milligrams per liter if the liquid has a specific gravity equal to water or very nearly so. 1 liter of water = 1,000,000 milligrams.

1 ppm = 8.33 lbs. per million gallons

1 ppm = 1 milligram per liter

A sewage with 600 ppm suspended solids has $600 \times 8.33 = 4998$ lb. of suspended solids per million gallons.

Efficiency of Removal:

$$\frac{\text{ppm influent} - \text{ppm effluent}}{\text{ppm influent}} \; 100 = \text{per cent efficiency of removal}$$

Percent of Moisture:

$$\frac{\text{wt. of wet sludge} - \text{wt. of dry sludge}}{\text{wt. of wet sludge}} \; 100 = \text{per cent moisture}$$

Percent of Dry solids:

$$\frac{\text{wt. of dry sludge}}{\text{wt. of wet sludge}} \; 100 = \text{per cent dry solids}$$

Other calculated quantities that need no special explanation are:
Square feet of sludge drying bed per capita
Cubic feet of digestion space per capita
Cubic feet of sludge produced per day per capita
Cubic feet of grit per million gallons
Pounds of sludge per capita per day
Cubic feet of gas per capita per day
Kilowatt-hours per million gallons pumped

Specific Gravity: This is the ratio of the density of a substance to the density of water. There is no unit. Density = the weight of unit volume.

$$\text{S.G.} = \frac{(\text{wt. bottle with sludge}) - (\text{wt. of empty bottle})}{(\text{wt. bottle with water}) - (\text{wt. of empty bottle})}$$

1 gallon of water = 8.33 lbs.
1 cu. ft. of water = 62.4 lbs.
These vary slightly with temperature.
    Water at   32°F. = 62.417 lb./ft.³
    Water at   62°F. = 62.355 lb./ft.³
    Water at 212°F. = 59.7   lb./ft.³
    Ice   = 57.5   lb./ft.³

Problem: What is the weight of dry solids in 1000 gallons of 10% sludge whose specific gravity is 1.04?

$$1000 \times 8.33 \times 1.04 \times \frac{10}{100} = 866.3 \text{ lbs.}$$

Mixtures:

If two materials of different percentages are to be mixed to produce an intermediate percentage, it may be done by rectangle method.
Problem: We have 30 per cent and 50 per cent material. In what ratio shall they be mixed to produce 37 per cent material.

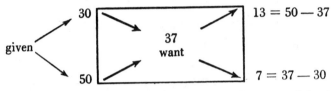

Desired ration is 13 parts of the 30 per cent and 7 parts of the 50 per cent. This will give us 20 parts of 37 per cent.

APPENDIX III

CHEMISTRY

A knowledge of chemistry is desirable for sewage treatment plant operators, first to control the processes occurring in their plants and, second, to measure the effectiveness of such treatment as is used.

Chemistry, in its broad sense, deals with the composition of matter and how it changes. A description of matter should include a statement telling of what it is made and the manner or state in which it exists. Thus a description of water should state that it is composed of hydrogen and oxygen in certain proportions and exists as a liquid. Ice also is composed of hydrogen and oxygen in the same proportions, but exists as a solid. Such a change in matter is called a physical change and takes place when its manner or physical state of existence is changed but its chemical composition remains unaltered.

A *chemical change* is an alteration of the composition of matter, as that which takes place when quick lime is slaked to form hydrated lime or when iron rusts.

Actions or measurements relating to physical changes, such as temperature, rates of settling, particle size, velocity of flow, etc., are dealt with under the science of physics. Chemistry deals with the composition and change in composition of matter. It may be subdivided into two branches. Analytical chemistry deals with the breaking down of matter into its fundamental components. Synthetic chemistry is concerned with the building up of matter from its elemental constituents. Years of investigations have shown that all matter is composed of combinations of one or more fundamental substances called elements.

Elements are substances which cannot be subdivided into simpler sub-substances by ordinary chemical change. Water can be broken down into hydrogen and oxygen, but it has not been possible to break down hydrogen or oxygen to produce simpler substances. Therefore, hydrogen and oxygen are elements. In all, there are 102 stable elements, of which less than twenty are of importance to the chemistry of sewage treatment. A partial list of chemical elements is shown in Table 11. Elements themselves are made up of unit particles called atoms.

Atoms are the smallest pieces of an element that can take part in a chemical change. You might consider atoms as extremely small building blocks, each one of any single element being chemically the same, but different from atoms of other elements.

Isotopes are elements that may contain two or more distinct kinds of atoms, identical in their general chemical properties but differing essentially in mass. Most of the ordinary elements consist of mixtures of isotopes. Thus, chlorine consists of a mixture of two isotopes of mass 35 and of mass 37 in such proportion that the average atomic weight is 35.46.

TABLE 11

Basic Data for Elements and Radicals Encountered in Sewage Treatment (only the most common valences shown).

	Atomic Symbol	Atomic Weight	Valence	Combining Weight
Elements				
Aluminum	Al	26.98	+3	8.99
Calcium	Ca	40.08	+2	20.04
Carbon	C	12.01	+4	3.00
Chlorine	Cl	35.46	−1	35.46
Copper	Cu	63.54	+2	31.77
Hydrogen	H	1.008	+1	1.008
Iodine	I	126.91	−1	126.91
Iron	Fe	55.85	+3	18.62
Magnesium	Mg	24.32	+2	12.16
Manganese	Mn	54.93	Several	
Nitrogen	N	14.01	Several	
Oxygen	O	16.00	−2	8.00
Potassium	K	39.10	+1	39.10
Sodium	Na	23.00	+1	23.00
Sulfur	S	32.06	Several	
Radicals				
Hydroxyl	(OH)		−1	17.00
Nitrite	(NO_2)		−1	46.01
Nitrate	(NO_3)		−1	62.01
Sulfate	(SO_4)		−2	48.03
Carbonate	(CO_3)		−2	30.00
Bicarbonate	(HCO_3)		−1	61.01
Phosphate	(PO_4)		−3	31.66
Silicate	(SiO_3)		−2	38.05
Ammonium	(NH_4)		+1	17.03

Atoms of an element may combine with each other or with atoms of other elements to form molecules. *Molecules* are the smallest portions of a substance that can exist and still retain the composition of the substance. If two atoms of chlorine combine, we have a molecule of chlorine gas, which is how the free element chlorine exists in nature. If one atom of chlorine combines with one atom of sodium, a molecule of ordinary table salt is produced. When atoms of different elements combine, the product is called a compound and the smallest piece of a compound that can exist and retain the composition of the compound is a molecule. If we again consider atoms as building blocks and the blocks cannot be subdivided, it must follow that atoms of elements combine with atoms of other elements in steps of one atom at a time. Thus, one, two or three atoms of one element can combine with one, two or three atoms of another element, but never with a fraction of an atom.

Law of multiple proportions. This idea that matter is composed of combination of blocks, called atoms, explains the fact that elements can only combine with each other in certain definite proportions or multiples thereof. This immediately brings some order out of what might be chaos. One atom of carbon will combine with one atom of oxygen to form carbon monoxide. If one atom of carbon united with two atoms of oxygen, the product would not be the same. Actually, when one atom of carbon combines with two atoms of oxygen, an entirely different compound called carbon dioxide is formed. If we think of compounds as consisting of an aggregate of molecules each of which is made up of a definite proportion of atoms of different elements, then we can understand why a pure compound is always exactly the same in composition, regardless of how it is made or where it is found. Water, made by exploding hydrogen and oxygen, always is one part hydrogen by weight, and eight parts oxygen. Water made from burning gasoline is exactly the same. Water in Timbuktu, and water in the jelly you eat is all composed of one part hydrogen and eight parts oxygen by weight.

Atoms are extremely small particles which cannot be isolated and weighed. However, the weights of atoms of different elements can be compared and a relative weight obtained for each. As oxygen combines with many elements, it is convenient to consider it as a sort of standard for weight comparison and further, if a weight value of 16 is assigned to oxygen no element will have a combining weight less than one.

As molecules are composed of atoms, it must follow that the weight of a molecule is the sum of the weights of each atom that makes up the molecule.

Molecular weight is the sum of the atomic weights of the elements in the molecule. Thus, water is composed of 2 atoms of hydrogen, each of atomic weight 1.0 and one atom of oxygen, atomic weight 16, making the molecular weight of water $2 \times 1 + 16 = 18$. Similarly, carbon dioxide is one carbon atom 12, and two oxygen atoms each 16, making the molecular weight $12 + 2 \times 16 = 44$.

Names—The names of elements have been generally derived from Greek and Latin roots descriptive of their character. Thus, iodine is named from its violet color, chlorine from its green color, others from localities where they were discovered, and others are derived from the names of minerals from which they were extracted.

When only two elements unite to form a compound, the name of the second element is modified to end in *ide*. Thus, when sodium and chlorine are combined to form a salt, it is called sodium chloride. Compounds of one element with oxygen are called oxides and when more than one oxygen atom is present, the Greek prefix *di* for two and *tri* for three is added. Thus, sulfur dioxide and sulfur trioxide describe sulfur compounds containing two or three atoms of oxygen for each atom of sulfur.

Symbols. To illustrate chemical changes, symbols have been developed for the different elements which indicate one atom of the element. Thus, an atom of chlorine may be written as Cl and of oxygen as O. Generally, the symbol is the first or first and second letter of the name of the element, although often the English name of the element is given but the abbreviation of the Latin or Greek name is used as the symbol. Thus, sodium is Na, the abbreviation of natrium, and iron is Fe, the abbreviation of ferrum. These symbols, together with the names of the common elements, are given in Table 10.

Formulae. By use of these symbols it is possible to write formulae which indicate the number and kinds of atoms making up a molecule. For example, HCl means that a molecule of hydrochloric acid is composed of one atom of hydrogen and one atom of chlorine. When more than one atom of an element occurs in a molecule, it is indicated by a number written under the symbol. Thus, H_2SO_4 means that a molecule of sulfuric acid contains two atoms of hydrogen, one of sulfur and four of oxygen. When a group of atoms is enclosed in parenthesis and a subscript number used, it means the whole group occurs in the moleule as many times as the value of the subscript numbers. For example: $Fe_2(SO_4)_3$ means iron sulfate contains two atoms of iron and three sulfate groups each containing one atom of sulfur and four atoms of oxygen. This is done because certain elements combine to form groups which react with other elements in a manner similar to a single element. The group is called a radical and will be discussed more fully under solutions. See Table 10. Another type of group symbol is used to indicate the association of molecules of complex compounds with molecules of simpler compounds. The latter can enter into or be expelled from the complex molecule without themselves being changed. For example, aluminum sulfate is $Al_2(SO_4)_3$ but if prepared by cyrstallization from a water solution it will retain molecules of water and have the formula $Al_2(SO_4)_3.18H_2O$, which is chemically like filter alum. This means that for every molecule of $Al_2(SO_4)_3$ present in the compound there are also eighteen molecules of water. However, if the compound is heated, the water as such can be expelled from the compound. Formulae of common chemicals with their common and chemical name are given in *Table 12* below.

Equations. By use of these formulae it is possible to write chemical changes graphically. Thus, $CaCO_3 + H_2SO_4 \rightarrow CaSO_4 + H_2CO_3$ means that when calcium carbonate and sulfuric acid react or combine, calcium sulfate and carbonic acid are formed. Similarly, when iron rusts it combines with oxygen to form iron oxide. This can be written $4\,Fe + 3\,O_2 \rightarrow 2Fe_2O_3$. However, one of the laws of chemistry is that matter can neither be created nor destroyed. Hence, in any chemical change there must be the same number of atoms in the substances produced as were present in the original compounds. Therefore, the above reaction must be "balanced" to produce an "equation" having an equal number of atoms on each side of the equation. Iron oxide, the product of the above reaction, contains two atoms of iron and three atoms of oxygen. To balance the equation there must be the same number of atoms of iron and oxygen reacting as exists in the product, Fe_2O_3. We might try to write the equation $2Fe + 3\,O \rightarrow Fe_2O_3$, but this cannot be true because we know oxygen gas consists of two atoms or O_2. To make the equation conform to the facts, we then multiply everything by two. Thus, $4\,Fe + 3\,O_2 \rightarrow 2Fe_2O_3$. Now we have said that four atoms of iron react with three molecules of oxygen gas to produce two molecules of iron oxide, and the number of atoms on each side of the equation are equal.

TABLE 12

Common Name	Chemical Name	Formula
Ammonia gas	Ammonia	NH_3
Ammonia	Ammonium hydroxide	NH_4OH
Filter alum	Aluminum sulfate	$Al_2(SO_4)_3.14H_2O$
Limestone	Calcium carbonate	$CaCO_3$
	Calcium bicarbonate	$Ca(HCO_3)_2$
Hydrated lime	Calcium hydroxide	$Ca(OH)_2$
Quick lime	Calcium oxide	CaO
	Chlorine	Cl_2
	Chlorine dioxide	ClO_2
Blue vitriol	Cupric sulfate	$CuSO_4.5H_2O$
	Ferric chloride	$FeCl_3.6H_2O$
Muriatic acid	Hydrochloric acid	HCl
	Sulfuric acid	H_2SO_4
Salt	Sodium chloride	$NaCl$
Soda ash	Sodium carbonate	Na_2CO_3
Soda	Sodium bicarbonate	$NaHCO_3$
Lye	Sodium hydroxide	$NaOH$
	Sodium phosphate	$Na_3PO_4.12H_2O$
	Water	H_2O
	Hypochlorous acid	$HOCl$
Chloride of lime	Calcium oxychloride	$CaOCl_2$
	Aluminum hydroxide	$Al(OH)_3$
Gypsum	Calcium sulfate	$CaSO_4$
	Carbon dioxide	CO_2
	Carbonic acid	H_2CO_3
	Monochloramine	NH_2Cl
	Dichloramine	$NHCl_2$
	Nitrogen trichloride	NCl_3
	Methane	CH_4
	Calcium hypochlorite	$Ca(OCl)_2$

From Table 11 we find the atomic weight of iron is 55.85 and of oxygen is 16.0. Then, 4 atoms of iron are equivalent to $4 \times 55.85 = 223.40$. A molecule of oxygen equals two atoms or $2 \times 16.0 = 32.0$, the molecular weight. Three molecules equal $3 \times 32.0 = 96.0$. A molecule of iron oxide equals $2 \times 55.85 = 111.70$, the weight of two atoms of iron, plus $3 \times 16.0 = 48.0$, the weight of three atoms of oxygen, or a total of 159.70. Two molecules of iron oxide $= 2 \times 159.70$ or 319.40.

The calculations would be:

$$4\,Fe \quad + \quad 3\,O_2 \quad = \quad 2\,Fe_2O_3$$
$$4 \times 55.85 \quad + \quad 6 \times 16.0 \quad = \quad 319.40$$

Now we can say that 223.40 parts of iron react with 96.0 parts of oxygen to produce 319.40 parts of iron rust, and they always will do so because the law of multiple proportion states that elements combine only in definite proportions. Suppose we had a piece of iron that had rusted and we wanted to know how much iron had been lost. If we carefully gathered and weighed all the rust and found it to be 79.84 grams, then we can calculate by proportion that $79.84 : 319.40 = ? : 223.40$, so the weight of iron that rusted must have been

$$\frac{79.84 \times 223.40}{319.40} = 55.84 \text{ grams}$$

To illustrate how this is of value to a sewage treatment plant operator, let's suppose you wanted to know how much alkalinity was in the sewage you had to treat. It might be for control of a chemical precipitation process or possibly in connection with corrosion control. Suppose you have available a solution of sulfuric acid containing 2 mg H_2SO_4 in each ml. By titration, which will be explained in the laboratory, you find that 5.6 ml of the acid neutralizes all the alkalinity in a 100-ml sample of water. Calling alkalinity $CaCO_3$, the equation is $H_2SO_4 + CaCO_3 \rightarrow CaSO_4 + H_2CO_3$. From the atomic weights, we find that 98 parts of sulfuric acid react with 100 parts of calcium carbonate. We found that 5.6 ml of a solution of sulfuric acid containing 2 mg per ml reacted with the alkalinity in the sample. Thus, by proportions,

$$\frac{5.6 \times 2}{98} = \frac{X}{100} \text{ and we find } X = 11.5 \text{ mg } CaCO_3$$

Therefore, this weight of calcium carbonate must have been present in the 100 ml of sample. If we wish to express the concentration as parts per million, the answer would be 10×11.5 or 115 mg per liter of sample, which is equal to 115 ppm. Actually, in doing the test, the concentration of acid is adjusted so that the titration in ml multiplied by 10, if a 100-ml sample is used, gives the answer directly without any calculation.

Equations commonly used in water and sewage treatment are:

$$CH_4 + 2_2 \rightarrow CO_2 + 2H_2O$$
$$Cl_2 + H_2O \rightleftarrows HCl + HOCl$$
$$Ca(OCl)_2 + Na_2CO_3 \rightleftarrows 2NaOCl + CaCO_3$$
$$Al_2(SO_4)_3 + 3CaCO_3 + 3H_2O \rightleftarrows 2Al(OH)_3 + 3CaSO_4 + 3CO_2$$
$$CO_2 + H_2O \rightleftarrows H_2CO_3$$
$$CaCO_3 + H_2CO_3 \rightleftarrows Ca(HCO_3)_2$$
$$Ca(HCO_3)_2 + Ca(OH)_2 \rightleftarrows 2CaCO_3 + 2H_2O$$
$$Ca(HCO_3)_2 + Na_2CO_3 \rightleftarrows CaCO_3 + 2NaHCO_3$$
$$NH_3 + HOCl \rightleftarrows NH_2Cl + H_2O$$
$$NH_2Cl + HOCl \rightleftarrows NHCl_2 + H_2O$$
$$NHCl_2 + HOCl \rightleftarrows NCl_3 + H_2O$$
$$CaCO_3 + H_2SO_4 \rightleftarrows CaSO_4 + H_2CO_3$$
$$Ca(HCO_3)_2 + H_2SO_4 \rightleftarrows CaSO_4 + 2H_2CO_3$$

See list of chemicals on page 249 for identification of these chmeicals.

Ionization. Somewhat different conditions prevail when chemicals are dissolved in water. You might consider that molecules of water enter between the atoms making up the molecules of the chemicals. The force that holds the atoms together is electrical. If they are separated by the molecules of water, each atom has an electrical charge. This splitting of the molecules, when dissolved in water, into charged atoms is called ionization. The charged atoms are called ions. Sodium chloride, when dissolved, ionizes into sodium ions and chloride ions.

$$NaCl \rightarrow Na^+ + Cl^-$$

The ions must be of equal and opposite charge or else the solution itself would have a charge, which is not true. When a salt such as ferric chloride ionizes, the ferric ion must have three positive charges to offset the negative charges of the three chlorine atoms.

$$FeCl_3 \rightarrow Fe^{+++} + 3Cl^-$$

Radicals. Under the heading Formulae, groups of atoms called radicals were discussed and it was said the groups reacted similarly to single elements. What was meant was that salts of the radicals ionize to form charged radicals instead of splitting into their component atoms. Thus, sodium sulfate ionizes to form sodium ions and sulfate ions and not charged sulfur or oxygen atoms.

$$Na_2SO_4 \rightarrow 2Na^+ + SO_4^{--}$$
$$Fe_2(SO_4)_3 \rightleftarrows 2Fe^{+++} + 3SO_4^{--}$$

Not all compounds ionize to the same degree. Some in dilute solutions are very nearly completely changed to ions, others are so little ionized that for practical purposes they may be considered un-ionized. Others vary anywhere between the two extremes. Actually, the ionization of salts is a reversible reaction and at equilibrium, which is rapidly established, as many molecules of a salt ionize as ions combine to form molecules. The reaction then should be written.

$$Fe_2(SO_4)_3 \rightleftarrows 2FE^{+++} + 3(SO_4)^{--}$$

to indicate it is proceeding in both directions at the same time and at the same speed. It is well known that similar electrical charges repel each other and opposite charges attract each other. This explains why not all elements will react. If the electrical charges on the atoms are the same, no chemical reaction will take place. If the charges on the atoms are different, then combinations can generally be made to take place.

Acids. One of the characteristics of an acid is that it will ionize in water to produce positively charged hydrogen ions.

$$HCl \rightleftarrows H^+ + Cl^-$$

Not all acids ionize to the same degree. In dilute solution the "strong" acids such as hydrochloric, sulfuric and nitric acids ionize practically completely. This is why they are called "strong" acids, as the activity of an acid is determined by the degree of ionization. "Weak" acids only partially ionize. Thus, an equal amount of a "weak" acid would produce only a fraction of the amount of hydrogen ion that a "strong" acid under similar conditions would produce.

Acids are also classified according to the number of hydrogen ions produced by one molecule of the acid.

Example: Monoacid—$HCl \rightleftarrows H^+ + Cl^-$
Diacid—$H_2SO_4 \rightleftarrows 2H^+ + SO_4^{--}$
Triacid—$H_3PO_4 \rightleftarrows 3H^+ + PO_4^{---}$

Bases or alkalis are compounds which ionize in water to furnish hydroxyl ions (OH^-). As with acids, bases ionize to different degrees.

"Strong" bases such as sodium hydroxide, and calcium hydroxide ionize to a high degree while "weak" bases only partially ionize.

Similar to acids, they are classified depending on whether one, two or three hydroxyl ions are produced by one molecule of base.

Example: Monobasic—NaOH $\rightleftarrows$ OH$^-$ + Na$^+$

Diabasic—Ca(OH)$_2$ $\rightleftarrows$ 2OH$^-$ + Ca^{++}

Tribasic—Al(OH)$_3$ $\rightleftarrows$ 3OH$^-$ + Al^{+++}

Equivalents. An equivalent weight of an acid is that weight of an acid which will furnish one molecular weight in grams of hydrogen ion. For monoacids, it equals the molecular weight of the acid in grams, for diacids it is half the molecular weight in grams, for triacids it is one-third of the molecular weight in grams.

Similarly, an equivalent of a base in the molecular weight in grams that will furnish one molecular weight of hydroxyl ions (17 grams). It is equal to the molecular weight divided by the number of hydroxyl radicals per molecule.

An equivalent weight of a salt is the molecular weight divided by the number of charges on the ions produced in solution.

pH value. Water ionizes to a slight degree to produce both hydrogen ion and hydroxyl ion.

$$H_2O \rightleftarrows H^+ + OH^-$$

Thus, water might be considered both an acid and a base. Actually, because the concentration of both ions is the same, it is considered neutral. The concentration of both (H$^+$) and (OH$^-$) in pure water is 0.0000001 expressed in terms of gram ions per liter. Rather than use decimal figures for measuring hydrogen ion concentration, a pH scale has been adopted to record concentration in whole numbers.

The following has been prepared in which the concentration of hydrogen ions is expressed in values which are decimal multiples of ten.

Ionic concentration as Grams of Hydrogen Ions (H$^+$) per Liter of Solution		pH Value
1.0		0
0.1		1
0.01		2
0.001		3
0.0001		4
0.00001		5
0.000001		6
0.0000001	neutral	7
0.00000001		8
0.000000001		9
0.0000000001		10
0.00000000001		11
0.000000000001		12
0.0000000000001		13
0.00000000000001		14

The pH value is the number of places after the decimal point in the expression for the concentration of hydrogen ions per liter. It will be noticed that as the concentration of hydrogen ion decreases the pH value in the opposite column increases.

For reasons beyond the scope of this discussion, the number of (H^+) ions multiplied by the number of (OH^-) ions always gives the same value. That is, if the number of (H^+) ions is increased ten fold, then the number of (OH^-) ions will be automatically reduced to one tenth of what they were before.

$$(H^+) \times (OH^-) = k \text{ (a constant value)}$$

Because of this relationship, a scale of p(OH) values could be prepared in which the p(OH) value would always be that number which when added to the pH value would equal 14. That is, a solution having a pH of 3.0 would have a p(OH) of 11 and a pH of 9.0 would correspond to a p(OH) of 5.0. Because of this fact, a measurement of pH is also, indirectly, a measure of the OH^- ion concentration and a second scale is therefore not necessary. pH values greater than 7.0 indicate alkaline characteristics.

Returning to the idea of "strong" and "weak" acids, if "strong" acids are highly ionized and produce a high concentration of hydrogen ion, then the pH value will be low. If an equivalent amount of "weak" acid produces less hydrogen ion, then the pH will be below 7.0 but not as low as in the "strong" acid solution.

Neutralization of acids and bases. Consider what happens when an acid solution and alkaline solution, each containing one equivalent of acid and base, are mixed:

$$HCl \rightleftarrows H^+ + Cl^-$$
$$NaOH \rightleftarrows OH^- + Na^+$$

The resulting solution would contain one equivalent of H^+, one equivalent of OH^-, plus the Na^+ and Cl^-. It was stated that water ionizes to H^+ and OH^- and their concentration from water is only 0.0000001 equivalents per liter. Thus, in the mixed solution the H^+ and OH^- would combine to produce water until the concentration of each was reduced from one equivalent of each to 0.0000001 equivalent of each.

$$H^+ + OH^- \rightleftarrows H_2O$$

In solution there would be left the $Na^+ + Cl^-$, which is what is obtained when NaCl is dissolved.

$$NaCl \rightleftarrows Na^+ + Cl^-$$

Both the acid and base would have disappeared. This mutual reaction of acids and bases is called neutralization. One equivalent of any acid will exactly neutralize one equivalent of any base with the production of a salt and water.

This is the basis of the determination of alkalinity in water. Under "Equations" it was shown how the alkalinity could be calculated if a solution containing a known amount of acid was used. However, if the acid solution is adjusted so that it contains a definite number of equivalents of acid, then one volume of the acid will neutralize an equal number of equivalents of base and no calculation is necessary.

Normal solution is one which contains one equivalent of acid or base per liter. Hence, equal volume of normal acids and bases exactly neutralize each other, or, if the acid is twice the normality of the base, half the volume will be required to neutralize one volume of base.

$$\text{ml} \times \text{normality of acid} = \text{ml} \times \text{normality of base}$$

To determine alkalinity, a 1/50 normal acid solution is used to neutralize the alkalinity in 100 ml of sewage. If 5.6 ml of acid was required, then 5.6 (the ml of acid) multiplied by 1/50 (the normality of the acid) divided by 100 (the volume of the sample of sewage equals the normality of the sewage).

$$\frac{5.6 \times 0.02}{100} = \text{N of the sewage}$$

A normal solution of alkalinity equals the molecular weight of $CaCO_3$ divided by 2 or 50 grams per liter. If the normality of the sewage as determined is multiplied by 50, the concentration of $CaCO_3$ in the sewage would be found in grams per liter. But the result desired is milligrams per liter, so that the grams per liter are multiplied by 1000 to change them into milligrams per liter or parts per million.

$$\frac{5.6 \times .02}{100} \times 50 \times 1000 = 56 \text{ ppm}$$

It will be noticed that all the factors cancel, leaving the answer obtained by multiplying the milliliter of acid used by 10, if 100 ml sample is used, or 20 if a 50 ml sample is used. Thus, to actually do the test all that is necessary is to titrate 100 ml sample of sewage, measure the volume of acid used in milliliters and multiply this volume by ten to obtain the alkalinity in parts per million.

Acidity, alkalinity and pH. Acidity of water is a measure of the *total* amount of acid substances (H^+) present in water expressed as parts per million of equivalent calcium carbonate. It has been shown that one equivalent of an acid (H^+) equals one equivalent of a base (OH^-). Therefore, it makes no difference whether the result is expressed as acid or base and for convenience acidity is reported as equivalnt of $CaCO_3$ because many times it is not known just what acids are present.

Alkalinity is a measure of the *total* amount of alkaline substances present in water and is expressed as parts per million of equivalent $CaCO_3$. Again this is done because the alkalis present might not be known but at least they are equivalent to the amount of $CaCO_3$ reported.

The activity of an acid or alkali is measured by the pH value. Thus, the more active the acid characteristics the lower will be the pH, or the more active the alkalis, the higher the pH will be. Alkalinity and pH are not the same, neither can be calculated from the other.

This can be illustrated as follows. If 1/1000 equivalent of a strong acid is added to 1 liter of water it will produce 1/1000 equivalent of H^+. From the table on page 13 it is shown that 0.001 equivalents of H^+ per liter equals pH 3.0. If 1/1000 equivalents of a weak acid, 10% ionized, is added to one liter of water, it will produce only one-tenth as much H^+ or $0.001 \times .1 = 0.0001$ equivalents of H^+ per liter and thus have a pH of 4.0. In both solutions the acidity or total amount of acid is the same, but one has a pH of 3.0 and the other 4.0. The one with the lower pH would more actively corrode iron than the one with the higher pH.

Organic Chemistry. The discussion so far has been concerned only with those compounds of mineral origin. There is another vast field of chemistry concerned with compounds of living matter or substances that had once been living matter. These are composed mainly of carbon, hydrogen and oxygen in many different proportions such as sugar, cellulose, or gasoline. Most of them do not ionize in water. Some, such as proteins, contain small amounts of nitrogen, sulfur and phosphorous. One characteristic of such compounds is that they volatilize on heating or burning, leaving no ash. The vegetable extract in natural water that causes the light yellow color similar to dilute tea is an organic compound. Algae, both dead and alive, are organic in nature, as is phenol, all of which cause taste and odor in water even in concentrations of only a few parts per billion instead of parts per million.

Most of the solid material suspended in sewage and a substantial part of the dissolved matter also is organic in nature. In fact sewage treatment is essentially a process for decomposing organic material into simpler chemical substances rapidly and under controlled conditions.

Solutions, Colloids and Suspensions. If small quantities of such common substances as salt, sugar or baking soda are added to water, the substances will disappear and the water will be just as clear as it was originally. Such a combination is called a solution and no chemical reaction has taken place between the dissolved substance, called the solute. and the dissolving liquid, called the solvent. The mixture may be thought of as molecules of the solute uniformly dispersed throughout the solvent such that there is no apparent interference with the passage of light through the solution.

On the other hand, if soil is mixed with water it will not disappear, but will prevent the passage of light through the water in proportion to the amount of the soil present. Such a mixture may be called a suspension and the permanency of the suspension is dependent on the coarseness and settleability of the soil particles.

If the soil contains very fine material, such as certain clays, some of it will remain uniformly dispersed throughout the water, but will still be visible and will diffuse a beam of light as it shines through. Such a mixture may be called a colloid or, as sometimes designated, a colloidal suspension.

The three terms, suspensions, colloids and solutions are thus used to differentiate progressively finer degrees of dispersion of substances in a liquid. The limit of the zones to which these terms apply is somewhat indefinite, arbitrary and beyond the scope of this chapter.

Colloidal suspensions are commonly found in sewage treatment. Raw sewage. Imhoff tank effluent, the supernatant liquor from sludge digestion tanks all exhibit more or less turbidity which is colloidal in nature. The purification effected by trickling filter units is due in part to removal of colloidal material from the sewage by the jelly-like coating on the surface of the filter stones.

The Chemistry of Sewage Organic Matter. Most of the organic matter in domestic sewage consists of food scraps, fecal and urinary wastes from human bodies, vegetable matter, mineral and organic salts, and miscellaneous materials such as soap, synthetic detergents, etc. Some of these are solids, some are in solution, and some may be in colloidal suspension.

The food scraps are largely carbohydrates, proteins or fats. Fecal matter is made up of bits of undigested food, intestinal bacteria, and cellular waste from the body. Chemically it is probably largely body protein with some fats and considerable carbohydrates. The urinary wastes contain most of the nitrogen which is not retained in the body. This is in the form of ammonia or urea. Urea is a chemical compound which is easily decomposed to yield ammonia and carbon dioxide.

The vegetable matter in sewage is essentially garbage derived from kitchens of the community. Soaps, synthetic detergents, and mineral salts are, of course, waste products from domestic activities involving dish-washing and laundering.

Saprophytic bacteria, always present in sewage, will decompose sewage organic matter, reducing the complex proteins, fats, and carbohydrates to simpler substances with production of simple gases such as carbon dioxide, hydrogen sulfide, methane, and ammonia and more complex substances such as organic acids, alcohols, etc. The course of the digestion and the resultant products are dependent to a large extent on the availability of oxygen. The products of digestion of sewage solids when oxygen is absent are quite different than the products of the digestion of the same material when oxygen is available. Digestion in the absence of free oxygen is called anaerobic digestion while that in the presence of free oxygen is called aerobic digestion.

Anaerobic digestion of sewage solids. The first stage of the digestion is characterized by the production of organic acids. Proteins, carbohydrates, and fats are decomposed by the anaerobic bacteria and the products of the decomposition are organic acids. This digestion stage is evident in sludge by a lowering of the pH and the presence of a disagreeable sour odor. Unless the amount of acid produced is excessive, the digestion will normally proceed to the second stage. With excess acidity, such as is obtained when the addition of fresh solids is too rapid, the bacteria will be destroyed and the process will end with the first stage.

The second stage is characterized by liquefaction of sewage solids under mildly acid conditions. The bacteria, by enzyme action, convert the insoluble solids material to the soluble form. This is in accordance with the requirements of the bacterial cells that all food material must be in solution before it can pass through the cell wall.

The third stage of digestion is characterized by production of gases, carbon dioxide, methane, and hydrogen sulfide; as well as an increase of pH and the production of carbonate salts.

The operator of a sewage plant can exert considerable control over the digestion process by taking steps to favor the orderly progression from one stage to another. In a properly operated sludge digestion tank, all three stages of digestion are progressing simultaneously but in different zones or layers within the tank. Physical and chemical tests for pH, the volume and identification of the gases produced, the relative amount of volatile material in the sludge solids and the drainability of the sludge when put on drying beds or on vacuum filters will reveal how well the process is going.

Aerobic digestion. In the aerobic digestion of sewage organic matter such as occurs in streams where the organic load is not excessive or on trickling filter units, the decomposition of the proteins, carbohydrates, and fats proceeds without the production of foul smelling organic acids and gases. The saprophytic bacteria have ample free oxygen available with which to accomplish the chemical transformations involved in decomposition of the complex compounds and the fixation of carbon, hydrogen, phosphorous, and sulfur elements into simple gases, relatively inert humus-like material, and mineral salts. Sewage plant operators are familiar with aerobic digestion which takes place in trickling filter units. The saprophytic bacteria are embedded in the gelatinous growth coating the stones, and humus material produced by the digestion periodically "unloads" from the filter and appears in the effluent.

The activated sludge process is another example of aerobic digestion of sewage organic matter. In this instance the consumption of free oxygen by the filamentous bacteria which are incorporated in the activated sludge is so rapid that extraordinary volumes of air are supplied by air compressors.

APPENDIX IV

BIOLOGY-BACTERIOLOGY

The science of biology is concerned with the study of living organisms, their habits, food requirements, and general functions. Among the myriad types of living organisms which inhabit this planet, the bacteria form a very important part. The study of biology and of bacteriology is of basic importance since these sciences are the foundations upon which sanitation and sewage treatment are based. Without knowledge of the fundamental factors concerning these living organisms and their relation to one another and to human beings it would be difficult to understand the principles upon which sewage treatment processes are based.

BACTERIOLOGY

Bacteria are minute living organisms, each consisting of a single cell. These organisms are so small that they can be seen only when magnified under a microscope. Thus they are included in the term microorganisms. Food assimilation, waste excretion, respiration, growth and all other activities are carried on through the action of the one single cell. Many bacteria have characteristics ordinarily associated with the animal kingdom and others generally applied to the plant kingdom. In some respects, they form a link between these two types of living organisms. There are many different kinds of bacteria, varying widely in size, shape and function.

The cells of the bacteria consist of an outer shell or membrane, an inner jelly-like material called protoplasm, and a nucleus within the protoplasm of the cell. As with all other living organisms, bacteria can reproduce, but they do this by a process known as fission. The adult cell constricts in the middle, the constriction increases until finally the cell divides into two smaller cells, each a complete living organism. These two daughter cells grow and in turn divide to continue the process. It is estimated that the average bacterium will divide at intervals of 20-30 minutes. Thus, the increase in the number of bacteria under favorable conditions is tremendous in a short period of time, such as 12 hours, if all the daughter cells were to survive. (Figure 29).

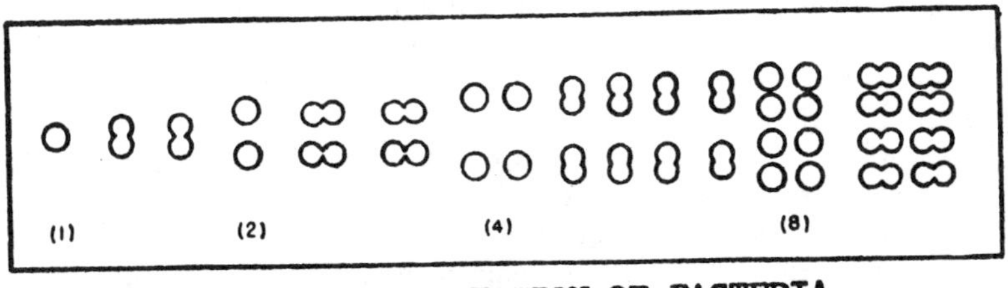

FIGURE 29 - REPRODUCTION OF BACTERIA

Bacteria are found everywhere in our environment. They are present in the soil, and thru the agency of dust they are suspended in the air. They are found in water as the result of passage of rain through the air and the various water sources flowing through and over the ground. Bacteria are present in the bodies of all living organisms and many of them carry on very useful and necessary functions related to the life of the larger organism.

Bacilli are rod-shaped cells, some longer or shorter than others with the different kinds also varying in width. A single rod-shaped cell is called a bacillus.

Cocci appear as round or spherial cells. Some occur as pairs and are called diplococci, others as chain and are designated as *streptococci*, still others are arranged in irregular shaped groups and are called *staphylococci*.

Other bacteria have different shapes, such as a comma or crescent, others are spiral. Each is designated by a special name but the bacilli and cocci are the most common.

Flagella are hair-like projections from the shell of a microorganism. Movement of these flagella provide a means of locomotion for the cell which can then move in its environment, a process generally ascribed to an animal. Not all bacteria have this property and as such, are more nearly like plants.

Saprophytes are bacteria that can carry on an independent existence, finding their own food supply, adapting themselves to the conditions of their environment and carrying on their work without stimulus from other organisms.

The saprophytic bacteria, in general, obtain their food from dead organic matter which they attack and decompose or break down into simpler substances. Thus, they can obtain the food supply that is necessary for their continued growth, while at the same time carrying on the very useful function of destroying the dead matter. Without the action of the saprophytic bacteria, it would be impossible for other organisms to live on this planet since there would be no way to dispose of the dead organisms which would eventually cover the earth, preventing growth of plants and the carrying on of natural functions essential for living organisms. Saprophytic bacteria break down the complex organic components of matter through the process known as decay or decomposition into simpler substances. These, in turn, serve as a food supply for plants, which become a food supply for animals, and the cycle of life is continued without the loss of matter. As an illustration of the changes in dead organic matter that are brought about by the activity of the bacteria, we might consider the natural process of decay and decomposition of organic compounds containing nitrogen, as shown by the nitrogen cycle. (Figure 30)

All living matter contains nitrogen bound with carbon, oxygen, hydrogen and other elements to form organic molecules. When these organisms die, the dead material is immediately a source of food for the saprophytic

236

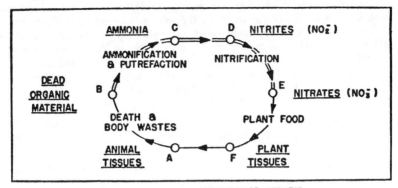

FIGURE 30 – THE NITROGEN CYCLE

bacteria, which change these complex organic molecules to simpler forms of nitrogenous matter, thence to ammonia, then to nitrites, and then to nitrates. The nitrates are the end product and the simplest and most useful form in which nitrogen exists. The nitrates are the basis of fertilizers and serve as a food for plants, which grow and become the food for living animals, which in turn grow until finally they die, and the cycle is completed and continues on and on. Thus, there is no loss of matter and complete usage is made of all of the elements composing living matter. In a similar manner, organic compounds containing sulfur, phosphorous, carbon and other chemical elements are decomposed through serving as a food supply for saprophytic bacteria.

Parasites, as contrasted to the saprophytic organisms, are bacteria that cannot live an independent existence, cannot find their own food supply, but must remain in close association with some other living organisms, from which they can obtain food already prepared. Parasites are dependent on the body of the host organisms to secure the environmental conditions upon which their existence and growth depend. They, however, carry on a similar type of decay and decomposition of this food supply, producing as a result end products which are necessary for the nourishment of the host. Most of these parasitic bacteria are beneficient and are necessary for the proper functioning of the living organism with which they are associated.

Pathogens. Among the parasitic bacteria are some which produce end products of their growth that are poisonous to the host organism and which produce a condition that is called disease. Some of them are pathogenic only to human beings in that they produce disease only in the body of human beings. Others are pathogenic to certain types of warm-blooded animals and some are pathogenic only to plants. There are a few types of saprophytic bacteria which have all of the characteristics of that class but which can, if they find entry into the body of an animal, produce end products which cause disease, such as anthrax or tetanus, in the body of the invaded animal. These particular saprophytic bacteria are also termed pathogenic.

Bacterial Growth. All bacteria require food for their continued life and growth and all are affected by the conditions of their environment. Like human beings, they consume food, they respire, they need moisture, they require heat, and they give off waste products. Their food requirements are very definite and have been, in general, already outlined. Without an adequate food supply of the type the specific organism requires, bacteria will not grow and multiply at their maximum rate and they will, therefore, not perform their full and complete functions.

Aerobic Bacteria. All bacteria require oxygen for their growth processes. Some require oxygen in its elementary gaseous form, which they obtain from the air. Such bacteria are designated as aerobic.

Anaerobic Bacteria. Some bacteria cannot live in the presence of free gaseous oxygen, but must obtain the oxygen needed for their respiration by decomposing or breaking down complex substances. These bacteria are designated as anaerobic.

Facultative Bacteria. There is a third type of bacteria which, though normally aerobic, can accustom itself to living in the absence of free gaseous oxygen or which, though normally anaerobic, can accustom itself to living in the presence of free gaseous oxygen. These are termed faculative bacteria.

Temperature Requirements. Bacteria are very sensitive to heat. Some live best at ordinary outdoor temperatures, varying from 60° to 68°F. Some, particularly the parasitic forms, require higher temperatures, approximately that of the body of living animals, 98°F. Some can live only at very cold temperatures, just above the freezing point of water. Any marked change from the optimum temperature requirements of specific bacteria causes a reduction in the activities of the bacteria, and if severe enough, may cause their death. If the temperature of the environment is raised to the boiling point of water, nearly all types of bacteria are destroyed.

Moisture Requirements. Bacteria require a moist environment for their most effective activities. If removed from such an environment for any length of time and drying takes place, most bacterial cells are destroyed. Under the most optimum environmental conditions of temperature, moisture, food supply and oxygen, the bacteria will multiply and grow at their maximum rate, producing their maximum amount of work. Any changes in the environmental conditions will cause an immediate decrease in the rate of growth, and possibly the death and destruction of the living forms.

Spore Formation. Some bacteria, particularly those of the saprophytic type, when obliged to live in a very unfavorable environment with an inadequate food supply for any length of time, develop into a resistant form called a spore or seed. These spores are not affected by the environment, no food is required for their existence, and no growth results. A nucleus of life, however, is maintained and when the spore is again placed in a favorable environment it will sprout or develop into an active cell again. Parasitic bacteria, in general, do not form spores while saprophytes frequently do.

NORMAL CHARACTERISTICS OF SAPROPHYTIC
AND PARASITIC BACTERIA

	Saprophytes	*Parasites*
Optimum temperature	Atmospheric	Body
Normal food material	Dead organic	Living
Oxygen requirements	Aerobic and anaerobic	Most anaerobic
Spore formation	Usually	Seldom
Effect on animals	Mostly non-pathogenic	Pathogenic and non-pathogenic

Mutual Activities. In the process of growth all bacteria produce waste products just as all other organisms do, and if these waste products were allowed to accumulate, they would destroy the particular form which produced them. However, other types of bacteria may find these waste products a satisfactory food supply, grow in their presence, and carry decomposition of the organic matter a step further until in turn their food supply is exhausted or their waste products accumulate to a sufficient degree to cause their destruction. Thus, the decay of organic matter is continuously carried on by many different types of bacteria, each of which carries the process of chemical decomposition forward. This is essentially what occurs in familiar process of sewage solids digestion.

When the food supply is plentiful it is possible for two or more varieties of bacteria to exist side by side provided that the waste production of one strain is not toxic for the other. If the food supply lessens, or if waste products produced by one strain are toxic to other strains, the phenomena known as overgrowth may appear. This is a condition where one strain of organism may predominate to the exclusion of all others. Eventually however, waste products of the metabolism of the organism, unless they are removed, will become deleterious to the organism itself and the number of cells in a culture will decrease.

Toxic Agents. Living bacteria are sensitive not only to changes in the environment but can readily be poisoned or destroyed by many chemical substances. Such things as large concentrations of salt will destroy certain types of bacteria and this process has been used for many centuries to preserve such dead organic matter as meat or fish. Others are destroyed by strong acids or strong alkalis and by the addition to the environment of such chemical substances as chlorine, iodine or bromine. The destructive action of chemicals is a time-concentration effect. Thus, a low concentration will kill when present in the environment for a long period of time and a large concentration will kill in a short time.

WATER BIOLOGY

Bacteria. Bacteria are so widely distributed in nature that it is not surprising that all natural waters contain a fairly large variety. Some of these are saprophytic bacteria leached from the soil, others may be parasitic. Even pathogenic bacteria may be present in the water through contamination by waste matter of human or animal origin. Any water supply contaminated by sewage is certain to contain a bacterial group called "coliform." This is a group comprising more than 20 individual

239

strains and termed coliform because of the fact that they have their natural habitat in the large intestine of human beings and animals. These bacteria are not usually pathogenic. The presence of pathogenic bacteria in water, as a result of contamination by sewage, is dependent upon an individual contributing to that sewage being ill of an intestinal disease and upon the survival of the pathogen in an environment which is not favorable to it. Coliform bacteria, on the other hand, are always present if sewage is present and are, generally much more hardy than pathogens. It is for this reason that the bacteriologic evaluation of water is always based upon a bacteriologic analysis to determine if coliform bacteria are present and in what concentration.

PLANKTON

In addition to bacteria other living organisms are commonly found in water and sewage. These are plankton. They are higher in the life scale than bacteria. They range in size from minute one-cell organisms only slightly larger than bacteria to much larger forms easily visible to the unaided eye. Some are plants, other are animals; some are capable of independent motion while others are not. Some idea of the complexity of size, shape, and metabolism of plankton may be gained by consideration of some characteristics of the most important groups of organisms included under that designation.

Algae. This is a very large group of plant forms distinguished by the fact that they contain chlorophyl—the green coloring matter of plants. Under favorable conditions they grow prolifically in water and sewage and heavy growths are easily detected by the presence of green-colored scum or "bloom." Under the influence of sunlight, chlorophyl-bearing plants absorb carbon dioxide and evolve oxygen. Pond waters which have heavy growths of algae frequently are saturated with oxygen during the daylight hours although the oxygen level decreases as darkness advances. Using water, carbon dioxide, and mineral matter secured from the environment, algae synthesize the complex proteins, fats, and cellulose constituents which made up their cell structure. The growth of algae is stimulated by the presence of nitrogen and phosphorous salts and also to some extent by calcium and magnesium salts. Growths in hard water are therefore usually heavier than in soft waters. Some algae are very tiny and have a single cell structure, other are multicellular and grow in a variety of forms, including branching plant-like structures hundreds of feet long. Many have pigments other than chlorophyl so that the actual color may be green, blue-green, or even red or brown. They are found most often in relatively pure water although not exclusively so. Some of the blue-green varieties are capable of growing quite well in heavily polluted water and even in sewage.

Fungi. Fungi are also plants, but in contract to the algae they do not contain chlorophyl. They are filamentous type organisms. For the purposes of simplicity, when we speak of sewage fungi we include filamentous bacteria and filamentous algae although, strictly speaking, these latter are not fungi. Fungi are commonly found in water and sewage and in the latter they are often observed growing in gray-colored cottony masses

240

which attach themselves to the walls and structures in sewage treatment units. A common organism of this type is known as sphaerotilus. Fungi masses frequently clog the pipes and screens in the sewage plant and reduce the flow in channels. Their metabolism is dependent upon the availability of oxygen and a plentiful supply of organic matter.

Protozoa. Animals coming under the heading of plankton include, among other forms, protozoa. These are generally considered to be higher forms of life than the algae. They are frequently motile and are usually associated with sewage pollution. There are very many varieties and most of them feed on other microscopic organisms, primarily bacteria. They are frequently found growing in large masses as well as individual cells suspended in the water. There are thousands of varieties ranging in size from submicroscopic to macroscopic.

Crustaceae. These are small animals ranging in size from 0.2 to 0.3 millimeter long which move very rapidly through the water in search of food. They have recognizable head and posterior sections. They form a principal source of food for small fish and are found largely in relatively fresh natural water.

Rotifera. These are tiny animal forms which are characterized by the presence of cilia—short hair-like appendages which serve the double purpose of providing locomotion and creating a current in the water so that food will be drawn to the organism. Rotifera feed on decomposing organic matter and are found in bodies of water where such matter is present.

Worms. Flat worms or nematodes are varieties of worms which may be found in water and in sewage. Flat worms feed principally on algae and are found in the lower depths of ponds because they dislike and avoid light. They range in size from the fraction of a millimeter to several centimeters. Nematodes are parasitic worms living on other organisms, including man. It is believed that those which are parasitic in man are usually associated with contaminated food rather than contaminated water. Nematodes are very hardy and will survive over wide variations in temperature and humidity. They even survive under prolonged drying. They are very abundant in sewage sludge and are believed to play an important part in the stabilization of sludge.

Water Borne Disease. Pathogenic bacteria, which cause certain diseases, when discharged into water, can survive and be transferred through the agency of the water from one person to another. Among these so-called water-borne diseases are typhoid fever, dysentery, cholera, and various types of diarrheal ailments designated as gastro enteritis. Thus, the presence of these organisms in water causes a contamination of the water and renders it both unfit and unsafe for consumption. People who drink the water containing these particular pathogenic bacteria can readily acquire the corresponding disease in this way.

Safe Water. Obviously, then, the removal of bacteria is a necessary step in making water suitable for human consumption. Another necessary step is to prevent these pathogenic bacteria from getting into a water supply. Only water free from pathogenic bacteria can be considered of safe and satisfactory quality.

Laboratory Control. To determine if water is safe or if our precautionary methods are eliminating waste, and thus pathogenic bacteria from water, it is necessary that some means be devised for detecting the number of bacteria in water. To actually detect such pathogenic bacteria as those causing typhoid fever, dysentery, or other water-borne diseases is a very laborious, time-consuming process. Contrary to the opinion of most people, such examinations of water are not made. Rather, it is desirable to determine whether polluting material in the form of waste products from living animals has entered the water and to prevent further contamination from this means, or to remove the bacteria from water which has already received this type of polluting material. The procedure used is to determine the presence of an organism indicative of contamination of a water supply by the waste products from the intestinal discharges of warm-blooded animals.

Coliform organism. All warm-blooded animals harbor in their intestinal tract parasitic bacteria of various types. All members of this one specific group are designated as the coliform group of bacteria. These microorganisms are not normally pathogenic and function in the digestive processes of the host organism. They are discharged from the intestinal tract in tremendous numbers. They will always be present in large numbers in sewage, which usually contains at least 4,000,000 to 5,000,000 coliform bacteria per ml. If sewage enters a water, the bacteria are carried with it and will survive there for long periods of time. Thus, their presence provides positive evidence of pollution and the possible presence of the pathogenic bacteria from the discharges of the animal bodies. Their detection by laboratory examination is relatively simple.

Index of Pollution. The number of these bacteria that are present in any definite volume of water is a measure of the amount of sewage or waste which has been discharged into that water, and can be interpreted as a measure of the safety of the water for human consumption. If large numbers of these bacteria are present, there will be a large amount of pollution and the water is unsatisfactory and potentially unsafe. A smaller number of these microorganisms, of course, shows a lesser concentration of pollution. A very few coliform bacteria, less than one per 100 ml of water, indicates that the amount of pollution is too small to present a definite hazard and that it can be considered of safe quality.

VOLATILE ACIDS IN SEWAGE SLUDGE

Sludge digestion proceeds in stages (Chapter 8). During the first stage of digestion, bacterial action produces quantities of water-soluble fatty acids (volatile acids). These are chiefly mixtures of acetic, propionic, and butyric acids. In later stages of digestion, these acids are decomposed by other species of bacteria and their absence in the sludge indicates that digestion has proceeded beyond the first stage. Determination of the concentration of volatile acids in the sludge permits an estimation of the efficiency of the digestive process. A progressive rise in their concentration over a period precedes failure of the process.

Volatile acids are separated from sludge by steam distillation in an apparatus illustrated below

Sampling. Collect a sample of sludge of at least 1 liter volume in accordance with directions given in Chapter 11, p. 129.

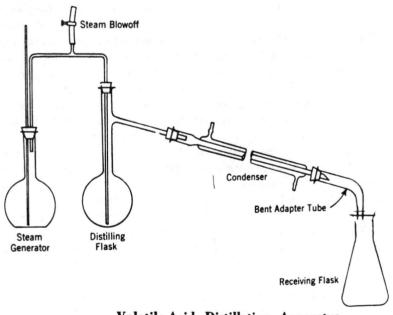

Volatile-Acid Distillation Apparatus

Equipment. Sludge sampling device, steam distillation apparatus having a steam generator of 1 liter capacity, distilling flask of 1 liter capacity, straight wall condenser at least 30 inches long, 1 liter Erlenmeyer-type receiving flask, bent glass adapter, glass tubing, rubber stoppers, etc. to connect the units of the apparatus. Ring stand supports and gas burners for steam generator and distilling flask are also required. Also 250 ml. measuring cylinder, 5-½ inch Buchner-type funnel, medium porosity filter paper to fit Buchner-type funnel, suction flask and source of suction (water aspirator or vacuum pump), pH meter or pH test kit.

Reagents. Sulfuric acid (1+1) - equal parts by volume of acid and water. Pour acid into water (do not pour water into acid) in small increments with stirring. Allow solution to cool between additions.

Sulfuric acid, standard solution 0.1N

Sodium hydroxide, standard solution 0.1N

Ferric chloride solution ($FeCl_3$. $6H_2O$) 82.5 g/l

Diatomaceous silica filter-aid (Johns-Manville Corp. Hyflo Super-Cell or equal).

Magnesium sulfate, crystalline ($MgSO_4$. $7H_2O$)

Phenolphthalein indicator solution

Procedure. Add sulfuric (1+1) in small increments to 500 ml of sludge with swirling after each addition. Check pH of the mixture after each mixing and continue additions until a pH of 3.5 is attained. If pH goes below 3.5, bring it back with sodium hydroxide solution. Add 6 ml of ferric chloride solution and 50 g of filter-aid to the sludge and mix. Prepare a Buchner filter by attaching the funnel to a suction flask connected to a source of suction. Apply suction to the flask, put filter paper in funnel and pour a water suspension of filter-aid over the filter. Sufficient filter-aid should be applied in this manner until the entire area of the paper has a thin coating. Pour the sludge into the filter funnel with the suction on. Wash the residue 3 - 4 times with 20 - 25 ml. of water.

Adjust pH of the filtrate to 11.0 with 0.1N sodium hydroxide solution. Concentrate with heat until the volume is about 150 ml and cool in a refrigerator.

Adjust the pH of the cooled filtrate to 4.0 with 0.1N sulfuric acid and pour it quickly into the distilling flask. Add magnesium sulfate solution to the flask in increments (swirl gently after each addition) continuing the additions until a slight excess of undissolved magnesium sulfate persists.

Apply heat to the steam generator with the blow-off open. When steam comes from the blow off, reduce heat to keep steam production at a low level but continuous. Apply heat to the distilling flask until temperature approaches the boiling point, then close blow-off and steam distill at a rate of about 200 ml of distillate in 25 minutes. Increase the distillation rate to a convenient maximum and collect about 600 ml of distillate. If foaming occurs, adjust heat under both flasks to reduce it.

Titrate* the distillate with 0.1N sodium hydroxide using phenolphthalein indicator.

Calculation.

$$\text{mg/l total volatile acids as acetic acid} = \frac{\text{ml O.1N NaOH} \times 6000}{\text{ml sample}}$$

*Sodium hydroxide solution, unless it is carefully preserved, changes its normality by absorption of carbon dioxide from the air. Sulfuric acid, on the other hand, is stable; therefore, standardize the sodium hydroxide solution against the O.1N sulfuric acid each time a test is run and base the calculations for volatile acids on the result.

Thus   ml/l total volatile acids as acetic acid =

$$\frac{\text{ml of Na OH solution} \times 60{,}000 \times \text{normality of NaOH solution}}{500}$$

References

1. American Public Health Association, American WaterWorks and the Water Pollution Control Federation, Standard Methods for the Examination of Water and Wastewater, 1960, 11th ed., New York Amer. Pub. Health Assn.

2. Heukelekian, H. and Kaplovsky, A.J., Improved Method of Volatile-Acid Recovery from Sewage Sludges, Sew. Works Jour., 1949, 21, 974 —

Dissolved Oxygen Test For Activated Sludge Mixed Liquor

Determination of dissolved oxygen in activated sludge requires a special reagent and special sampling technic to cope with the problem of interference due to 1., the high percentage of organic matter in the sludge; 2., the biochemical oxygen demand of the sludge floc which rapidly and continuously uses up oxygen present in the sample and 3., the probable presence of nitrites in the sludge.

Reagents. All the reagents required for the determination of dissolved oxygen in sewage and, in addition an inhibitory solution which stops biochemical oxygen demand, destroys nitrite and coagulates the sludge thereby promoting settling of solid matter.

Inhibiting solution. Dissolve 50 g of copper sulfate ($CuSO_4.5H_2O$) in 500 ml of distilled water. Dissolve with stirring (no heat!) 32 g of sulfamic acid (NH_2SO_2OH) in 475 ml of distilled water. Mix the two solutions, add 25 ml of glacial acetic acid and mix again.

Equipment. A glass-stoppered bottle of at least 1 liter capacity and a glass siphon in addition to the equipment listed for dissolved oxygen in sewage.

Sampling. Add 10 ml of inhibiting solution to the 1 liter bottle, or, if the bottle is larger than 1 liter size, 1 ml of the inhibiting solution for each 100 ml of bottle capacity. Collect sample in this bottle by lowering it on its side into the aeration tank in such manner that the sludge flows gently into the bottle without agitation. Fill the bottle to overflowing, insert the stopper without entrainment of air, mix by repeated inversion and set the bottle aside to allow the floc to settle. When the floc has settled and a clear supernatant over the solid material is available, carefully siphon the supernatant into a 300 ml BOD bottle without agitation and without entrainment of air. Procedure for measuring of dissolved oxygen in sample in the 300 ml bottle is the same as the test for dissolved oxygen in sewage.

Reference

Ruchhoft, C. C. and Placak, O. R. "Determination of Dissolved Oxygen in Activated Sludge - Sewage Mixtures". Sew. Works Jour. Vol. XIV, No. 3, 638-649, May 1942.

BIBLIOGRAPHY

Imhoff, Karl and Fair, G. M. "Arithmetic of Sewage Treatment Works."

Imhoff, Karl and Fair, G. M. "Sewage Treatment." John Wiley & Sons, Inc., New York

Hardenbergh, W. A. "Sewerage and Sewage Treatment." International Textbook Co., Scranton, Pa.

Metcalf, Leonard and Eddy, Harrison P. "Sewage and Sewage Disposal." Second Edition. McGraw-Hill Book Company, Inc., New York

Babbitt, H. E. "Sewerage and Sewage Treatment." Sixth Edition. John Wiley & Sons, Inc., New York

Whipple, G. C. "The Microscopy of Drinking Water." Fourth Edition. Revised by G. M. Fair and M. E. Whipple, 1927. John Wiley & Sons, Inc., New York

Phelps, E. B. "Stream Sanitation." 1944. John Wiley & Sons, Inc., New York

New York State Public Health Law—Articles 11 and 12

"Manual for Sewage Treatment Plant Operators." Second Edition. Texas Water and Sewage Works Association, Austin, Texas

Keefer, C. E. "Sewage Treatment Works." First Edition 1940

Standard Methods for the Examination of Water, Sewage and Industrial Wastes Tenth Edition. American Public Health Association, New York, New York

Eldridge, F. F. "Industrial Waste Treatment Practice." McGraw-Hill Book Co., Inc., New York

Besselievre, E. B. "Industrial Waste Treatment." McGraw-Hill Book Co., Inc., New York

Gurnham, C. F. "Principles of Industrial Waste Treatment." John Wiley & Sons, Inc., New York

Fair, G. M. and Geyer, J. C. "Elements of Water Supply and Waste-Water Disposal." John Wiley & Sons, Inc., New York

"Standards for Sewage Works." Upper Mississippi River Board of Public Health Engineers and Great Lakes Board of Public Health Engineers

King "Handbook of Hydraulics." McGraw-Hill Book Co., Inc., New York

Glassary—Water & Sewage Control Engineering